Helene Hanff captured the hearts of readers everywhere with *84, Charing Cross Road*, the account of her love affair with an antiquarian bookshop in London. She studied playwriting at the Theatre Guild in New York and wrote dramatic scripts in the era of live television. She has written many books for children, as well as articles for the *New Yorker* and *Harper's* magazines, before becoming the author of *Underfoot in Show Business*, *The Duchess of Bloomsbury Street*, *Apple of My Eye* and *Q's Legacy*. More recently, her witty broadcasts for BBC Radio's 'Woman's Hour' were published as *Letter from New York*. She has lived all her adult life in New York.

The Helene Hanff Omnibus

Underfoot in Show Business
84, Charing Cross Road
The Duchess of Bloomsbury Street
Apple of My Eye
Q's Legacy

WARNER BOOKS

A *Warner* Book

This edition first published in Great Britain in 1993 by Warner Books

THE HELENE HANFF OMNIBUS Copyright © 1993 by Helene Hanff

Previously published separately:
UNDERFOOT IN SHOW BUSINESS first published in Great Britain in 1980
by André Deutsch Ltd.
Published by Futura Publications in 1981, reprinted 1986, 1989.
Copyright © 1961, 1962, 1980 by Helene Hanff
84, CHARING CROSS ROAD first published in Great Britain in 1971
by André Deutsch Ltd.
Published (with *The Duchess of Bloomsbury Street*) by Futura Publications in 1976,
reprinted 1981, 1982 (twice), 1983 (twice), 1984, 1987 (twice), 1989, 1990 (twice),
and by Warner Books in 1992.
Copyright © 1970 by Helene Hanff
THE DUCHESS OF BLOOMSBURY STREET first published in Great Britain
in 1974 by André Deutsch Ltd.
Published (with *84, Charing Cross Road*) by Futura Publications in 1976, reprinted 1981, 1982
(twice), 1983 (twice), 1984, 1987 (twice), 1989, 1990 (twice) and by Warner Books in 1992.
Copyright © 1973 by Helene Hanff
APPLE OF MY EYE first published in Great Britain in 1977 by André Deutsch Ltd.
Published by Futura Publications in 1978, reprinted 1978 (twice), 1984, 1985, 1987, 1988,
and by Warner Books in 1992.
Copyright © 1977 by Helene Hanff.
Q'S LEGACY first published in Great Britain in 1985 by André Deutsch Ltd.
Published by Futura Publications in 1986.
Copyright © 1985 by Helene Hanff

The moral right of the author has been asserted.

A CIP catalogue record for this book is available from the British Library.

ISBN 0 7515 0600 1

Typeset by Leaper & Gard Ltd, Bristol, England
Printed and bound in Great Britain by Clays Ltd, St. Ives plc

Warner Books
A Division of
Little, Brown and Company (UK) Limited
165 Great Dover Street
London SE1 4YA

CONTENTS

Underfoot in Show Business

The day I finished the book, I celebrated by phoning Maxine in Hollywood.

'Do you want to hear the dedication?' I asked her.

'Go ahead,' said Maxine.

So I read it to her.

To all stagestruck kids who ever have,
or ever will,
set out to crash the theatre.

'What do you think of it?' I asked.

'It's MUCH too sentimental,' said Maxine. 'Why don't you just dedicate it to me?'

So what the hell—

This book is for Maxine

Contents

To the Reader

You may have noticed this book was not written by Noel Coward. It's a book about show business, where fame is the stock in trade, and it's written by a name you've never heard of and probably can't pronounce. There is a simple explanation for this.

Each year, hundreds of stagestruck kids arrive in New York determined to crash the theatre, firmly convinced they're destined to be famous Broadway stars or playwrights. One in a thousand turns out to be Noel Coward.

This book is about life among the other 999. By one of them.

Helene Hanff

1

Flanagan's Law

We'll begin with the law that governs the life of every one of the 999 from the day he or she first arrives in New York, which was first explained to me by a stage manager named Bill Flanagan. Flanagan's law of the theatre is:

No matter what happens to you, it's unexpected.

You can even work it backward. Thus if you know I never got anywhere in the theatre you can deduce from Flanagan's Law that my theatrical career must have got off to a magnificent start. And it did, back home in Philadelphia on the shining day when I got a letter from Theresa Helburn, co-producer of the Theatre Guild.

This was at the tag end of the Depression, and after one year of college I'd had to quit and go to work. I got a job as typist in the basement of a diesel-engine school. Twelve dollars a week and all the grease I could carry home on me. In my spare time I wrote plays. And one evening when I came home from work, my mother told me she'd heard on the radio that an organization called the Bureau of New Plays was sponsoring a playwriting contest. It was open to 'young people of college age' and the three winners were to be awarded $1,500 fellowships.

'I sent away for an application blank for you,' she said. The application blank arrived and informed me I could submit as many plays as I chose. I'd already written three, but reading them over I didn't like any of them much. It was only October and since the deadline for submissions was January 1, I decided to write some new ones for the contest.

In the next three weeks, during lulls in the diesel-engine basement and at home in the evening, I wrote a new three-act play, since writing a three-act play takes no time at all when you haven't got any idea what you're doing. At the end of the three weeks I was fired, leaving me free to write three more plays during November and December. I sent all four off to the contest. And then, since the results weren't to be announced till March 15, I put the whole thing out of my mind and went job-hunting.

I landed a nice quiet situation as secretary to two musicians – a band leader and a saxophone player-teacher – who shared an office. The dance band played mostly subdebutante parties. In order to sell his band to the subdebs' mothers, Van, the band leader, had to know well in advance when the approved boys' schools had their Christmas and Easter vacations, since no mother scheduled a party without assuring her daughter a good long 'stag line.' So part of my job was to write haughtily condescending letters to the headmasters of Andover, Exeter, Hotchkiss, Lawrenceville and so forth, requesting the dates of their holidays 'in order to facilitate the planning of the coming social season.' I signed the letters *Baroness Helena von Hanff, Social Secretary.*

My two bosses played in a luncheon-music ensemble in the Ritz-Carlton dining room so they were entitled to a Ritz mailbox and enough Ritz stationery for me to write the letters on. After I mailed the letters, I'd stop in at the Ritz every few days on my lunch hour to collect the answers.

Now it's one thing to sound like a haughty noblewoman on paper, and quite another to look it. I didn't look it. I had a dumpy little figure and the clothes I bought off the sale racks in Wanamaker's basement didn't improve it. I had straight mouse-colored hair which I couldn't afford to have cut or set very often, I wore glasses, and I had as much poise as any young girl who's never been anywhere or done anything and most of the time isn't exactly sure who she is.

Thus equipped, I had to lope up to the Ritz-Carlton desk, tell the clerk I was Baroness von Hanff and ask for my mail. This so unnerved me it was a positive pleasure to get back to the office and work on my current second act through a two-hour saxophone lesson.

That's where I was working when, on a Friday early in February, the letter came. My father and my two older brothers all got home from work that evening before I did. I walked into the living-room and found the whole family gathered in awed silence around a white envelope that lay on our wobbly marble-topped coffee table. My mother handed me the letter. On the back of the envelope was the printed legend, HOTEL DORSET, NEW YORK CITY. Above this was written in ink, 'Theresa Helburn.'

I stared at it and my knees went weak. I sat down abruptly on the worn blue sofa and stared round at my parents and my brothers, and still nobody spoke. Nothing so momentous had ever happened in our family.

Both my parents were passionate theatregoers. My father in his youth had run away from college to go on the stage as a song-and-dance man. His show-business career lasted only two years. He got stranded in Montana and wired home for money, and my grandmother sent him a train ticket instead.

'When he came home,' my mother told me, 'he had lice or something, and your grandmother threw him into the bathtub, burned all his clothes, and told him he was through with the theatre.'

So he became a shirt salesman, married my mother and settled down. But Philadelphia was a favorite tryout city for Broadway plays, and my father spent the rest of his life swapping shirts for passes with all the box-office men in Philadelphia. This was an ideal arrangement in the thirties because box-office men had too many empty theatre seats and not enough shirts. So throughout the Depression, though the taxes on our house weren't paid or the installments on the old secondhand car, and though the prescription for my mother's new glasses went unfilled, every Monday night our whole family went to theatre.

We always brought a program home, to be pasted in the Theatre Book, a large album in which my parents kept the program of every show they saw, each program marked with a pencilled letter in the upper right-hand corner: E, G, F, or R. E for Excellent, G for Good, F for Fair, R for Rotten. On rainy evenings, my brothers pored over the book, scanning the cast lists of 1920s plays for the names of bit players who had since become Hollywood stars: Humphrey Bogart,

Bette Davis, Barbara Stanwyck. But in our house such names never carried the weight of genuine theatre names – Shaw and the Lunts, Noel Coward and O'Neill.

To my parents, the theatre was a large, many-mansioned religion. The *sanctum sanctorum* of this religion was the Theatre Guild, then presided over by its co-producers, Theresa Helburn and Lawrence Langner. The Theatre Guild was the most prestigious of producing organizations, celebrated for its lofty dedication to the theatre as Art. Even my brothers, though agnostic as they grew older, had been firmly reared in this faith and, like my parents, regarded the Guild with awe. Now here they all were, contemplating a letter from the High Priestess herself – addressed to Sis. I come of a noisy family, and never before or after were they so quiet as when they watched me open that letter.

'Dear Miss Hanff,' it read. 'I am interested in your work. Can you come to New York to lunch with me on Tuesday? I enclose the fare.'

Enclosed was a check for five dollars.

During dinner we all shouted happily at each other that the Bureau of New Plays must be the Theatre Guild in disguise and Terry Helburn must be the contest judge and wouldn't she be pleased to learn my family never missed a Theatre Guild production.

I went through the weekend in a fog. On Monday, I showed the letter to my two bosses, who said I could have Tuesday off. All day Monday I worried about what to wear, and wished I had the money to have my hair done.

On Monday night, my father triumphantly brought home for me a new green rayon suit which he had got wholesale from a friend. The suit was a brighter green than I would have chosen, and not precisely my size, but my mother took it in at the waist and let it out at the hips and cut off the row of threads that hung from the hem, and we decided it looked great.

On Tuesday morning, wearing my old blue winter coat with the grey fur collar over the new green suit, I boarded the train for New York armed with a round-trip ticket and enough money for a cab to the Hotel Dorset.

It was an ostentatiously quiet residential hotel with an elegantly uniformed doorman. But if you had a personal appointment with Theresa Helburn you were not to be intimidated by a doorman.

Reeking with poise, I sailed grandly past him into the plush lobby and up to the desk and informed the lady behind it that I wished to see Miss Theresa Helburn.

'She's expecting me,' I added graciously.

The desk clerk looked surprised.

'I don't think she's here,' she said. 'I think she moved out.'

My *sangfroid* evaporated.

'She must be here!' I said in a high-pitched bleat. 'She wrote to me on your stationery!'

I showed the lady my envelope with HOTEL DORSET and 'Theresa Helburn' on the back. She nodded pleasantly but without conviction.

'Just a minute, I'll see,' she said, and disappeared into a small office beyond the desk. Then she came back.

'Miss Helburn moved out,' she said. 'Try the Warwick.' And she turned away to greet a pair of mink-clad arrivals.

I left the lobby and went out to the sidewalk and stood there in a panic. I didn't know where the Warwick was; I didn't have money for another cab so I'd have to find it by bus or on foot, with no guarantee Theresa Helburn would be there when I found it.

The Dorset doorman must have sensed the commotion in me because he bowed in courtly fashion and asked if he might be of assistance.

'I'm looking for Miss Theresa Helburn,' I quavered. 'She wrote and told me to meet her here, and now they say she's moved out, and I know if she moved she'd have let me know!'

Once more I produced my envelope. The doorman raised an arm and pointed a forefinger at a residential hotel directly across the street.

'She moved back to the Warwick,' he said. Then he leaned down and whispered conspiratorially: 'Flop!'

'Pardon?' I said.

'Miss Helburn lives at the Warwick,' he explained. 'But when the Guild has too many flops in a row she decides the Warwick is bringing her bad luck and she moves over here to us.'

'Doesn't she have flops here?' I asked.

'Oh, yes,' he said. 'Then she moves back to the Warwick.' He gave me a prodigious wink. 'You go on over there; you'll find her.'

So I went across the street to the Warwick and through another elegant lobby to the desk and asked the desk clerk tensely whether

Miss Helburn was registered. And when he said he'd ring her suite, relief flooded through me.

While he rang, I watched the parade of glamorous people through the lobby. It was almost one o'clock, and sleekly beautiful women buried in furs were on their way to the dining-room, where they were met by full-chested, middle-aged men. I became conscious of my old blue coat and took it off and draped it over my arm to let my new suit show.

The desk clerk gave me a suite number and told me to go right up. I was the only passenger in the elevator, and now that I was actually going to come face to face with Theresa Helburn my heart pounded so loudly I was afraid the elevator operator would hear it. He let me out at the tenth floor and I went down the long carpeted hall to a door at the end and pressed the bell. Chimes rang mellowly inside, and I hoped it would be a maid instead of a butler who opened the door, but I straightened to my full five-feet-three and prepared to deal with either.

Terry herself opened the door, and I gawked at her: she was barely five feet tall, making me feel suddenly large. She had short, fluffy white hair, bright blue eyes, a blunt square nose and a blunt square chin – and awed though I was, she reminded me then and ever after of a shrewd, friendly toy bulldog.

'Hello, dear,' she said. 'Come in. Give me your coat.'

I stepped into the spacious, impersonal hotel living-room, and Terry took my coat and waved around at a sofa and a couple of armchairs and said:

'Sit down, dear.'

Being awkward as well as nearsighted, I lunged at the nearest armchair and tripped over what appeared to be a grey-and-white fur coat lying on the floor beside it – whereat the grey-and-white fur coat rose to its four feet with a mildly indignant bass bark.

'Go away, Blunder, and sit down somewhere,' Terry advised the fur coat. Blunder was one of those mammoth, improbable Old English sheepdogs with a face so immersed in shaggy fur you had to guess where his eyes were. I sat down in the armchair and Blunder walked off to the middle of the rug and sat down facing me.

'When I bought him,' said Terry, 'everybody called him "Terry's blunder" so that's what I named him. I'll put some lipstick on and we'll go down to the dining-room.'

She went off to the bedroom and I got up and stole a look in the mirror over the sofa. My hair needed combing, my skirt had acquired a thousand small, knifelike creases, and a whole new crop of threads had sprouted from the hem. I didn't have a comb, I didn't have scissors and I didn't have nerve enough to ask for either. I sat back down, very low in my mind, and the sight of my unhappy face obviously moved Blunder because he got up, walked over to me, put his massive front paws on my shoulders and gave me a broad, wet kiss.

Terry meanwhile was calling questions about my education, job and taste in plays. While I answered, Blunder got as much of himself onto my lap as would fit, kissing me in a transport of enthusiasm which removed the last vestiges of powder and lipstick.

And so, as I trailed Terry into the Warwick dining-room, past a gantlet of chic women who called to her from every table, my green suit with the threads hanging from it was covered evenly from shoulder to hem with grey-white sheepdog hair.

Terry sailed to a back table where, she said, we could talk in peace. A waiter brought imposing menus, and Terry, after studying her menu for a minute and me for another minute, announced I was too young to drink in the middle of the day and advised me to try the creamed chicken. The ordering thus disposed of, she got down to business.

'Your plays are terrible,' she told me, beaming. 'Just terrible!' And she laughed. 'Never mind. You have talent.'

She told me the Bureau of New Plays was financed by several Hollywood studios and that she herself had nothing to do with the contest, though the Guild 'might do something for the winners.'

'I lent them my secretary as a playreader,' she said, 'and when she finds a script she thinks shows talent, she steals it for me.' She grinned at me. 'I've got all four of your plays, but the judges don't know it. I'll put them back when I'm through with them.'

Lunch arrived and she stared at the creamed chicken and then allowed that Play No. 4 wasn't as bad as the others and after lunch she'd show me how to rewrite it. Then she asked whether I planned to change my name. I said it hadn't occurred to me. For the next ten minutes, between bites of her chicken, Terry repeated my name aloud ten or twelve times, with varying inflections. Then she nodded decisively.

'Keep it,' she said. 'If anybody ever gets it straight, they'll remember it.'

After coffee, we went back up to her suite where she worked all afternoon with me reconstructing Play No. 4. When I left her at five, she said:

'Bring me the first-act revisions next Tuesday. If you don't have the fare, borrow it from your parents and I'll reimburse you. And bring me a copy of the play for myself so I can put this one back.'

She told me which Fifth Avenue bus would take me to Penn Station and I floated home to Philadelphia.

For the next six weeks, from early February to mid-March, I went to see Terry every Tuesday. My two bosses had to close their office and go their separate ways so I was out of work again, but Terry said it was just as well because I needed to study. She had me buy Aristotle's *Poetics* and Stanislavski's *My Life in Art* and *An Actor Prepares* and Lawson's *Theory and Technique of Playwriting* and quizzed me on certain key passages in each to make sure I understood them.

The Broadway season was then at its height. Terry was looking in on rehearsals of a new Guild play, she was overseeing the road company production of another play about to tour the Guild's subscription cities, and she was working with two authors whose plays the Guild had under option. All afternoon every Tuesday as we worked, the phone rang, the desk sent up importunate messages from stars, agents, directors, and Terry's harassed secretary hurried in and out with reminders of auditions and backers' conferences and memos on contracts and run-throughs, vainly trying to keep Terry from wasting the whole afternoon on me. And week after week, Terry went on wasting it.

The Tuesday before March 15 – when the contest winners were to be announced – she said to me over lunch:

'I don't know what three names the judges have picked, dear, but if you're not one of the winners don't worry about it. I can take care of you.'

And I was so moved I couldn't even thank her, I just nodded dumbly. At dinner that night, I explained airily to my family that I really didn't care whether I won a fellowship or not.

Which was a good thing because March 13 and 14 came and went, with no word from the Bureau of New Plays. Since the winners were to go on the radio to accept their fellowships at a ceremonial dinner on the fifteenth, I thought it unlikely that word would come as late as that morning. And sure enough, nothing came in the mail on the morning of the fifteenth.

In spite of Terry's warning, I was disappointed. To console myself, I went downtown and shopped for a spring outfit to wear-to-New-York-on-Tuesdays. I bought a navy suit with a white collar and navy shoes and bag, but it took me all day since the less you have to spend the longer it takes you to find what you want. So it was five o'clock when, lugging my bundles, I turned the corner of our block, started up the street toward our house – and stopped in my tracks.

Camped on our doorstep were half a dozen reporters and photographers talking to my mother. She saw me and beckoned frantically, and I loped into a run, bundles flapping.

'Miss Helburn's on the phone,' my mother called as I came within earshot. 'She wants to know where you are.'

I ran up the front steps and into the house, my mother following and the press bringing up the rear.

'You won,' my mother said. 'You're the only girl. You're the youngest. The newspapers got a telegram.'

I picked up the phone and said hello, but Terry had hung up. Feeling lightheaded, I sat down to be interviewed and photographed. Just as the press was leaving, the phone rang again and I hurried to answer it.

'Why aren't you in New York?' Terry demanded 'You go on the air at seven-forty-five!'

'I just found out about it!' I said. 'I wasn't notified. I didn't get a letter or a telegram or anything!'

'Well, you knew you won,' said Terry. 'You've been seeing me for weeks.'

It was no time to answer: 'But you said –.' I changed into the new blue suit, took the next train to New York and went on the radio with the other two winners to accept the fellowship. Two months later, Terry took me to Westport, Connecticut, to work as an apprentice at the Guild's summer theatre; and in the fall I moved to New York on my fellowship money, having been enrolled by Terry in a playwriting seminar to be conducted by the Theatre Guild.

And since nobody had told me about Flanagan's Law, I didn't realize that with a start like that, I was positively certain to get nowhere at all in the theatre.

Footnote to Chapter 1:

It Doesn't Pay
to Educate Playwrights

Before I'd been in New York a month, I made the shocked discovery that most people who worked in the theatre made fun of the Theatre Guild. You mentioned the Guild at Sardi's (shyly and proudly) and everybody died laughing.

What baffled me about this was that the laughers included the stars and playwrights, directors and designers who were most impressed by the Guild's artistic standards and most eager to be involved in Guild productions.

Then what was so funny?

Consider the saga of the Bureau of New Plays and its fellowship winners, and the playwriting seminar the Guild conducted for them. It was the sort of high-minded fiasco that could have happened only to the Theatre Guild.

The Bureau of New Plays had been founded one year earlier and had awarded two fellowships that year, giving the winners $1,500 each and sending them on their way. During the second year, when I was one of the winners, the Theatre Guild stepped in.

'You're doing this all wrong,' said the Theatre Guild to the Bureau of New Plays. 'It's a great mistake to give young writers money and send them wandering off on their own. Playwrights need training! So this year,' finished the Theatre Guild, 'you give them the money and we'll give them the training.'

Having hatched this lofty and commendable project, the Guild rounded up twelve promising young playwrights and enrolled us in a seminar. The Guild had its own building and theatre on West Fifty-second Street, and on a mild September afternoon we gathered in the third-floor boardroom for our first session, to be conducted by Lawrence Langner and Terry, the Guild's co-producers.

At first glance, it was a typical boardroom, large and quiet, with wide windows and a polished mahogany board table long enough to seat all of us. What gave the room its quality, and awed us into silence as we took our places at the table, were the faces that looked down at us from massively framed photographs on the walls.

There was Shaw, with a pixie smile and a note scrawled across the beard. There was O'Neill, staring somberly into space, the Lunts in a flamboyant scene from *The Taming of the Shrew*, Maurice Evans as Falstaff, and Ethel Barrymore and Gertie Lawrence, and George Gershwin with the original cast of *Porgy and Bess*.

The hallowed history of the Theatre Guild flowed out from those walls as Lawrence Langner looked into our solemn faces and told us the future of the theatre rested with us. Terry added her own welcome and then Lawrence outlined the seminar.

We were to meet in the board room three afternoons a week, in classes to be taught by producer Cheryl Crawford, director Lee Strasberg, and Guild playreader John Gassner. Occasionally Terry or Lawrence would lecture on production, and from time to time famous actors, actresses, playwrights and directors would be brought in as guest lecturers.

In addition, each student would attend morning rehearsals of a new Broadway play. There were several new plays to be produced by the Guild. Cheryl Crawford was also producing one; Lee Strasberg was directing one; and John Gassner had written one. Each of us was to be assigned to rehearsals of one of these productions. We would also be given tickets to Broadway plays.

Thus began the education of twelve young would-be playwrights, an intensive professional training the luckless winners of the previous year's fellowships might well have envied. Nothing was overlooked, no time or trouble was spared; and in March, when the seminar ended, everybody agreed it had been a great success.

There was, to be sure, one small hitch. We had attended rehearsals of our mentors' productions so that we might study and analyze the best new plays, those which had met the high standards of the Theatre Guild.

The play produced by Guild protégée Cheryl Crawford flopped.

The play written by Guild playreader John Gassner flopped.

The play directed by Lee Strasberg flopped.

All four plays produced by the Theatre Guild flopped.

But that's a detail. The worth of the seminar itself can fairly be judged only by the ultimate achievements of the twelve neophyte playwrights so carefully educated. What became of them?

One – Danny Taradash – became a screenwriter with an Academy Award to his credit. A second – John Crosby – became a famous TV critic.

No. 3 became a physician, No. 4 is a short-story writer, No. 5 manages a movie theatre, Nos. 6 and 7 are English professors, Nos. 8 and 9 became TV writers, Nos. 10 and 11 became screenwriters, and No. 12 has a private income and seems not to have done much of anything. (You'll find out soon enough which of these I was.)

The Theatre Guild, convinced that fledgling playwrights need training as well as money, exhausted itself training twelve of us – and not one of the twelve ever became a Broadway playwright.

The two fellowship winners who, the previous year, had been given $1,500 and sent wandering off on their own were Tennessee Williams and Arthur Miller.

2

'No Casting Today But Keep in Touch!'

When Maxine and I met and became best friends – in the backstage ladies' room of the Morosco Theatre – I thought she was the most glamorous creature on earth. Maxine was a bona fide Broadway actress.

We met during my fellowship winter when I was assigned to rehearsals of a comedy called *Yankee Fable*, in which Maxine had an impressively large role as the comedy-ingenue – impressive to me because Maxine was my own age. Sitting in the dark, empty theatre during the first two days of rehearsal, I had gawked more at the redheaded comedy-ingenue than at the star. It awed me that someone as young as I was should be so poised and assured and so thoroughly at home on a Broadway stage as Maxine was.

On the third day, I went into the backstage ladies' room to wash before lunch, and the redhead was standing at the sink. She was fussing with the straps under the shoulders of her white silk blouse, and when she saw me she turned beet-red. I smiled uncertainly, wondering what she was blushing at.

'Have you got a safety pin?' she asked.

'No, I don't,' I mumbled, tongue-tied in the presence of so much glamour. She turned away and went on fussing with the brassiere straps or whatever they were, and as I washed my hands I goggled at her covertly, never having seen a real actress at such close range.

Maxine had the kind of beauty people goggled at anyway. She had thick masses of hair the color of flaming autumn leaves that curled about her face in loose ringlets, a complexion like milk and one of those swan necks you see in 1890s portraits. It was when I had got as far as her neck that I noticed something peculiar below it. Maxine's left breast appeared to be a couple of inches higher than her right.

She saw my puzzled stare and her eyes suddenly filled with tears.

'What's the matter?' I asked.

'It's my damn falsies,' she said. 'I can't get them to stay put.'

'Can't you take them off?' I asked timidly.

'How can I go back onstage with no bosoms when I had them all morning?' she demanded. 'Everybody would notice!'

'Oh, I don't think they would,' I said earnestly. 'Listen, I've been watching you all morning. Why don't you take them off and walk up and down, and I'll tell you if I notice the difference.'

Maxine removed the falsies, buttoned her white blouse, threw her shoulders back and walked away a few steps to give me a profile view. Then she turned and faced me bravely.

'Nobody,' I stated positively, 'will notice a thing! You don't need falsies, you have a lovely figure!'

'I'm playing a sexy part, I wouldn't have got it if they'd known I was flat-chested,' said Maxine.

'You're wonderful in the part!' I said. 'They hired you for your talent, not your bust!'

'I nearly died when I felt them slip during the last scene,' she said, wrapping the falsies carefully in Kleenex and putting them in her handbag. 'I'm nervous enough in this company. They're all such pros.'

'Well, you're a pro!' I said.

Maxine giggled.

'I only graduated from the American Academy last June,' she said. 'The Guild took me out of the senior class and gave me my first job and when the show closed I went back and graduated. This is only my second show.'

'You must be terrific, if you made the American Academy of Dramatic Art and then got taken out of the senior class by the Theatre Guild!' I said. And I added, trying to sound offhand about it: 'You know, it's funny: I'm a Theatre Guild protégée, too.'

'I know,' said Maxine. 'I asked somebody who you were because nobody else in the company is my age, and they said you were a playwright sent over by the Guild. That's why I never had the nerve to talk to you.'

She saw the uncomprehending look on my face and explained:

'People with brains intimidate me.' And she added simply, 'I don't have any brains.'

I laughed. I think I knew that people who really have no brains don't know it. And having read my Stanislavski, I knew that acting demanded a high degree of intelligence. But I understood what she meant: we both grew up equating brains with college degrees.

'I don't have any brains either! I only went to college for one year,' I assured her. 'I don't even know anything about the theatre and you're a professional Broadway actress!'

'My name's Maxine Stuart,' she said. 'Have you got a lunch date?'

So we went to lunch together at Ralph's, an Eighth Avenue restaurant patronized exclusively by the 999 theatre hopefuls who couldn't afford Sardi's.

After that, we exchanged daily confidences in the backstage ladies' room under a large daisy-sprinkled wall poster that assured us 'Syphilis CAN Be Cured!' By the end of *Yankee Fable's* three weeks of rehearsal, I was firmly convinced Maxine was a finer comedienne than the show's star and she had read my latest play and pronounced it far superior to *Yankee Fable*. Damon and Pythias had met.

Yankee Fable went to Washington, D.C., for the usual two-week out-of-town tryout. It opened in Washington, closed in Washington and died in Washington. In two weeks, therefore, Maxine was back home living the normal everyday life of a glamorous young actress.

A young actress engages in three kinds of activity. First, there's physical training. An actress has to train everything from her vocal cords to her toe muscles, so that her body – known to Stanislavski disciples as her Instrument – will be in perfect condition for her life onstage. Second, there's 'making the rounds': paying daily or twice-weekly visits to the offices of producers rumored to be casting new shows, interspersed – not often enough – with auditions for producers and casting directors. Third, and rarest, there's the glorious achievement: rehearsing and appearing in a Broadway play.

I first learned about Maxine's method of training her Instrument on the Sunday after *Yankee Fable* died in Washington when Maxine invited me to her house for lunch.

Maxine lived with her parents in a big, comfortable apartment on West End Avenue, and in no time at all that apartment became my second home. Maxine's parents were a short, plump, benign middle-class couple comfortingly like my own parents. They knew I lived in a furnished room and ate my meals in the nearest cafeteria, and being warm-hearted people they got themselves rapidly trapped into feeding me oftener than the cafeteria did.

Maxine's mother opened the door to me at noon that Sunday. Beyond her I could see Maxine's father stretched out on the sofa with the *Sunday Times*. As I opened my mouth to say hello to both of them, there was a piercing scream from the bathroom down the hall.

'Oh, NO!' screamed Maxine, the 'NO' turning into a long, blood-curdling wail that raised the hair on my scalp.

'Did you have any breakfast, dear?' Maxine's mother asked, unperturbed by her screaming daughter. 'Would you like some orange juice?'

As I said no-thank-you, Maxine shrieked again, and Maxine's father said:

'If you want the theatre section it's in Maxine's room.' So as I went down the hall to Maxine's room I concluded she was rehearsing for an audition for some melodrama.

She wasn't; she was exercising her vocal cords. You do this by taking a very deep breath, opening your mouth very wide to achieve a full-throated scream, starting your 'Oh, NO' at high C and then wailing straight down the scale to the lowest bass note you can reach. Like this:

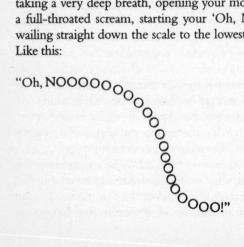

"Oh, NOOOOOOOOOOOOOOOOOOOOOOOOO!"

It greatly increases your vocal range, not to mention the tempers of the people living underneath you.

When she got through with her vocal cords, Maxine limbered up her tongue, teeth and palate. This limbering-up involved the Peter-Piper-picked-a-peck-of-pickled-peppers exercise, extended to include Sam-sometimes-sends-sister-Susie-sums, and Tom's-thumb's-thinner-than-Tim's-thumb-thus-Tim's-thumb's-thicker-than-Tom's.

Sam-and-Susie was the hardest because you had to pronounce the last *s* on 'sometimes' and the first *s* on 'sends' separately, and the last *s* on 'sends' and the first *s* on 'sister' separately. When you've got that one licked, try saying 'granddaughter,' pronouncing each *d* separately.

Once Maxine's cords, tongue, teeth and palate were loosened up for the day, she got to work on her resonance. If you want to be sure your stage voice will positively reverberate with resonance, start humming, and as you hum put your index fingers lightly on each side of the bridge of your nose and see whether your fingers can feel any vibration. (Your nose will vibrate lower down but this doesn't count; it has to vibrate up at the bridge.)

If the bridge isn't vibrating, you're humming back down in your throat instead of up front in your resonance chamber, which is in the same neighborhood as your sinuses. You have to bring your entire hum forward and then push it up and keep pushing it farther and farther up till your fingers can feel the bridge of your nose vibrate.

Once the bridge vibrates, you're on the right track but you've still got a long way to go, because to attain really first-class resonance you have to push your hum clear up through your nasal passages to the beginning of your forehead. Maxine eventually achieved this. She put my fingers between her eyebrows and hummed and I almost died of awe when I felt her forehead vibrate.

(After that, when I took my daily hike through Central Park – so my hips would be as slim and my posture as perfect as Maxine's – I worked on my hum. But I never even got it up to the bridge of my nose except once, and then it occurred to me that a playwright's resonance didn't come from the nasal passages so I gave it up.)

When she was working and in funds, Maxine augmented the training of her Instrument with singing and dancing lessons. It was during that first winter that Maxine told me she was starting singing lessons with a vocal coach recommended by Terry, and the phrases 'singing lessons' and 'vocal coach' filled me with respectful admiration. After that, she began talking learnedly about Vocal Technique and Projection. But one day when we were window-shopping on Fifth Avenue and talking about a new musical, I began to sing one of the songs from it under my breath. Maxine joined in, in her authoritative, resonant voice, and after two bars I stopped and stared at her.

'You're singing it all on one note!' I said.

'I know,' said Maxine. 'I can't carry a tune.'

I don't know how many singing teachers wore themselves out trying to teach Maxine to carry a tune. None of them ever succeeded. Which was unfortunate, because producers assume that any actress can sing passably enough to manage the refrain of a popular song if a scene in a play happens to call for it.

So a procession of vocal coaches worked long and hard before they abandoned their efforts to teach Maxine to sing and, instead, taught her to manipulate her speaking voice and project it in a large theatre. With phenomenal results: Maxine's powers of projection were such that she could turn to me, in the first balcony of Loew's Eighty-third Street movie theatre, and whisper:

'Do you think it's safe to use the ladies' room here? I have to go,' and be heard clearly by everybody sitting below us on the orchestra floor and above us in the second balcony, not to mention the people on our own level who turned to stare at us from rows around.

Then there were dancing lessons. In pursuit of that grace and lightness necessary to the perfection of her Instrument, Maxine decided to take up ballet. For a whole year, we took ballet lessons from a Greek who taught us a little Greek classic dancing on the side. I went along, partly because Maxine said it would tone up my system, but mostly because I was studying Greek at the time and had visions of carrying on chatty conversations with the ballet teacher in beginner's ancient Greek.

(Studying Greek was one of the things I was doing to perfect *my* Instrument. My Instrument was the English language – and since the English language derives so largely from Latin and Greek, how could I hope to select the precisely right English word every time I wrote one, if I didn't know the Greek or Latin root of every word in the language? as I explained impressively to Maxine.)

Every morning after she trained her Instrument, Maxine prepared for her second activity – making the rounds – by spending a painstaking hour applying street makeup. First she pencilled feathery brown eyebrows over the pale pink ones God had thoughtlessly given her. Then she overlaid her pale pink eyelashes with feathery brown mascara. Next came rouge and lipstick, each chosen with no more care than the average girl would spend in choosing her wedding dress; and finally face powder, dusted on and then carefully brushed off. When her makeup was complete, Maxine looked as if she were wearing no makeup at all. This job done, she climbed into high heels and a chic suit and was off on her rounds of producers' and agents' offices.

In every one of these offices, there was a sign on the wall saying, *No casting today. Please leave your name;* or, more cheerily, *No casting today but keep in touch!* You could walk into the office of a producer who was casting a new musical, and find a horde of young actors and actresses who'd been summoned to audition overflowing the sofas, chairs and windowsills till late arrivals had to sit cross-legged on the floor, and above them on the wall a large sign stubbornly insisted, *No casting today.* The signs were like pictures; they were never taken down.

So kids making the rounds learned to ignore them. They also devised ingenious methods for forcing the attention of the receptionist in the producer's outer office, who was usually the only person they were permitted to see. Say you were a young actor or actress making the rounds and you walked into the office of a producer who was casting a new play. You stepped up to the desk and asked politely if you might see the producer.

'No-casting-today,' said the receptionist in a bored tone and without looking up. 'If-you-want-to-leave-your-name –' And her pencil moved to a pad, but she still didn't look up. This was very frustrating because you might have heard you were exactly the physical type the producer was looking for, and how could the receptionist know this if she didn't look at you? So you invented a trick to force her to focus on you. Bill Flanagan of Flanagan's Law, for instance, changed his first name to Brazelius and added the initial P. when he made the rounds.

'She asks you to leave your name,' he explained to me, 'and if you say "Bill Flanagan" she writes it down without looking up. But if you say

"Brazelius P. Flanagan" she looks up. She asks you how to spell it, she stares at you to see if you're serious – and she remembers the name later.'

He claimed he got a lot of work on the strength of that Brazelius. Of course, when he signed a contract, he reverted to Bill.

Maxine's trick was not to answer when a receptionist asked her name.

'You-wanta-leave-your-name?' the receptionist would mumble, pencil poised above her writing pad, eyes on her manicure. Maxine would stand silent until the receptionist was finally forced to look up to see if she was still there. Once the receptionist looked up, she saw Maxine's mop of flaming red hair, which was dramatic enough to be remembered.

Having made the rounds of producers' and agents' offices faithfully, Maxine was regularly rewarded by being asked to audition for some new Broadway play. Those auditions not only aged her parents considerably and ruined their digestion and mine; they also conformed to Flanagan's Law by simply defying expectation.

Take, for example, the afternoon when an agent named Eddie sent for Maxine to tell her she was to audition the next morning for the producer and director of what promised to be the new season's outstanding production. The playwright was famous, the two stars were internationally known, the director was the most sought-after. The cast was set except for the comedy-ingenue.

'You are so right for the part,' said Eddie, 'that after they've seen you I don't think they'll bother to hear anybody else read for it! Provided' – and he paused solemnly – 'pro*vided* – you give the best damn audition you've ever given. This is a top-drawer production, dear. I don't want to send you over there unless you feel you can give a top-drawer reading.'

Now in the best of times and under tranquil conditions, Maxine was by nature highly emotional. (We were both by nature highly emotional.) Under the conditions Eddie had created, she was Joan of Arc and *The Snake Pit* combined.

She phoned me that evening and, with death in her voice, asked me to come to her at once; she couldn't stand to be alone and she couldn't stand to be with her parents and she was feeling nauseous and so forth. I hurried up to West End Avenue, arriving just as Maxine's parents were leaving for the movies (I gathered they couldn't stand to be with her either), and Maxine's mother, looking careworn, said:

'She's in her room, dear. You'd better knock.'

I went down the hall and knocked timidly on Maxine's bedroom door. When she opened it, I said, 'Hiya' hollowly, took off my coat and hat and dropped them on the bed – and Maxine promptly had hysterics. That's how I found out it was bad luck in the theatre to put hats on beds.

When we both stopped crying I asked her what kind of temperament the role called for.

'I don't know,' said Maxine coldly. 'It's a secret! I don't know whether to look ingenue or sexy or sophisticated. First Eddie says I'm exactly right for the part, now he admits he hasn't seen the script! Nobody's seen the script!'

She plucked an invisible eyebrow and glared at me in the mirror, her brown eyes snapping with fury.

'. . . incredible people, they have the bloody play MIMEOgraphed and then they dig a hole under the subway and BURY all five hundred copies, God forbid anybody who's going to audition for it should *read* it!'

'What else has Eddie sent you out for?' I asked. 'What type does he think you are?'

The tweezer froze in Maxine's hand. She stood a moment in the attitude of one listening to the distant roll of the tumbrel. And she whispered in horror:

'I'm coming down with a cold.'

In Maxine's life this was the overriding catastrophe. A cold ruined you, it ruined your looks, your resonance, your projection, everything.

'It's not a cold, it's just nerves,' I said.

'There's a prickle in the back of my throat, I'm getting a cold!' She went out to the kitchen and heated a kettle of water and draped a towel over her head and spent the rest of the evening steaming her sinuses while we discussed what she should wear to the audition, what material she should use if they asked her to do her own material, and whether she should tell the blonde star that redheads look very well under pink lights so the star wouldn't veto her as interfering with blonde lighting.

At midnight, when I left her, she was icily calm. She stood in the doorway in her blue bathrobe and bare feet, her fiery hair stuck up in curlers, her nose slathered with freckle cream and her face beet-red from the long steaming, and said in a remote voice:

'I may not call you tomorrow. I know definitely now I'm going to give a ghastly audition.'

'You're going to give a wonderful audition,' I said.

We were both wrong. You were always wrong. You persisted in assuming there were two possibilities and there were always three: the two you thought of and the one that happened.

Maxine arrived at the producer's office and the secretary ushered her into an inner office where four men were waiting for her: producer, director, author, casting director. One sat behind the desk, one was in an armchair, the other two were on the sofa. Having announced Maxine's name, the secretary withdrew, leaving Maxine standing alone in the middle of the room.

The four men stared at her. Nobody spoke. Nobody asked her to sit down, nobody introduced himself, nobody asked her to read. The silence lasted for several minutes during which they went on staring at her. Finally, one of the men spoke.

'I don't see it,' he said.

'I told Eddie what we wanted!' (That was the casting director.)

'I don't see this at all,' the third man agreed. The fourth man said nothing. He had a hangnail and he was working on it. The first man pressed a buzzer and the secretary appeared. Looking past Maxine as if she didn't exist, the first man said to the secretary:

'Who else is out there?' The secretary named another young actress, and the producer said: 'All right, send her in.'

The secretary ushered Maxine out. The audition was over. Maxine met me for lunch afterward at the Astor Drugstore, which was a theatre kids' hangout, and she had even the countermen clutching the walls for support as she acted out the audition for everybody.

There were auditions where she walked out on stage to read and was stopped before she opened her mouth because she was too tall, or too short, for her scene with the leading man. There were auditions where they decided they didn't want a redhead or had thought she was British.

And there was the winter when she was in Florida with a stock company and got a telegram from an agent saying CAN YOU FLY UP

SUNDAY IMPORTANT AUDITION MONDAY MORNING and she flew up and phoned the agent and discovered she was to audition for the New Opera Company.

Nothing daunted, she went out on the New Opera Company stage and did her best comedy material, after which the fat little director came hurtling down the aisle crying:

'Magnificent, liebchen, absolutely perfect for ze part! Now let's hear you zing zomezing.'

Boom. Don't–call–us–we'll–call–you.

Never mind. Once a year came the audition when she actually got the part; and on that day, my friend Maxine owned the earth. She sailed down Fifth Avenue or floated up Broadway in a radiant glow that caused people to stare after her, bemused. Or, as one of her beaux observed to me with a wistful sigh (he wasn't in the theatre):

'Maxine with a job is !ike any other woman in love.'

Of course, after the successful audition came the first five days of rehearsal during which Maxine and her parents and I all lived in a permanent state of acid indigestion because during the first five days of rehearsal, an actress could be fired. Not till the sixth day was she given a contract. I spent the five probationary evenings cueing Maxine in her lines (while she steamed her sinuses) and saying hello and good-bye to her parents who went off nightly to the movies looking more and more careworn.

From the day she signed the contract, there was nothing more to worry about till the night before the opening when pre-opening night nerves set in. At 11 P.M. on the night before one opening, she threw the New York telephone directory at me (I can't lift it myself without using both hands), whereupon I stalked off and went huffily home to bed, to be awakened at 1 A.M. by the telephone conveying weeping apologies from West End Avenue. (Such evenings consoled me for what I put Maxine through when I was out of work and no producer would buy my play, which was most of the time.)

On opening nights, Maxine's parents were lucky: they weren't allowed to go; they might make her nervous. They went on the second night when the crisis was past.

I was allowed to go to the opening. I sat through each one with my stomach churning and all my fingers crossed. Maxine never gave a bad opening-night performance, but most of the plays she appeared in were the kind of total flops we referred to as 'dawgs.' I'd sit through the three acts gamely and, as soon as the final curtain fell, hurry backstage to Maxine's dressing-room and say the wrong thing.

An actor I knew did a very funny act at parties in which he mimicked the well-meaning friends who always came backstage after an opening to offer foot-in-mouth congratulations. The funniest bit in his act mortified me because it was what I invariably said to Maxine after every one of her openings. I'd hurry backstage, knowing the play was a dawg that wouldn't last a week, walk into Maxine's dressing-room and say earnestly:

'*I* LIKED it! I really did!'

If you can't do better than that, just leave a note with the stage doorman telling your friend she was sensational and go on home.

Maxine appeared in eleven Broadway plays, most of which opened on a Tuesday night. On Wednesday came the flop notices, on Thursday an empty house, on Friday the closing notice went up, on Saturday the show closed and on Sunday Maxine slept it off.

And so, on Monday, she was once more to be found in her parents' apartment on West End Avenue ready to resume the normal daily life of a glamorous young actress by screaming 'Oh, NO!' in the bathroom.

3

If They Take You to Lunch
They Don't Want Your
Play

When a young playwright – temporarily starved out of New York and back in the bosom of her family in Philadelphia – receives two phone calls from two Broadway producers in the same afternoon, and each producer says: 'You've written a wonderful play. When can you come to New York to see me?' the playwright naturally assumes that both producers want to produce her play.

Not until she has hurried off to New York and seen both producers and been left stranded at Penn Station at three in the morning with thirty-five cents and her play unsold does it occur to her that there must have been a flaw in her thinking. Somehow or other, she has failed to understand how producers' minds work.

The phone calls came on a Tuesday in March, a month after I'd gone home for a second wind. I'd hung on in New York for a couple of years after my fellowship year ended, keeping alive on dreary office jobs, from which I was regularly fired for typing my plays on company time. That February, I'd lost the one job too many and when my capital had shrunk to the price of a one-way ticket to Philadelphia, I'd packed my bags, left a new play at my agent's office, said a tearful good-bye to Maxine and crept mournfully home.

The first of the two calls came early in the afternoon as I was trying to get a whole cigarette out of my brother.

My oldest brother was married by then but the middle one was still living at home. I wouldn't say he was exactly working at the time, but he was earning money, which I wasn't. (He later became a big wheel in industry so I'm not allowed to say that his earnings came from playing pool and duplicate bridge in local contests. He was so expert at both games that rich men backed him, won heavily on him and gave him a percentage of their winnings.)

Since my parents were feeding and housing me, I didn't need cash for anything but cigarettes and these my father generally remembered to buy for me. It was when he forgot that I was forced to appeal to my brother's better nature – such as it was. I'd ask him for a cigarette and he'd ponder the request.

'I'd be glad to give you one,' he'd say earnestly, 'but one cigarette won't help you. You'll smoke it – and in half an hour you'll be out of cigarettes again. Now what I'd like to do is find a way to give you enough cigarettes to last you awhile.'

He'd take six or seven cigarettes out of his pack, hold them half-out to me and ponder them. And the minute I reached for one, he'd yank them back and say:

'I know how to do it!'

And he'd take a penknife out of his pocket, cut all six or seven cigarettes in half, and hand me the butts thus accumulated. This was before king-size cigarettes had come on the market, so you know how long half a cigarette was. You couldn't light it without burning your upper lip and the tip of your nose.

I did not stand idly by while he mutilated six cigarettes. But it's very difficult for a girl to get cigarettes by force from a brother who's bigger and taller than she is and has an open penknife in one hand. So as I said, I was trying to appeal to his better nature when the phone rang.

'Miss Hanff?' said a woman's voice at the other end. 'Just a moment, please. Oscar Serlin calling from New York.'

All the blood left my head. Oscar Serlin had produced *Life With Father*, then in its fourth or fifth year on Broadway and with road companies across the country, including one in Philadelphia that was breaking records there in its second year. Of all Broadway hits, this had been the biggest.

'Miss Hanff?' said Oscar Serlin in a deep baritone voice. 'I've read your play. I'm very impressed. When can you come to New York to see me?'

We settled on Friday afternoon and when I hung up I was shaking. I managed to tell my brother the news and he was so impressed he gave me a whole cigarette. I'd only just finished it when the second call came. This one was from a producer we'll call Charlie. He also had a play running on Broadway. It had got mixed reviews but it had been running since early October and was by no means a flop. Said Charlie, without reservation or preamble:

'I think you've written a marvelous play. I want to produce it.'

He went on for half an hour about the characters and the dialogue, which he said were both marvelous, and about the theme of the play which was also marvelous.

'I have some friends who are interested in it and we all want to meet you,' he said. 'When can I give a small dinner party for you?'

I said I was coming to New York on Friday and Charlie said Friday evening would be ideal for the dinner party. He gave me his address and told me again how marvelous the play was and we hung up. I phoned my agent, who congratulated me and ordered me not to set foot in either producer's lair until I'd seen her first.

On Friday, wearing my good spring suit and carrying a new silk blouse (charged to my mother on my prospects) to change into for the dinner party, I set out for New York, with the fare donated by my father, and a nearly full pack of cigarettes and fifty cents for buses donated by my brother.

Hoarding the fifty cents for emergencies, I walked from Penn Station to my agent's office. She welcomed me warmly and gave me instructions. Oscar Serlin, she said, was one of Broadway's most discriminating producers and I was to let him have the play. However, I was to be very, very nice to Charlie because, while she didn't think too highly of his current production, one simply never knew what next year might bring.

I phoned Maxine from my agent's office and told her the news. She was in rehearsal for one of the bombs she was periodically cast in and we shrieked congratulations at each other over the phone.

'Listen, I'll be home all evening,' she said. 'Call me and tell me what happened!'

'I'll phone you before I leave town,' I promised. And wouldn't I just.

I left my agent's office and went around the corner to Oscar Serlin's office in Rockefeller Center. Even the receptionist's room was quietly opulent. I gave the receptionist my name and she smiled and said: 'Oh, yes!' and rang Mr Serlin on the intercom, and then told me to go right in.

I opened the inner-office door and saw, across a vast expanse of carpeting, an imposing desk at the far end of the room from behind which a man rose and held out his hand. Oscar Serlin was over six feet tall and built like a football player. He gave me a warm handclasp, drew up a chair for me, offered me a cigarette from a silver box, lit it for me with a silver lighter, fixed his liquid brown eyes on me and said:

'Tell me about yourself,'

and as far as I was concerned, he was Shakespeare, Sir Galahad and President Roosevelt fused.

I gave him my ten-cent autobiography and he nodded. Then he picked up the blue-bound copy of my play, which was on his desk.

'This is a very bad play,' he said conversationally. 'Your construction's lousy. Your two central characters are very interesting and your dialogue is excellent. But you have to be a carpenter before you can be a cabinet-maker. Let me show you.'

And leaning back in his chair, he reconstructed the entire play for me so easily and brilliantly it left me tongue-tied. When I could speak, I told him I knew I could rewrite it exactly as he'd outlined it and that I thought I could finish it within the standard three-month option period.

It was then that he explained – with some surprise, I thought – that he didn't want to produce the play. He'd just wanted to meet me.

'I want you to keep in touch with me,' he said, 'and I want to see your next play. When are you moving back to New York?'

'I'm trying to find a job in Philly so I can earn enough to come back,' I said, 'but I haven't had any luck so far.'

He nodded and wished me well and walked me to the door; and sadly relinquishing the dream of having my play produced by this god, I left his office and went over to the Taft Hotel to change into my new blouse in their ladies' room.

The Taft Hotel ladies' room charged me a nickel for the use of their john, which is the one health service I thought nobody ought to have to pay for, and I left there vowing never to patronize the Taft Hotel again.

Charlie lived way up on Riverside Drive. I caught a Fifth Avenue double-decker bus, climbed to the top and took the front seat so none of the other passengers could watch me counting my remaining funds. I had a return ticket, thirty-five cents and six cigarettes. Deduct a dime for a bus to Penn Station and another for a bus home from North Philadelphia station, and I had fifteen cents left over – exactly the price of a fresh pack of cigarettes for tomorrow – so l decided to make the six cigarettes last me till I got home to Philadelphia.

Charlie turned out to be a pleasant, bustling little man who welcomed me with enthusiasm and presented me proudly to the assembled dinner guests. They included an elderly lady backer who was deaf and had to be shouted at; a German baron who wrote poetry and planned to direct my play for Charlie though he'd never directed a play before; and a pair of homosexual male twins who were dying to act in my play, which had no parts for them. But everybody was enthusiastic about the play, the martinis were excellent – and all over the living-room, on every table, were wooden boxes and crystal holders chockful of free cigarettes.

We drank to the play, we discussed possible stars for it, we debated whether the Booth Theatre was too small or the Belasco too big, and by the time Charlie led the way into the dining-room I was carelessly dismissing Oscar Serlin as shortsighted.

All I remember about that dinner is my traumatic experience with the first course. Did I tell you I'm very nearsighted? Well, in those days, as Dorothy Parker observed, men never made passes at girls who wore glasses. Being young and female, I never wore mine at a dinner party, certainly not at a dinner party given in my honor by a Broadway producer. The first course arrived in the kind of sherbet glasses my mother used for shrimp cocktail, and all I could see of the stuff in the glass in front of me was that it was white. Peering narrowly down at it, I decided it was crab meat, of which I am very fond, and I took a hungry mouthful of it – and discovered, with apoplectic results, that it wasn't crab meat. I didn't know what it was, but I knew I couldn't swallow it. So, before the fascinated gaze of the entire dinner party, I spit it out.

'It's herring,' Charlie told me. 'Don't you like it?' – a question I bitterly resented since it would be rude to say no and having just spit it out I could hardly say yes. So I can't tell you what else we ate or what we talked about; I spent the rest of the dinner hour patching together the remnants of my aplomb.

After dinner, the other guests departed and Charlie took me to see his current Broadway play. The production was the kind usually described as 'shabby': the sets didn't quite work, the direction was awkward and the play was embarrassing where it was meant to be moving. After the theatre, we adjourned to Sardi's – to talk.

At Sardi's, it turned out that while my play was still marvelous, it wasn't quite marvelous enough. It would be, however, as soon as Charlie rewrote it. What he had in mind was a contract making him co-author. He would then rewrite the play his way and if his version was approved by his backers, he'd produce it.

Had Oscar Serlin offered me such a contract I'd have jumped at it (though Oscar would have found the suggestion that he rewrite an author's play simply bizarre). But where Oscar's revised construction of the play had sounded brilliantly right, Charlie's sounded terrible. Nor did he bolster my confidence in him by telling me what changes he'd personally made in his current play. The scenes I'd found embarrassing were the scenes Charlie had written.

I explained this to Charlie. (Every year I make a vow to learn tact or keep my mouth shut but so far nothing has come of it.) We argued and we talked and we argued and we arrived at no conclusion. Sardi's, on the other hand, did: I looked up and noticed that the waiters were putting chairs up on tables and that we were the only customers left in the restaurant. I plucked Charlie's sleeve as he was finishing a sentence.

'I think Sardi's wants to close,' I said.

We looked at Charlie's watch; it was nearly 3 A.M.

With many apologies, Charlie put me in a cab, gave the driver a dollar and said:

'Take the young lady to her hotel.'

The cab drove off and I told the driver to take me to Penn Station. At Penn Station, the lone night clerk informed me that the next train for Philadelphia was due at 6:35. I couldn't wake up Maxine's family at three in the morning to ask to sleep there. So I sat down on a Penn Station bench to wait for the 6:35.

It was a raw March night, there wasn't anybody else in the waiting room, and Penn Station was saving heat. I'd been sitting there for fifteen chilly minutes trying to get up the nerve to ask the night clerk if he had a blanket, when the stationmaster came along. He stopped, looked down at me and asked politely what I was doing there.

'I'm waiting for the six-thirty-five to Philadelphia,' I said.

He clucked.

'A nice young lady,' he said, 'doesn't want to sit all night in a railroad station!'

And I thought: You won't get any argument out of me, mister, there's no place I wouldn't rather sit.

'Wouldn't it be much better,' he said, 'to go across the street to the Governor Clinton Hotel and get a good night's sleep?'

I don't know why I couldn't tell him I only had thirty-five cents, but I couldn't. And since I was wearing my good suit and silk blouse he couldn't guess it.

'How will it be,' he suggested jovially, 'if I escort you there myself?' And he bowed and offered his arm.

I stood up and he took my arm and we left the station and walked across the street to the Governor Clinton, where the stationmaster explained to the desk clerk that this charming young lady had missed her train and needed a room for the night.

And don't think he didn't stand there at my side till the desk clerk gave me a little cellophane bag with a nightgown and toothbrush in it and summoned a bellhop to take me up to my room.

The bellhop took me up and unlocked the door and switched on the lights for me, and I tipped him a quarter – leaving me a total capital of ten cents, minus the cost of the room (and the nightgown and the toothbrush), which I hadn't had the courage to ask about.

I undressed, decided it was a lovely hotel, crawled into bed at quarter to four and slept like a baby till eleven-fifteen next morning.

At eleven-sixteen I phoned Maxine. It was Saturday and I prayed her rehearsal wasn't scheduled till noon, which was usual on a

Saturday. God heard me and Maxine herself answered the phone.

'You have to come down and get me out of here,' I said. 'I'm at the Governor Clinton in a room I can't pay for. I don't even know how much it costs.'

'Hang up, the operator may be listening in,' said Maxine. 'I'll be right down.'

And she came down and paid the hotel bill. Since her play had been in rehearsal for three weeks and was due to open the following Tuesday (and close the following Saturday), Maxine was in funds and bought me a lavish breakfast before we had another weepy farewell and I went back to Philadelphia.

My mother brushed aside the bad news about the play.

'You've got a job!' she said. 'In the press department of *Life Wtth Father*. It's on the second floor of the Walnut Street Theatre, you start Monday. A man just called an hour ago.'

Oscar Serlin had given the press agent's assistant a paid vacation for the remaining six weeks of the play's run in Philadelphia – just to make room for me, so could I earn my way back to New York.

Oscar and Charlie were only the beginning. During my two months in the *Life With Father* press office, through the two summer months when I worked as prop girl at a summer theatre in Philadelphia and on through September when I finally moved back to New York, I was positively besieged by producers. If producers Nos. 1 and 2 had conformed to Flanagan's Law, the rest of them positively shouted it.

Producer No. 3 was elderly and semiretired but he'd had a legendary career in his day.

'Yours is the first play he's been interested in in five years,' said my agent, impressed. 'He wants to take you to lunch.'

I met the legendary producer for lunch at the Algonquin, where for two hours he talked of his producing days, the great stars and playwrights he'd discovered and the contrasting sorry state of the contemporary theatre. When we parted, he wished me every success and certainly hoped one of these younger fellows would have the sense to produce my play. (Agent's translation: 'I guess he's broke.')

Producer No. 4 telephoned me at midnight. I'd never heard of him but what did that matter?

'I've just read your play and I'm so excited I can't sleep!' he said.

'Can you lunch with me tomorrow?'

We lunched. He was an attractive young man and I gathered he had a private income. I asked what plays he'd produced.

'None yet,' he said. 'I've been looking for the right play for five years. Thanks to you, I've finally found it!'

He took a three-month option on the play. He wanted revisions, and during the next three months while I was rewriting, we met weekly to discuss the revisions over long and expensive lunches. At the end of three months, he read another playwright's play and realized that *that* was the one he'd spent five years looking for, and he dropped his option on mine and took an option on the new one. Three months later still, he dropped the second play, having found a third to take an option on and have long expensive lunches over.

This man was what might be called a pretend-producer. There were quite a few of these. There was one man who sat in the same office for sixteen years reading plays. He never produced one. If you dropped in at his office, at your agent's suggestion, he told you he just hadn't been able to find the exactly right play. But he was still looking – and as a matter of fact, he had one play in mind, a French play, and if the author was willing to rewrite – and if the American rights were available – and if he could find the right adapter for it, which was going to be tough because it was a very special script, but as he'd told your agent, as soon as he got a decent translation he wanted you to read it because you just might be the right adapter for it, he wasn't sure. . . .

Producer No. 5 sent for me and when I walked into his office he said: 'How-d'ya-do' impatiently, and then before I even found a chair: 'The whole thing goes haywire in the second act, you're going to have to do the whole play over. Sit down, I'll show you what I want you to do.' This one meant business.

He told me how he wanted the play rewritten. He was going to Hollywood for two months and he wanted the revised play ready for production when he came back. He asked whether I'd be willing to quit my job and live on the option money, which he would mail to my agent, so that I could work on the play full time. I said yes.

I was working as secretary to a press agent and I quit the job and went to work on the revisions. The producer sent me a long, encouraging letter from Hollywood but he forgot to send my agent the option money. The night before he was due back in New York, I sat up till 4 A.M. to finish typing the revised draft and put it between covers. At noon the next day I went to his office with the finished play.

His secretary took my name in. Then she came back. The producer, she said, was about to go into rehearsal with a new play and wouldn't have time to read mine. But he sent me greetings and wished me lots of luck with the play. (None of us was so sordid as to mention the unpaid option money.)

Producer No. 6 was a very fine actor who wrote me from Hollywood that he wanted to produce the play and star in it as soon as he completed the film he was making. And he very well might have done so if, three weeks after he wrote to me, he hadn't happened to drop dead on the golf course of a heart attack.

And that was the end of the furor over that particular play.

Since this history was to be repeated, with minor variations, every time I hatched a play (and I had them like rabbits), I learned to understand how producers' minds worked.

When a producer phones a playwright and says: 'You've written a wonderful play. When can you come and see me?' it doesn't mean he wants to produce the play. But whether it means (a) he wants to meet the playwright, or (b) he wants to rewrite the play himself to make it producible, or (c) he'd produce it if he had the money, or (d) he needs a play in reserve, to hold his backers' interest till he finds one he really likes, his motive stems from the same economic fact. That fact told me why the odds against me would always be so much greater than the odds against Maxine.

If you're a young actress who has never set foot on a professional stage, a producer can take a small gamble on you by giving you a bit part in his next production. If you do well, he'll trust you with a larger part next season. Eventually, he may trust you with a leading role.

But if you're a young playwright, the situation is different. There's no such thing as a bit play. It's going to cost a Broadway producer just as much to produce your play as to produce Tennessee Williams's. He can't take a small gamble on you; he's got to gamble all the way.

He reads your play and it's clearly not worth gambling the fortune required to produce a play on Broadway. But there's a fine central character and the last scene in the second act is terrific – and what about your next play? So he wants to meet you. And he definitely wants to see your next play.

He gets your next play a year later and it's not very good but it's better than the first one. And what about next year? Maybe your great play is just around the corner, maybe you just need to be nursed a little longer. So instead of returning the script to your agent with a flat rejection, the producer phones you.

'I've read your play and I'm very impressed,' he says, which is true as far as it goes. 'When can you lunch with me?'

And you lunch with him. For the first five years. After that, you don't bother unless you need the lunch because you know from experience, if they take you to lunch they don't want your play.

4

If She Takes You to Lunch She Can't Sell It

A couple of times in the last chapter I mentioned my agent without telling you who she was. The truth is couldn't remember who she was. (I say 'she' because in the forties and fifties, as almost all producers were men, almost all agents were women.)

'Agents' in this book, of course, refers exclusively to Broadway play agents — 'playbrokers,' they were once called. Those I knew were affectionate, warm-hearted women who belonged body and soul to their clients — unlike many Hollywood agents and New York literary agents who were rumored to be Uncle Toms (ostensibly working for their writers but actually far more zealous in looking after the interests of the Hollywood studio or the New York publishing house). But though I have fond memories of every playbroker who ever handled my plays, I managed to use up seven of them (that I can remember), some of them twice.

Beginning in my fellowship year, when the older playwrights in the seminar were already complaining about their agents, I noted a fact that became increasingly evident as the years went on. Since all (but one) of the unsuccessful playwrights I ever knew were men, I hope they'll excuse me for stating this fact in the male gender:

The average unsuccessful playwright goes through life with the firm conviction that his agent is persecuting him. She's giving him ulcers and sinus trouble and he complains about her to his friends and to the psychoanalyst she drives him to.

I couldn't afford ulcers or an analyst, so on the night when I discovered my agent was giving me a severe postnasal drip, I realized the time had come to figure out how agents' minds worked. Having run through three of them by then, I made a discovery which from then on was my salvation:

All playbrokers are alike.

Herewith the biography of a play agent, or what you need to know before you set foot in her office with your new play.

She begins her career by renting a small office and installing a phone, on capital saved while she was assistant to an older agent. She has pirated away two or three of the older agent's youngest clients, and she scouts around and corrals a few more potential playwrights, say eight in all. Her real assets are in herself: she is friendly and sympathetic, she is brilliantly critical, highly intelligent, shrewd and slightly ruthless.

She goes to work to sell her eight plays, sending each play to Broadway producers, and phoning and pestering selected stars and directors until they, too, agree to read her plays. As fast as a play comes back rejected, she sends it out again. And then one day, she sells one of the eight plays. It opens, it's a hit, and overnight the author is a big name on Broadway.

The agent now has Mr Big to pay her office rent and phone bill. She has seven unsold plays, which six Broadway producers have read and rejected, and a dozen producers have not yet seen. They never will see those seven plays. Because now that the agent has Mr Big, eight new clients drift in, wanting her to handle their plays. She's Mr Big's agent: if she's good enough for him, she's good enough for them. So the agent gets to work on the eight new plays, and puts the seven old ones on a closet shelf marked *Dead*.

Well, why doesn't she try to sell all fifteen? Because she hasn't time. Why not? It doesn't take her all day to send out the new plays, does it? No – but she has Mr Big.

Now that his play is a hit, she's busy negotiating a screen sale, she's attending rehearsals of the road company and sitting in on auditions for the London company – because having a big-name client means that the agent's not just an agent any more: she's Mr Big's business manager, press representative, legal adviser, play doctor, confidante and best friend. She's his buffer in every argument he has with his producer, his director or his star, no matter how many arguments there are or how far into the night they run. If he has a second play trying out in Boston, she has to fly up for the opening: he needs her. If his New York hit opens in London, she has to fly over. Her time is not her own, her soul is not her own, they both belong to Mr Big. And why not? He's paying the rent, the phone bill, the secretary's salary.

She therefore puts the old plays on the *Dead* shelf and goes to work to sell the new. She sells one. It opens and flops, but she unloads it on Hollywood for a small fortune. The author of this one isn't a big name, but he's made her some money, she has faith in his future and he needs help on his new play, the second act's giving him trouble. Meanwhile, of course, several of *his* friends bring her *their* plays because she's *his* agent: she got him all that Hollywood money and if she's good enough for him she's good enough for them.

So the agent puts the second batch of unsold plays on the *Dead* shelf and goes to work to sell the third. By which time, of course, the original seven unsold plays are so far down on the *Dead* shelf she's forgotten about them.

The authors of them, unfortunately, haven't.

The author of one of them, not having heard from his agent in several months, phones her one day to find out what's happening with his script.

'Just-a-minute-I'll-see-if-she's-free,' says the secretary who answers his call. This is followed by a three-minute pause, during which the agent debates whether to duck the playwright or take the bull by the horns. She decides to take it by the horns. She gets on the phone.

'HelLO!' she says in a warmly personal voice. 'When can we lunch?'

They lunch. Over the bloody Marys, the agent tells the author what the last producer who saw his play said about it – not realizing she told him this three months ago and is exposing the fact that she hasn't sent it anywhere since. Over the entree she tells him the latest theatre gossip ('He was drunk last night when he made his third-act entrance, it's not his fault, poor soul, the man is Sick, he is So Sick!'). Over coffee, she asks the playwright when he's going to write a new play, he's too talented to be so lazy!

Now any idiot should know by this time that the agent has given up on his play. Our hero, however, refuses to believe it without further proof. In search of which, he strides briskly into her office one day between 1 and 3 P.M., when he knows she's out to lunch. (Agents transact much of their business over lunch so lunch invariably takes two hours.)

'I'd like to pick up a copy of my play,' he says. 'Olivier wants to read it.'

He tells the secretary the title of his play and she looks puzzled: she's only worked here four months and she's never heard of that play.

'I'll see if I can find it,' she says, and moves innocently, unerringly, toward the closet shelf marked *Dead*. The playwright, hard on her heels, stares over her shoulder and sees, in shocked outrage, all six copies of his play, all very dusty. The truth is there and he faces it squarely: this friendly, sympathetic, brilliantly critical, highly intelligent, shrewd and slightly ruthless woman hasn't been sending his play around.

Six Broadway producers have seen it. Twelve or fifteen producers haven't, and as things now stand, won't. What can he do about it?

Well, he can go home and call up his friends and tell them all what a slob his agent is, and wind up with ulcers, a psychoanalyst and a persecution complex. But will that get his play read by all the Broadway producers who haven't seen it? No, it won't. Then what's the solution? How is he to get his script into the hands of all the producers who haven't yet read it? The answer lies in that basic fact about agents: *All playbrokers are alike.*

This being so, when you find all six copies of your script on your agent's *Dead* shelf, this is what you do:

You wander into her office, unannounced, late one afternoon when you know she's finished work for the day and has time to talk. She welcomes you warmly (they always do), if defensively (ditto), and tells you to come on into her private office and talk to her.

You tell her honestly that you're sorry your play wasn't good enough for her to sell. And you love her dearly but would she be terribly hurt if you took it to some less important agent, who might be willing to send it to off-off-Broadway and little-theatre groups, which you realize she herself hasn't time to do.

Up to now, the agent's been feeling guilty about you, since along with her other virtues and contrary to general opinion she also has a conscience. And here you are, offering to take one guilt source off her mind. She's so grateful she smiles at you almost with tears in her eyes.

If she couldn't sell your play, she says, she hopes you know it wasn't for lack of trying, or lack of faith in you or affection for you. And what's more, she means it; and what's still more, realistically speaking it's true. So you tell her, with tears in *your* eyes, that you never doubted that. You and she part company with mutual affection and esteem. But – if by some chance you don't know their names by heart – before you leave, you ask her to give you a list of the six producers who rejected the play.

Armed with your list, and your six scripts, you proceed to the office of another agent and ask if she'll read your play. She has a Mr Big too, of course, but he's in Hollywood at the moment so she has a little free time. She reads your play, she thinks its salable and she offers to send it around. In her stable, you're a brand-new dark horse. She sends the play to the six best producers who haven't seen it. (Two of the six want to meet you, one takes you to lunch, and the other three reject it without all the ceremony.) Three months go by and you phone the agent to ask what's doing with the play. And she says:

'HelLO! When can we lunch?'

And a week after that, you have a frank heart-to-heart talk, you part with mutual affection and esteem, and you are off, with your list of producers who have rejected the play, to agent No. 3. By the time the third agent is through with it, every producer on Broadway has read it and rejected it and you can forget it. But you've probably written a new play by then.

Now it's true, as Maxine once observed, that if you follow my system for five or six years you'll have 'run through every agent on Broadway like a dose of salts.' But by the time this happens, three former assistants to three of your former agents have set up shop for themselves and are looking for their first batch of clients. So you go to each in turn.

And then? Why then, you just go back to the beginning and start over. You carry your new play into the office of good old agent No. 1.

She's delighted to see you again. You parted with mutual affection and esteem; your old play showed promise; for all she knows, your new one may be the hit of the season. And if she can't sell it, you won't make her feel guilty; you didn't last time. So she welcomes you with the enthusiasm reserved for new clients and sends your script to the six best producers who haven't yet seen it.

Only the second time round, when you telephone to ask what's doing, and she says:

'HelLO! When can we lunch?' you say:

'Oh, honey, can I have a raincheck? I'm working like a dog on a new first act —'
because by this time, you know damn well if she takes you to lunch she can't sell it.

5

The Underfoot
Free Enterprise System

Since kids trying to crash the theatre require expensive instruction (which includes seeing the best plays and films) as well as expensive clothes in which to be Seen on occasion, and since they never have any money, they have to master the delicate, illegal art of getting everything for nothing. In the cultivation of this art, my friend Maxine had no equal.

Maxine and I saw every Broadway show and neighborhood movie free. I went to producers' lunches attired in Saks's best, Maxine took vocal lessons and I was tutored privately in Latin and Greek, and none of it cost us a dime. All I can remember us paying for were the ballet lessons we took from the Greek gentleman. Thanks to Maxine's negotiations, we paid him a dollar a week in a class where everybody else was paying two dollars.

What specially equipped Maxine for this art, besides an unflagging imagination and the nerve of Napoleon, was her unique ignorance of finance. I couldn't add or subtract too well, but Maxine's innocence in money matters was so total it amounted to a whole new theory of economics. I'll give you an example:

The autumn when I finally got back to New York after a six-month exile in Philadephia I had difficulty finding a job. My capital finally dwindling to $15, I told Maxine I couldn't meet the $10 weekly rent on my hotel room the next week unless I cut down to one meal a day. We were riding on the upper deck of a double-decker Fifth Avenue bus at the time, on our way up to Maxine's house for dinner, and Maxine stared thoughtfully out the window and down at the street as she worked on the problem.

'All right,' she said finally. 'The ten dollars a week for rent you can manage by putting a little away every day. Put fifty cents away every day; that way you won't miss it. And I can get the money for food for you. As long as I'm working part-time, you can collect my unemployment insurance; it's just sitting there!'

Given a mind like that, it's easy to evolve your own economic theory. Maxine's was simply stated:

Nothing should cost anything.

It went into operation that fall, when I finally got a job as assistant to a press agent. Salary: $25 a week. Ten dollars paid for the hotel room, three dollars went toward paying off a large dental bill, and the remaining twelve dollars were flung away carelessly on food, cigarettes, toothpaste, typing paper, typewriter ribbons, nylons, shoe repairs, carfare, semiannual haircuts and taxes. So by the time Friday – payday – came around, I was wiped out.

Since Maxine was living at home, her room, board and essential clothes were supplied. She was also working part-time taking street-corner surveys at one dollar per surveying hour. Surveys of corporation vice-presidents paid two dollars, but you didn't get this work often, and when you did, half the vice-presidents coldly refused to be surveyed; and since you got paid per vice-president instead of per hour, even that didn't pay too well. Her average weekly gross for four or five afternoons was twelve to fifteen dollars, which was distributed among hairdressers, theatrical makeup, street makeup, professional photos, Equity dues, audition accessories, nylons, cigarettes, carfare, agents' commissions, taxes and a monthly lunch at Sardi's. (If-you're-an-actress-you-have-to-be-Seen.) So as a rule, she had even less cash than I did.

I was therefore mildly startled when, shortly after I got the job, Maxine phoned me at the office on a Wednesday morning and inquired casually:

'Do you feel like seeing the new Odets tonight?'

I said I had $1.85 to last me till Friday if that answered her question.

'I don't mean buy tickets!' said Maxine impatiently. 'Where would I get the money to buy tickets? I mean Just Go.'

I had no idea what Just Go meant but I said I'd love to.

'Meet me at the drugstore on the corner of Forty-fifth Street at quarter to nine,' she said. 'Don't wear a coat.'

It was a chilly November evening and the curtain time for Clifford Odets's play was eight-thirty, but I did as I was told. Maxine met me at the door of the drugstore and said briskly:

'We're all set. I phoned the box office and they're not sold out; they have a few seats downstairs.'

We climbed on stools and ordered coffee and Maxine explained the Just Go method of seeing every show in town. We made our coffee last twenty minutes, during which we took turns running to the front door, at two-minute intervals, to glance up the street at the theatre where the Odets was playing. At nine-ten, it was my turn to be lookout and I saw the theatre doors open and the crowd begin to stream out onto the sidewalk for intermission.

We left the drugstore and hurried up the street to the theatre, to light cigarettes and mingle with the crowd of smokers on the sidewalk. After a few minutes, we drifted into the lobby and mingled with the smokers there. And when the bell rang, we mingled into the theatre along with the paying customers who went down the aisle to their seats. We stood at the back while Maxine, under pretext of wanting a last puff on her cigarette, cased the house for empty seats. These were easy to spot because they had no coats or programs on them. Maxine saw a pair down front on the side and said: 'Come on.'

She sailed down the aisle, her burnished head arrogantly high above her best black cocktail dress, her mother's marten scarf dangling negligently over one shoulder, and me pattering nervously behind her. She said, 'Excuse me' graciously to a man sitting in the aisle seat and we climbed past him and sat down in the two empty seats. Maxine shook out her fur, draped it over the back of her chair and turned to survey the house.

'There are two better seats back there in the center,' she said, and stood up. 'Come on.'

'You go if you want to,' I said. I was pale with terror.

'Is this really your first time?' she asked sympathetically. I nodded and she sat back down.

'All right,' she said. 'We forgot to get programs. After the second act, remind me.'

The house lights dimmed and I sat frozen in the certainty that at any second an usher's hand would drop to my shoulder and a waiting cop would haul Maxine and me off to night court. But no usher materialized: we saw the second act of the Odets, which was excellent; and after the second intermission we picked up a pair of programs and moved to the better seats on the center aisle.

From then on, we went to theatre several nights a week. We never saw a first act, but in a three-act play nothing ever happened in the first act. Of course, it wasn't always smooth sailing. Occasionally the house proved to be more crowded than the box office had indicated when we phoned; and as the houselights dimmed, we'd find ourselves still standing at the back or, worse still, wandering up and down the aisle looking for empty seats – at which moment an usher was likely to loom up and helpfully ask to see our stubs.

'I'm afraid we've lost them,' Maxine would explain in her best stage diction. 'We must have dropped them in the lobby during inter-mission.' And we'd flee out to the lobby and across the street, and wait around to mingle with the intermission crowd at the musical there. (Musicals were in two acts instead of three and had a single later intermission.)

Since the biggest hits somehow always opened in the winter months, we caught a lot of colds. You can't mingle into a theatre with an intermission crowd in your winter coat. The ushers would spot you at once as a gate-crasher, since no matter what the weather theatregoers always leave their coats behind on their seats when they go out for a smoke. So on cold nights, Maxine caught sore throats walking to her subway and I got coughs standing on windy corners waiting for my bus. But if you go to theatre regularly, it ought to cost you *some*thing. Especially if the show was a rare and wonderful one like *Lady in the Dark*.

Lady in the Dark was the only musical ever to win the hearts of us two serious students of the drama. It had Gertie Lawrence, who had been our idol in half a dozen Broadway comedies, and it had an astonishing new comedian named Danny Kaye. We must have mingled into it half a dozen times and I remember the night when we made a momentous decision and spent our own money to see the first act. And still, when the show finally closed, our appetite for it was unappeased.

Soon after it closed, it went on the road and opened in Philadelphia. Philadelphia being my home town, I considered it squarely up to me to get us there. My father knew the box-office men, so getting in to see the show free would be no problem. The problem was the fare to Philly. Neither of us had it.

On the Monday *Lady in the Dark* was to open in Philly, I brooded over the problem during breakfast at the cafeteria. Then I opened the *Times* and turned to the theatre section. In the middle of one page, an ad announced that tomorrow evening, the Philadelphia Orchestra would give its regular Tuesday concert at Carnegie Hall. Right there, the problem was solved.

On my way from the cafeteria to the office, I worked out a story to give my boss about having to go to Philadelphia Wednesday for a funeral. Then I phoned Maxine.

'Meet me at Carnegie Hall at eight-thirty tomorrow night,' I said. 'Bring a nightgown. Tell your folks you'll be back Wednesday night late.'

I had in my adolescence been one of several thousand bobby-sox worshippers of Leopold Stokowski, conductor of the Philadelphia Orchestra. With all my friends I had got happily in the orchestra's hair, I knew all the first-desk men personally and was especially palsy with Marshall Betz, the orchestra librarian.

Therefore when Maxine met me at Carnegie Hall, we went around to the stage door and said hello to Marshall, who passed us in to hear the concert. During intermission we went backstage to say hello to my many friends in the orchestra and put through a call to my father on the Carnegie Hall office phone asking him to meet us at Broad Street Station at approximately one in the morning. We heard the rest of the concert and then rode to Philadelphia on the Philadelphia Orchestra's private train.

I had one bad moment on the train when Maxine, looking extremely high-fashion in a dark green wool suit and her mother's fur jacket, turned to me and said simply:

'Stick close to me, will you? I only have a nickel.'

My father drove us home and we slept in the twin beds in my old bedroom. *Lady in the Dark* was sold out, of course. But we got passed in to hang over the back rail at the matinee performance, dined with my parents, hung over the back rail again for the evening performance and touched my father for the fare back to New York. He also drove us to the station so that when we reached New York, Maxine still had her nickel. It took her home on the subway.

We had an easier time seeing neighborhood movies free. We only had to miss the credits, and the M-G-M lion or J. Arthur Rank's naked friend banging his gong. Maxine and I were selective movie-goers: we only saw half a dozen films a year, but we saw each of them five or six times. We'd get a crush on James Mason, say, or Humphrey Bogart, and follow his current film from the upper West Side to lower Third Avenue. We saw *The Maltese Falcon* seven times and *I Know Where I'm Going* six. With *The Seventh Veil*, I lost count. This kind of moviegoing was ideally suited to Maxine's system, which ruled out patronizing any one movie theatre often enough for the box-office girl to get to know our faces.

What we did was, we phoned the box office and asked when the last feature started. If the box office said eleven o'clock, we'd get to the movie house at eleven-ten, and lurk outside a few minutes till the box-office girl closed up and went home. Then we just walked in and sat down. Any usher not in the men's room changing into his street clothes was asleep in the back row.

Only once did we have to wait outside an extra ten minutes till the manager came out and went home. This was at a movie theatre where, on a previous nerve-racking evening, we had unexpectedly bumped into him coming out as we were going in.

You may have noticed I was careful to specify neighborhood movie houses. Only once did we attempt a first-run Broadway house. The Broadway movie palaces were great, plush Hollywood temples crawling with doormen and uniformed ticket takers and different grades of ushers, and you couldn't possibly sneak in free, even at midnight. It was this impasse that led Maxine and me to commit our only prison offense.

I was working late that evening at the press office, folding, inserting sealing and stamping five hundred press releases which had to be mailed that night to newspapers all over the country on behalf of a second-rate tenor who was going on a cross-country tour. I was dining on a sandwich and a container of coffee and folding the last hundred letters when Maxine wandered in. She'd had a late rehearsal at a theatre across the street and had seen the light in the press office window.

'The new Bogart opened today at the Capitol,' she remarked.

The Capitol being a very overstaffed palace, I told her plainly I only had ninety cents. She only had ten. As tickets were $1.25 per person, I considered the subject closed. I went on folding and Maxine sat down and inserted the letters for me and we sealed and stamped them. As I put away the leftover releases and envelopes and the leftover sheets of stamps, Maxine rose.

'I think I'll phone the Capitol,' she said.

She found the number and dialed it. I took a last mouthful of coffee and then nearly choked to death on it as I heard Maxine's most gracious stage voice inquire of the Capitol box office:

'Do you accept stamps?' There was a brief pause, and then Maxine amplified:

'Postage stamps. In exchange for tickets.' She listened a minute, said, 'Thank you' warmly and hung up.

'They'll take them,' she said. 'Where did you put them?'

'It's stealing!' I said.

'On what you're paid?' said Maxine coldly. 'You were supposed to leave an hour ago. Are you being paid for overtime?'

So a few minutes later we pushed two dollars and fifty cents' worth of stamps across the counter at the box office of the Capitol Theatre and went to see Humphrey Bogart in *Casablanca*.

While free entertainment was something we both required, free clothes were needed only by me, since Maxine's parents were still happy to keep her supplied with Bendel's best. My clothes problem was chronic but I was blessed with affluent friends who were always generously deciding they never wore that old plaid suit anymore, or With skirts getting longer that raincoat was really much too short. And if a skirt was too large at the waist or a dress, in Maxine's phrase, 'hung like a bag' on me, I'd early resigned myself to the fact that I couldn't sew and couldn't afford alterations and I went around unconcernedly pinned together. So whenever Maxine and I were strolling on Fifth Avenue and she wanted to stop in at Bergdorf's or Bendel's, she'd pause on the sidewalk in front of the store, run an eye over my conglomerate outfit and say simply:

'You wait out here.'

But of course there were critical producers' lunches and large romantic evenings for which I had to look the part. On most of these occasions I just borrowed Maxine's clothes, having had the fore-thought to get thin enough to wear them. But every now and then, both of us had important engagements for the same day or evening and Maxine would report with distress that she didn't have two suitably elegant ensembles in hand.

In such emergencies I followed her instructions. I went to Saks, bought a beautiful dress or suit on my charge account, took it home, wore it on my big date, and returned it to Saks the next day. (Except that, being sloppy, I generally got a spot on it, in which case I kept it and paid it off at the rate of five dollars a month for a year or two so that by the time I threw it out it was all paid for.)

Maxine borrowed my clothes only once. She borrowed a ruffled organdy blouse handed down to me by some sadist, my five-year-old black suit and a beanie my mother had knitted, which was my hat wardrobe that season.

'What do you want them for?' I demanded. Maxine looked evasive. 'I'll take care of them,' she said.

Two weeks later, when she returned them, I found out she'd worn them on location in a rooming house in Brooklyn, where she'd played the lead in a documentary film on gonorrhea.

When it came to vocal lessons for Maxine, and Latin and Greek lessons for me, we hit our first snag. I'd been trying to teach myself Latin and Greek and she'd been trying to teach herself to carry a tune and neither of us was doing too well.

Private instruction being both necessary and expensive, Maxine decided that the solution for both of us was to Sell Something. This led to two exhausting Saturdays, the first spent haggling with the Empire Diamond and Gold Buying Service over the value of my high school graduation ring and a ring my parents had given me with a minute diamond in it, for both of which Empire gave me a stingy fifteen dollars, and since this wouldn't buy much Greek I bought Shaw and Shakespeare with it instead.

The second Saturday we spent trotting from secondhand clothing store to secondhand clothing store trying to sell Maxine's mother's fifteen-year-old Persian lamb coat. That coat gave Maxine nothing but trouble anyway. Her mother had passed it on to her a couple of years before, and for a whole season Maxine had worn it with chic assurance. But during the second season, she made the mistake of wearing it on a picket line she had volunteered for. You turn up on a line of starving strikers wearing a Persian lamb coat and you are liable to be stoned to death. Maxine escaped without injury but she lost her taste for the coat, so one hot Saturday in August we lugged it to the Ritz Thrift Shop ready to trade it in for vocal lessons.

'How much are you asking?' said the man at the Ritz Thrift Shop, running a practiced eye over the coat.

'I thought two hundred,' said Maxine in a tone that managed to be both haughty and friendly.

'Oh, we can't even talk!' said the man. When pressed, he allowed the coat might be worth forty dollars to him. Outraged, we stalked out of there and lugged the coat in and out of all the secondhand stores on Sixth Avenue and Eighth Avenue and then we went across town and lugged it down Second Avenue and up Third, and at five o'clock we gave up and lugged it back to the Ritz Thrift Shop and Maxine took the forty dollars, which paid for eight vocal lessons.

The problem of my Greek and Latin lessons remained unsolved. I wrote dignified letters to all the free city colleges, none of which, it turned out, gave free night courses in Latin and Greek. I took my one remaining piece of jewelry – a lapel watch – down to the Empire Diamond and Gold Buying Service and they wouldn't even make me an offer. Just as I was getting completely discouraged, Maxine, as usual, came through with the solution.

'Why don't you run an ad in the Personals column of the *Saturday Review*?' she suggested.

'The problem isn't finding a tutor,' I said. 'It's finding the money to pay him!'

'That's all right,' said Maxine reasonably. 'Just mention in the ad that you can't pay anything.'

And if you think I got no response to an ad that read:

> Wish to study Latin and Greek.
> Can't pay anything.

you underestimate the readers of the *Saturday Review*. I got five offers, one from a German refugee who said he would teach me the Latin and the Greek if I would teach him the English, two from retired professors, and one from a Lebanese rug merchant who didn't know Latin but offered to teach me modern Greek and Arabic instead.

The fifth letter came from a young man who wrote that he'd graduated from the Roxbury Latin School and Harvard; and after careful consideration, Maxine advised me to award the coveted post to him.

'In the first place, he's young and he might be cute,' she pointed out. 'And in the second place, you can't do better than Harvard.'

So Tom Goethals, who turned out to be six-feet-four, lean and shy-looking, and whose grandfather had built the Goethals Bridge, put his Roxbury Latin School and Harvard education to use by teaching me to read Catullus and trying to teach me Greek grammar.

Maxine phoned me after the first lesson.

'How was he?' she asked.

'Oh, he's great!' I said.

'I told you to stick to Harvard,' she said. 'Taking somebody second-rate would be like sneaking into theatre and sitting in the balcony, or borrowing clothes from Gimbel's instead of Saks. If you're getting things for nothing, it's just as easy to get the best.'

We always got the best.

6

'Sumer Is Icumen In...'

'I have to stay home tonight,' I told Maxine on the phone one April evening when she wanted to go to theatre. 'I have to write my summer-theatre letters.'

'I'm set, thank God,' said Maxine. She'd been hired for the summer as a member of the resident company trying out new plays at the Theatre Guild's summer playhouse in Westport, Connecticut.

The summer-theatre furor always began in April when the new *Summer Theatre Directory* appeared on the Times Square news-stand. The day it came out, you tore down to Times Square along with every other brat in show business, bought your copy and took it home, and spent the evening making a list of first-, second-, and third-choice barns to spend the summer in, as a member of the acting company, the backstage crew or the producer's staff.

Somehow, anyhow, you got yourself set for the summer, and in June you quit your winter job and set out for the Adirondacks or the coast of Maine where you had an absolutely wonderful two months on a schedule that would have put a normal person in a sanitarium and at a salary Charles Dickens would have refused to believe.

There were two kinds of summer theatres: the pre-Broadway tryout house, like the Guild's playhouse in Westport, and the 'package' theatre, where each week a star arrived with an acting company (the 'package') with which he or she was touring the summer circuit in some old war-horse like *Candida* or *Charley's Aunt*.

I didn't care which kind of theatre I worked in, and that night I wrote to a dozen summer-theatre producers offering myself as prop girl, scene painter, assistant stage manager or typist willing to double as usher. (The only category I omitted was box-office ticket seller. I can't add.) A few weeks later I landed a job and had myself a superb summer but it got off to a demoralizing start.

One of my letters had gone to a man who ran the Bucks County Playhouse in New Hope, Pennsylvania, not far from Philadelphia. He had phoned me, interviewed me and engaged me as his secretary for the summer. I was to report at Bucks on June 20.

On June 20, I arrived in New Hope and hauled my two suitcases into the playhouse office. The producer looked up from his desk and stared at me blankly.

'What can I do for you?' he asked. I told him he'd hired me as his secretary for the summer. 'Oh!' he said. 'That was last spring, wasn't it? I thought my secretary was going to be working for Bela Blau up at the Deertrees Theatre in Maine. I talked her into staying with me.' I must have turned pale because he added: 'Maybe they haven't replaced her yet. Why don't I phone and see if they can use you at Deertrees?'

He phoned Deertrees, chatted a minute, hung up and said:

'They can use you.'

I was to go back to New York and report to Bela Blau's office. Two members of the Deertrees staff were driving up that afternoon and Bela would phone his office and tell them to wait for me.

First I took a bus to Philadelphia, having a filial urge to see my parents and borrow the fare to Maine in case something went wrong in New York. Then I took a train back to New York and lugged my suitcases into Bela Blau's office and met the Deertrees stage manager, Bill Flanagan of Flanagan's Law, and the assistant stage manager who drove us to Maine in his elderly cream-colored Ford called the Beige Bee because he'd bought it with money he'd earned on a radio show called The Green Hornet.

The town of Harrison, Maine, lay between two lakes with mountains rising beyond them and was as beautiful a spot as I've ever seen. It was a tiny town – pop. 200 – with three streets. We found the theatre just beyond the third street and it was as enchanting as its setting. The handsome log-cabin playhouse stood in the center of a hushed clearing circled by pine woods. As we walked around to the back of the theatre to Bela Blau's office, the ground under our feet was a thick carpet of pine needles.

Bela shook hands with me and said, beaming:

'Your partner will be very glad to see you! She's a local girl and she almost quit when she thought she was going to be in there by herself. She's never worked in a box office before.'

I did not say 'In a *where*?' and I did not tell him I couldn't add. If Bela Blau wanted me looking after his finances for the summer, that was his problem. Mine was to get myself installed in a summer theatre. After a day of considerable mental anguish I was finally installed in one and I wasn't leaving.

Still, as I crawled into bed that night, in an airy bedroom in an old-fashioned frame house that let rooms to 'summer people,' I couldn't help feeling Bela Blau was in for a nerve-racking summer. And boy, was I right.

I met Reta Shaw, my cell-mate, the next morning. Reta was a stout schoolteacher with a pretty face and the most cheerful, unruffled disposition I've ever had the privilege of working alongside. She must have caught Theatremania in that box office because the next year she gave up teaching and went to New York to crash the theatre – and did. She began turning up on Broadway as a comedienne in *Gentlemen Prefer Blondes* and *Picnic* and *The Pajama Game* and so forth; she was very much in demand for years.

She couldn't add either.

The two of us were on duty in the box office from 9 A.M. to 9 P.M. daily including Sunday. Salary: $17 a week. Eight of it paid the rent on the furnished room with breakfast thrown in, a dollar went for cigarettes (thirteen cents a pack in Maine that summer) and the remaining eight dollars bought seven lunches and seven dinners. The town of Harrison had one restaurant: Ken's Koffee Kup. If you didn't feel like eating there you could always starve. I have fond memories of Ken's place. The *cuisine* may not have been very *haute* but you got a lot of food there for eight dollars a week.

Deertrees ran on the package system. In successive weeks, we had Tallulah Bankhead, Ethel Barrymore, Grace George, each with her touring company and her ancient hit. Grace George, who had been a reigning star when my father was a chorus boy, had long since grown old enough and rich enough to spend her summers sensibly in

Europe. Instead, she was touring the summer circuit in *Kind Lady*.

She arrived with her company at nine o'clock of a rainy Sunday night, having spent the day on the road from New Jersey where she'd played the week before. She announced that she would run through the play then and there, so that she and her company could accustom themselves to the new stage before the Monday night opening. But as I said, it was raining. Grace George walked into the theatre and realized there was going to be a hitch in her plans.

Deertrees was built entirely of pine logs, by somebody who didn't realize that the sound of steady rain on pine walls and a pine roof is deafening. During a heavy downpour, the players' voices were completely drowned out and the show simply stopped. When the rain let up – ten minutes or two hours later – the show resumed. So at nine o'clock that Sunday night, Grace George and her company sat down in the damp playhouse to wait out the storm. The crew and staff drifted in and we all sat around, listening to the racket and batting at the bugs which had hurried in out of the wet. At ten, we began to wonder when Miss George would give up and go to bed.

At a little before eleven, the rain stopped. And Grace George went up onstage with her company, and instead of walking through the play as the old lady held prisoner by two strangers and their half-witted daughter, gave a harrowing, electrifying performance that froze us to our seats. The performance ended at 1:30 A.M., after which Grace George, seventy if she was a day, sashayed serenely off to bed, looking forward to eight performances in the next six days with another traveling Sunday at the end of the week and *that's* what I mean by Theatremania.

Her opening-night performance was fine, but no finer than the performance she'd given for the staff and crew at midnight the night before, so we toasted her at our regular opening-night gin picnic. Each week, every member of the staff and crew gave Flanagan thirty-five cents and he bought gin and pretzels with it, and after the opening we had a gin picnic on the playhouse lawn. One Monday night we drank two-hundred-proof hospital alcohol instead. One of the boys on the crew had a brother who was an intern at a local hospital and he filched us a bottle of hospital alcohol which we cut with Coca-Cola. You can get higher on that than you can get on Cutty Sark. You can get positively looping till after a while you can't feel your arms or legs or anything.

As I said, Maxine was spending the summer at a 'tryout' playhouse.
A letter from her described the daily Westport routine and at first
glance it seemed to be the standard schedule for an acting company at
any summer theatre where a new play was tried out every week.

9:30 A.M.	Breakfast.
10:00 A.M.	Everybody off to study his-or-her lines in next week's play.
11:30–4:30	Rehearsal of next week's play.
4:30–6:00	More studying of lines in next week's play.
6:00–7:00	A light supper.
7:15	Arrive in dressing room to mend and press costumes and apply makeup.
8:30–11:00 P.M.	On stage in this week's play.
11:30	Late supper and then home to bed at one in the morning, in order to be up at nine and start the whole thing over again.

Wednesdays and Saturdays the program changed to include a
matinee performance, and Sunday was entirely different: dress parade
in the morning, dress rehearsal all afternoon and evening and far into
the night.

Perfectly normal summer schedule. But Maxine's letter had been
written in somebody's car on the way to Mount Kisco, New York,
thus revealing an extra feature of the Westport company's schedule.

At Mount Kisco, which was forty miles from Westport, there was
a playhouse of the 'package' kind; and that summer Westport and
Mount Kisco traded plays. Every alternate week, Westport sent its new
tryout play to Kisco for a week's run, and Kisco sent its star 'package'
to Westport for a week. The 'package' company, of course, just moved
to Westport for the week. But the Westport company had to be in
Westport during the day to rehearse next week's play, so instead of
moving to Kisco the company commuted nightly.

So every second week, the six o'clock supper was sandwiches eaten
in the car on the forty-five-minute drive to Kisco, and the eleven-
thirty supper was sandwiches eaten in the car on the way back. It made
a nice change for everybody.

By comparison, Reta and I had an easy summer in the box office.
We whiled away the long hours between customers by playing word

games and paper-and-pencil games: Battleship and Hangman and Associations and Twenty Questions and What Is It? On non-matinee days each of us was allowed to take the box office alone for two afternoon hours while the other went swimming or rowing – or just stood outside and felt the sun and saw the sky, which all by itself was a change.

Those afternoons gave us the strength to face the trauma of matinee days. The trauma was due to a crisis which arose absolutely incessantly.

As regularly as Wednesday matinee time arrived, either (a) some camp descended on us, 200 campers and 15 counselors strong, demanding the tickets they'd sent us a check for – only we'd thought they were coming Saturday so we'd saved 215 Saturday seats and sold today's seats to 215 other customers, and since the theatre only seated 300, there was no place to put the camp; or (b) we had 215 seats saved for the camp and the camp never showed up, having meant their check to cover 215 seats for next Wednesday.

This crisis took a lot out of us every time, not to mention what it took out of Bela Blau. He was a very kind and good-humored man and he never once lost his temper with us, but after the first three or four matinee days he began to acquire a hunted look. By the end of July all the fight went out of him, and for the rest of the summer the three of us simply resigned ourselves to a succession of traumatic Wednesday and Saturday afternoons.

Saturday was frantic altogether. Ticket sale in the morning, then the matinee crisis, then the evening ticket-sale rush, and at nine o'clock, when we closed the box office to the public, we had the entire week's receipts to tot up and balance. Including subtracting the tax on each ticket. I suppose if you had any talent for math you could have totted up our week's gross in half an hour, but it took Reta Shaw and me from nine till midnight, even with Bela helping. And when we were all through we were usually a dollar short.

At midnight on Saturday, we went into the theatre for our voluntary job of keeping the backstage crew awake and on their toes all night as they struck last week's set and mounted next week's. Reta and I made coffee and played records for them till four or five in the morning while they hauled scenery under Flanagan's supervision.

I'll tell you how he happened to explain Flanagan's Law to me. It was on a horrendous night when the male star of the show arrived in his dressing room fifteen minutes before curtain time, roaring drunk. Flanagan came charging out to the box office to tell us the news and describe the uproar backstage. Since the play was a comedy, I said:

'He may get through it, drunk as he is. The audience may think he's just playing the part very broadly. Otherwise it'll be a fiasco and we'll have to return their money.'

'Neither will happen,' said Flanagan, 'because you predicted them. If you can predict it, it doesn't happen. In the theatre, no matter what happens to you, it's unexpected.'

So of course I bet him one or the other would happen.

Bela Blau held the curtain till nine, but the star was still too drunk to walk straight or talk distinctly, and it was impossible to keep the audience waiting longer. At nine, Reta and I closed the box office and hurried into the theatre and hung over the back rail and watched in suspense as the curtain rose and the two minor characters who opened the play began their ten-minute scene, at the end of which the star was to make his entrance.

Five minutes after the play began, there was a reverberating clap of thunder followed by a torrent of rain on the pine roof and walls and the play came to an abrupt halt. The curtain fell, the houselights went up and the audience settled good-naturedly to wait out the storm.

At a little after ten, the rain stopped – by which time the star had been dragged out into the rain and forced to swallow a vat of black coffee, and when the curtain rose again he was thoroughly sober.

The play proceeded without a hitch and I've believed in Flanagan's Law ever since.

7

'No Legs No Jokes No Chance'

It began in December of 1942, the morning after the opening of a Guild flop called *The Russian People*. Despite the fact that we'd waited up till 4 A.M. for the notices, Joe and I were at work at 10 A.M. as usual, composing ads that would fool the public into thinking the show was a hit. Joe was the Theatre Guild press agent. I was his assistant.

We'd only had four hours' sleep but we were both wide awake. You couldn't possibly get drowsy in the Theatre Guild press department, not in December. Our top-floor offices got whatever heat was left over from the casting department on the floor-below, the executive offices on the floor below that, and the theatre itself, which was on the ground floor.

The Russian People was a ponderous bore about the Nazis and the Russian front. But Joe, like the good press agent he was, had persuaded himself by opening night that it was the greatest thing since *Hamlet* and he took the notices hard. So we weren't talking much that morning. We just glumly pulled quotes for the ads.

Pulling quotes worked like this. If Brooks Atkinson, the *Times* drama critic, wrote: 'For the fourth time this season, the Theatre Guild has wasted a superb production on a dull and empty play,' you pulled out the two good words and printed at the top of your ad:

'SUPERB PRODUCTION!' – Atkinson; *Times*.

This sort of thing takes practice, but by the time *The Russian People* opened, we'd had a lot of practice. Not to beat about the bush, *The Russian People* was the Guild's sixteenth straight flop. It was only the eighth for me; I'd only worked there a year and a half.

I'd got the job when I came back from Deertrees. My agent phoned me one day and said Miss Helburn had read my new play and wanted to see me and the next afternoon I went to Terry's office.

'Dear,' she said, 'I don't like this play much. But I wanted to find out how you're getting on.'

I told her I was out of work and starving to death and Terry asked what jobs I'd had. When I mentioned Oscar Serlin's press department and the press agent I'd worked for the season before she nodded.

'Joe Heidt, our press agent, needs an assistant,' she said. 'He's on the fourth floor. Run up and tell him I said you need the job and you're very bright.'

So I took the elevator up to the fourth-floor attic and went down the hall past the auditor's office to the press department. Lois, Joe's secretary, was sitting in the outer office, surrounded by the usual press-department litter of newspapers, posters, glossy photos of stars and albums of press clippings. I asked if I might see Mr Heidt and she told me to go on into the inner office.

Joe was sitting with his feet up on the desk reading a newspaper. He had a round Irish face which peered at me above the newspaper inquiringly.

'Miss Helburn sent me up,' I said. 'She said you need an assistant.'

I stopped, being too shy to sell myself, and waited for him to ask where I'd worked before and whether I knew how to interview stars and write publicity stories for newspapers. I didn't realize the weight of the simple 'Miss Helburn sent me up.'

'Well, all right,' said Joe resignedly. 'You want to put your typewriter over there?'

And he peered into the outer office and pointed to a spot near Lois's desk. Lois and I got the former assistant's typewriter from the floor of a closet and put it over there, and I was assistant to the Theatre Guild press agent.

Part of my job was to go to all Guild openings to help Joe with the Critics Seating List. And at my first Theatre Guild opening it was heaven to be standing between Joe and Johnny, the casting director, all of us leaning our elbows on the broad, plush-covered railing behind the last row of seats as the last glittering couples in evening gowns and dinner jackets followed an usher down the center aisle.

Our eyes swept the packed rows of first-night celebrities, a sea of carefully groomed heads that rolled away to the stage. Then the houselights dimmed and went out and in the black theatre the footlights gleamed like a golden ribbon along the edge of the dark stage and as the curtain slowly rose I think I stopped breathing.

This heady excitement returned with each of the next three openings. Then it wore off. You couldn't possibly assist at the string of disasters the Guild produced that season and the next, and retain your starry-eyed enthusiasm for opening nights.

The first show I worked on was *Hope for a Harvest*, which flopped so badly that the stars, Fredric March and his wife, Florence Eldridge, took an ad in the newspapers the next day with a cartoon of a trapeze artist missing connections with his partner in midair and a caption reading, 'Oops! Sorry!'

Subsequent accidents included *Papa Is All*, which was Pennsylvania Dutch; *Mr Sycamore*, in which Stuart Erwin became a tree in the second act (that is not a misprint and you did not misread it); and *Yesterday's Magic*, in which Paul Muni, as an alcoholic actor, threw himself out the window in the last scene. Add a couple of ill-fated revivals of classics, a limp comedy called *Without Love*, which not even Katharine Hepburn had been able to prop up for long, and finally, on this morning in December, *The Russian People*.

Looming up ahead, according to the brochure we'd sent to Guild subscribers in nineteen subscription cities, was a new American Folk Opera. Like *Porgy and Bess*, we assured everybody. It was to be based on an old Guild flop, and in true operatic tradition it was to have a murder committed onstage and a bona fide operatic ballet.

Considering our track record on even the most standard fare, this projected opera had given everybody the jimjams. But it was to be the Guild's most expensive venture in years, and the rumor that reached us that morning put an end to our worries about the Folk Opera. The rumor was that after sixteen flops, the Guild was bankrupt. Word spread from floor to floor that Terry and Lawrence were planning to sell the Guild Theatre and the Guild building to pay their debts. When the sale was complete, the Theatre Guild would cease to exist.

People from the other departments wandered morosely up to our offices that day, to indulge in the usual morning-after castigation of the management. Our attic was ideal for this, since it was the one place in which Terry and Lawrence could be counted on not to set foot, especially in December. All day long, the wage slaves from casting, subscription, auditing, playreading came in to sing the usual litany freely and with feeling. This would not have happened (the litany began)

– if Terry didn't sit over at the hairdresser's letting some floozy pick her plays for her;

– if Lawrence didn't lie on the casting couch plucking lofty, expensive ideas out of that goddamn mustache, with a vast unconcern for what the public would pay to see;

– if, when the lofty ideas flopped, the two of them didn't embark on monster economy drives which consisted of cutting down the number of towels rented weekly for each office and threatening to take the water cooler out of the casting department because (said Lawrence) too many strangers were drinking our water;

– and if, year after year, they didn't insist on selling season tickets in nineteen subscription cities for 'six forthcoming Guild productions' when they had only four plays under option and disagreed violently about three of them.

And so on and so forth. It was an old refrain with lots and lots of verses. But on this December day the tone was particularly bitter. Not just because December was a very cold month in which to be thrown out of work, but because for all their talk nobody who worked there was eager to see the Theatre Guild close down. Most of them had been there for years. They remembered the great days of the Lunts, the Shaw openings and the five-hour O'Neill drama which the stage doorman was said to have referred to innocently throughout its run as 'Strange Intercourse.'

Joe and I finished making up the ads, and then he went down to get Lawrence's O.K. on them, and I went down to get Terry's.

She was in her office in an armchair, having tea. Her fluffy white hair was rinsed a deep, cerulean blue that season; her blunt nose and blunt chin were as cheerfully pugnacious as ever.

'Well, dear!' she said when I came in. 'We seem to be having a run of bad luck!'

I gave her the ads and she read them carefully, glancing at the reviews to check each quote, then running her eye over all the reviews and murmuring:

'I don't know what the boys want!'

Then she said the ads were fine and handed them back to me, and I started for the door. As I reached it she said, patting her hair casually:

'I notice Lawrence was first on the program again. That's twice in a row, isn't it?'

If the program for one show read 'Produced by Lawrence Langner and Theresa Helburn,' the program for the next show had to read 'Produced by Theresa Helburn and Lawrence Langner.'

I said I was sure Mr Langner hadn't been first twice in a row because Joe was always careful to check the last program before we made up the new one.

'All right,' she said agreeably. 'Just remind Joe: I'm first on the new one.'

My gloom evaporated. *The Russian People* hadn't been the one-flop-too-many after all. We were going to do another one.

We read about it the next day in one of the gossip columns. Joe came in with the afternoon dailies and said resignedly:

'Terry scooped her own press department again.'

She was always scooping us. She never told us anything about a new production for fear we'd tell somebody. (In the theatre, everything is a secret.) Then she'd go and confide in some columnist. It appeared that between acts of *The Russian People* on opening night, she'd told a columnist – in strictest confidence – that the composer and librettist had finished the new Guild opera and that it was to be called *Away We Go*.

Down the hall in his cage, Jack, the auditor, floating on a sea of unpaid bills, shouted at anybody who went past:

'What do they think they're producing an opera with? What're they using for money?'

And the question was indeed pertinent. During the next few weeks we heard they were holding backers' auditions, and that they had the promise of a third of the money needed, from Broadway's biggest single backer, though there were several ifs attached to his promise.

The New Year set in, *The Russian People* closed and the management plunged on with *Away We Go*. By the end of January,

Joe and I had all the names connected with it.

It wasn't your normal operatic cast. The male lead was to be sung by a young man who'd played the juvenile in *Yesterday's Magic* and the singing comedienne was the ingenue from *Papa Is All*. Both were unknown, of course. The leading comic was very well known in the Yiddish Art Theatre but hadn't done much in English.

The score had been composed by the leftover halves of two teams: an operetta lyricist whose composer partner had just died, and a musical-comedy composer whose lyricist partner had died. Add a Russian ballerina and an Armenian director from Hollywood, and our American Folk Opera was all set.

During February, people from other floors drifted into our office with progress reports. This was, they informed us, the damnedest musical anybody'd ever hatched for a sophisticated Broadway audience. It was so pure you could stage it at a church social. It opened with a middle-aged farm woman sitting alone on a bare stage churning butter, and from then on it got cleaner. They did not feel a long sequence of arty dancing was likely to improve matters on the farm.

The purity complained of was obvious on the day of the dress parade. As the girls walked across the stage in their period farm dresses, not an ankle or an upper arm was visible. I don't even remember seeing a neck. As I left the theatre, I heard Lawrence suggest to the costumer that the dresses might be cut a little lower here and there without spoiling the authenticity.

The show was to open in New Haven early in March and Joe went up a few days before the opening to 'beat the drum' for it. He was very worried. Not about the show. Joe admitted frankly that there was still some work to be done on it, but he believed that by the time it opened in New York it would be the greatest show since *Hamlet*. What worried him was that some drama editor, or some columnist's assistant like Winchell's Rose, would sneak up to New Haven and see the show before it was Ready. As of now, Joe did not feel it was Ready.

(It was always a producer's worry that somebody in a newspaper's drama department would sneak out of town to a pre-Broadway tryout and write a report that would kill the show before it ever opened. But no drama department editor scared them half as much as Winchell's

Rose. Walter Winchell's column appeared in cities across the country, including all the Guild's subscription cities, and was immensely influential. If Winchell's Rose – she must have had a last name but I never heard her called anything but Winchell's Rose – snuck out of town to see the tryout, the effect might be devastating.)

Away We Go opened in New Haven to mild but approving notices. Pleasant, pretty musical, they said; which cheered us. But about midafternoon, a newspaper reporter phoned and left word for Joe to call him as soon as he got back from New Haven. He said he had an important item for Joe; he didn't sound as if it were anything pleasant.

Joe came back to town, full of enthusiasm. The show, he assured us, was great. It had a few weak spots but they'd all be strengthened in Boston. Some wiseacre from an afternoon daily *had* snuck up from New York and had said bluntly the show was corn and wouldn't last a week on Broadway. But, said Joe, Terry and Lawrence were not worried. They knew they had a hit.

Lois gave him the reporter's message and Joe returned the call. He listened for a few minutes, thanked the reporter and hung up. Then he told us the news. According to the reporter, Winchell's Rose had gone to New Haven and seen the show and had wired Winchell her report on it. The wire had read:

NO LEGS NO JOKES NO CHANCE.

Winchell had shown the wire to the backer who had promised a third of the financing; and as a result, the backer was pulling his money out of the show.

Joe called Terry and Lawrence in New Haven. They'd heard about the telegram. Joe didn't mention the backer and neither did they. How they expected to finance the Broadway opening we didn't know, but when Joe left for Boston the show was still scheduled to open there the following Monday and in New York two weeks later. The show opened in Boston to fair notices – not nearly as good as those Boston had given some of our other flops and certainly not notices you could get last-minute financing on. So we still didn't know how the show was to open in New York till Jack tossed us the news casually with our mail the next morning: Terry and Lawrence had sold the Guild Theatre and building to a radio network. *Away We Go* would open on March 31, as scheduled.

Joe phoned from Boston with instructions about the opening-night press release to be sent to 10,000 Guild subscribers. He said that the whole second act had been thrown out, and that the company was working round the clock on a new second act. With a new second act, Joe felt, it would really be a great show.

For the next few days, Lois and I were busy addressing envelopes and grinding out 10,000 copies of the press release on the mimeograph machine to tell the world about the new American Folk Opera, *Away We Go*. We had about 8,000 mimeographed when Joe came back from Boston and broke the news to us that we'd have to throw them all away and start over. There had been a title change.

Nobody, it seemed, liked the title *Away We Go*. The composer had wanted to change it to *Yessirree*, but Joe was thankful to report he'd been talked out of it. The title finally agreed upon – thanks largely to Armina Marshall, Lawrence's wife, who came from out that way – was *Oklahoma*.

It sounds fine to you; you're used to it. But do me a favor and imagine you're working in a theatre and somebody tells you your new musical is to be called 'New Jersey.' Or 'Maine.' To us, 'Oklahoma' remained the name of a state, even after we'd mimeographed 10,000 new releases and despite the fact that 'Oklahoma' appeared three times on each one.

We had folded several hundred of them when the call came from Boston. Joe picked up the phone and we heard him say, 'Yes, Terry,' and 'All right, dear,' and then he hung up. And then he looked at us, in the dazed way people who worked at the Guild frequently looked at each other.

'They want,' he said in a faraway voice, 'an exclamation point after 'Oklahoma.''

Which is how it happened that, far into the night, Lois and I, bundled in our winter coats, sat in the outer office putting 30,000 exclamation points on 10,000 press releases, while Joe, in the inner office, bundled in his overcoat, phoned all over town hunting down and waking up various printing firms and sign painters. We were bundled in our coats because the heat had been turned off by an economy-minded management now happily engaged in spending several thousand dollars to alter house-boards, playbills, ads, three-sheet posters and souvenir booklets, to put an exclamation point after 'Oklahoma.'

We were not sold out for the opening, New York subscribers having dwindled to a handful after sixteen flops. Nor did we get any help from the weather. When I woke on the morning of March 31, with a cold, it was snowing.

By six that evening, the snow had turned to sleet and my cold included a cough. As I left the office to go home and climb into a drafty evening dress, Joe took pity on me.

'I don't need you there, dear,' he said. 'Don't come unless you feel like it.'

I felt guilty about not going as I ate a quick dinner in a cafeteria. But by the time I'd fought my way home through the sleet guilt had given way to self-preservation. I undressed and crawled thankfully into bed. In bed, I reached for the wet newspaper I'd brought home and opened it to the theatre page. Our big opening-night ad leaped out at me: *'Oklahoma!'*

Slowly, surely, with that foggy bewilderment you were bound to feel sooner or later if you worked at the Theatre Guild long enough, I saw that Terry and Lawrence were right. About the exclamation point.

I did not allow myself to speculate on the insane possibility that they might also be right about such brainwaves as a clean, corn-fed musical with no legs and no jokes and with a score by Richard Rodgers and Oscar Hammerstein II, who'd never collaborated before; a full-blown ballet by an unknown young choreographer named Agnes de Mille; and a cast of unknowns, including Celeste Holm, the ingenue from *Papa Is All*.

I switched off the lamp, thinking how typical it was of both this epic and the Guild that the notices would appear on the morning of April Fool's Day. I coughed, pulled up the blankets and, as I drifted off to sleep, said a silent Good Luck to Alfred Drake, the juvenile from *Yesterday's Magic*, who was at that moment strolling out onto the stage of the St. James Theatre, singing:

'Oh, what a beautiful morning!'

8

Large Furnished Rear with Kitchen Privileges

When a young writer sets out for New York to crash the theatre, she is prepared to starve in a garret for a while. She has read the solemn pronouncement of a turn-of-the-century writer named Richard Harding Davis, that 'a man who can afford a hall bedroom in New York City is better off than he would be if he owned 160 acres of prairie.' She has seen *La Boheme* and wept as Rodolfo gallantly tossed his poems into the fire to warm his garret on Christmas Eve. And she has seen *Stage Door* – both Broadway and film versions – describing life at the Rehearsal Club, a female 'residence club' where young actresses bolster each other's morale in charming dormitory rooms. She has gathered from all of these testimonials that starving in a garret is a rich, purifying experience, and she wants it. And she gets it.

And of course, *after* she gets it, it dawns on her that when Richard Harding Davis wrote that a New York hall bedroom was better than 160 acres of prairie he was no longer living in a New York hall bedroom, having grown rich enough to afford a town house and nostalgia; she types her play huddled in blankets and sourly informs Rodolfo he should be damn glad he's got a fireplace to throw his poems into; and she thinks that somebody in *Stage Door* might have mentioned that the Rehearsal Club has a special New York electrical system known as DC – direct current – which means that the day she moves in she's going to blow her radio, her iron, and all the building's fuses, and that while the fuses can be fixed, her radio and iron can't, which in turn means that till next Christmas she's going to have to do without a radio, press her skirts under the mattress, and iron her scarves, blouses and handkerchiefs by pasting them soaking wet to a mirror.

My first garret – not counting the Rehearsal Club, which took me in temporarily as a favor to Terry and kept me just long enough to ruin my appliances – was one of those hall bedrooms Richard Harding Davis was so crazy about. This was way back in my fellowship year. I rented a hall bedroom on the fifth floor of a brownstone walk-up rooming house on West Sixty-ninth Street. The upper West Side was lined with four- and five-story brownstone houses built in the 1880s as homes for the well-to-do. Fifty or sixty years later the houses were moldering, vermin-ridden rooming houses. Ours had a cavernous entrance hall and a great, gloomy, unlit staircase, the steps adorned with dirty shreds of ancient carpeting and creaking eerily all the way up – and if you passed a dead rat on the stairs you were just very thankful he was dead.

I used to creak my way up four flights each night, grope down the musty hall to the third room on the left, unlock the door, feel for the string attached to the twenty-five-watt bulb overhead and ask myself why I'd left Philadelphia.

My room looked out on a stone wall and I couldn't see to comb my hair, let alone type my play, so I went out and bought a seventy-five-watt bulb and climbed on a chair and several of my best books to install it. But when I came home that night, the seventy-five-watter was gone and the twenty-five-watter was back. Forced to take the landlady's hint about saving electricity, I told myself Shakespeare probably never used more than twenty-five candles at a time either.

The room had a chair, a dresser and a bed. Some of the rooms had closets, but mine, being a seven-dollar-a-week room, had nails driven into the wall for clothes.

I stood this hole for six weeks and moved out as a result of two stimulating experiences during the sixth week. The first happened on an unusually warm October night. There was no air in the room and I was lying awake, listening to the tubercular coughing of a man across the courtyard, when there was a knock on my door. Since I knew nobody in New York but the ten men and one woman in the seminar

with me, none of whom was likely to knock on my door at 1 A.M.,
I decided it must be a telegram. I climbed out of bed, put on my
bathrobe and opened the door. A large, beefy middle-aged man stood
staring at me. He gazed from the curlers in my hair down past my
blue-and-white-striped pajama-and-bathrobe set, to my bare feet.

'You Dolly?' he inquired.

'I'm afraid you have the wrong room number,' I said. He looked
me over carefully again.

'You open for business?' he asked.

It took me a few seconds to understand him. Then I slammed the
door, locked it, pushed the overstuffed chair in front of it, armed myself
with a scissors and stood shaking, waiting for him to batter the door
down. I knew the difference between rape and prostitution, but at one in
the morning in that rooming-house room I wasn't sure he did.

In a minute or two I heard his footsteps down the hall and a knock
on another door. I heard the door open; then it closed and there was
silence. I climbed back into bed and lay staring watchfully at the
barricaded door till I fell asleep.

Next morning I woke up with hives. The hives got worse all week.
On Saturday night I woke about 3 A.M. to find a wild thunderstorm
in progress and the wind blowing the rain in on my bed. I got up,
switched on the light and began to strip the wet top sheet off the bed.
As I did so, two shiny round black objects scurried across the bottom
sheet and they weren't hives.

It took me half an hour to pack. I could have packed all I owned
in fifteen minutes but it takes longer when you're having hysterics. At
3:30 A.M. I hauled my luggage – a suitcase full of clothes, my Girl
Scout camp duffel bag full of books, and my portable typewriter –
down the four flights of stairs and out the front door. I dragged
everything to the corner of Amsterdam Avenue. The rain had stopped
and I stood there wondering what to do next, when a cruising cab saw
me and pulled up. The driver leaned out and surveyed my tearstained
face.

'Whatsamatta, honey?' he inquired.

'I had bedbugs,' I said. 'I moved out.'

'Couldn'ya waited till morning?' he asked. 'They wouldn' hurt ya!'

He got out and put my luggage in the cab and when I climbed into
the back seat, he said:

'Where to?'

'I don't know,' I quavered. 'I've only been in New York two months. I'd like to move out of this neighborhood if there's any other neighborhood I can afford.'

He was careening down Amsterdam by then and without slowing down, much less stopping, he turned clear around to stare at me.

'Didn' you know you were living in a red-light district?'

'No,' I said. 'What is it?'

He turned back to his driving, shaking his head.

He turned east on a dingy West Side street and came to Central Park, shot through the park to Fifth Avenue and on over to Lexington and careened down Lexington.

I'd never been east of Fifth Avenue before. Even at four in the morning, staring bug-eyed out of the cab window, I could see that the driver had brought me into a noisy, dilapidated, hopeful New York I hadn't known existed.

'I like it over here,' I thought. And over here I've stayed ever since.

'I'm takin' you to a woman's hotel,' he said. 'It ain't the Ritz but it's respectable. You stay there till you know your way around. Hear?'

The hotel room cost eleven dollars a week, more than a third of my weekly thirty-dollar fellowship allowance. But if the room was as small and narrow as a convent cell it was also as clean. I crawled thankfully into bed and went to sleep.

When I surveyed the lobby the next morning I seemed to be the only guest in the hotel who was under sixty-five. This had one unfortunate consequence which I got used to. My dates never did, however.

A man from the seminar took me out one Saturday night and when he brought me home he walked me to the elevator, where we had to say good night since Men Were Not Allowed Above the Mezzanine. The elevator arrived, and as my escort leaned over to kiss me good night, two black-suited men stepped out of the elevator carrying a sack between them.

Old ladies were carried out of there at the rate of a sack a month – always late at night, and somehow I was always around to assist. Me and my date. The next morning there'd be a sign on the lobby bulletin board:

'FOR SALE: Matched luggage.' Or 'Caracul coat. Good condition.'

I took advantage of one of those sales to throw out my camp duffel bag. I bought a wardrobe trunk for eight dollars, in case one of my plays ever went touring.

From then on, I alternated between small hotel rooms and larger rooming-house rooms that were somehow always on the top floor of a walk-up where you trudged up four double flights of stairs and, with your foot on the top step, remembered you were out of cigarettes. Both the hotel manager and the rooming-house landlady locked you out of your room if they caught you using a hot plate to save the price of a cafeteria breakfast.

All this time I cherished the dream of finding the ideal garret, a room large and light enough to work in and with what I described to myself as 'hot plate privileges.' But a year after *Oklahoma!* opened, the need for such a room became acute. I left the Guild and took a part-time job which would give me more time for my playwriting (see next chapter), but this meant that I'd be working at home and earning less. In the narrow hotel room I was living in that season, I scanned the Furnished Rooms columns in the *Times* without finding anything suitable I could afford. And then, one bright morning, there it was:

> Lg. furn. rear. Share bath.
> Kitch. priv. $40 monthly.

Since I'd had to slog out to the nearest cafeteria for breakfast every morning for five years, rain, sleet or cold-in-the-head – which is a very good way to feel sorry for yourself, especially on a rainy Sunday – 'kitchen privileges' was the pot of gold at the end of the rainbow.

I hurried around to the address given, on a quiet upper East Side street. The building was a narrow greystone, sandwiched in between a vegetable market and a handsome, discreetly anonymous building on the corner.

I found the super and asked about the furnished rear. He said it had already been rented, but a large furnished front had just come vacant for a few dollars more. It was on the top floor and we rode up in an undreamed-of elevator to look at it. It was a big, sunny room with a studio couch, an armchair, and a table big enough to accommodate my typewriter during the day and two dinner guests in the evening.

The super led me halfway down the hall to show me the bathroom and then on down to the far end of the hall and into a big old kitchen with an assortment of battered community pots and pans; and I knew I was home. He explained that I would share the bath and kitchen with the four other seventh-floor tenants, all of whom, he could assure me, were Ladies.

(That was a very prissy building. The second floor was for bachelors only; the third, fourth and fifth floors were for couples only; and way up on the top two floors – Ladies.)

I moved in on Saturday morning. I tore around to Woolworth's and bought plates, cups and saucers, knives, forks and spoons, a frying pan and a coffee pot. On the way home, I bought coffee, bread, eggs and oranges for Sunday breakfast, which I was going to cook properly in a kitchen and eat in my bathrobe in my own room, like a lady.

I met the other four tenants in and around the bathroom on Saturday afternoon. Somebody had tacked to the bathroom door a Schedule for Bathroom Hours for each tenant, but natural processes being what they are, it was hard to stick to.

Like me, the other tenants all classified as the Middle-Class Poor. Down at the end of the hall in the room next to the kitchen was Maude E. Bird. We called her Birdie behind her back, or ran it all together and called her Maudiebird, and both names suited her.

Maudiebird was a small, frail, wispy old lady with a thin, prim voice in which she indicated that she had known better days and that this sort of community living was not what she was used to. In her prime, she had been governess to the children of the rich and had lived, we gathered, only in mansions and villas. You'd think such wealthy employers would have given her some sort of pension, but if any of them had, it obviously wasn't enough because Maudiebird earned a few dollars as companion to a sick woman a couple of days a week and hired out at thirty-five cents an hour as chaperone to small children who went skating in Central Park.

She made her own hats from hat frames bought at Woolworth's and covered with fabric from Third Avenue remnant stores. I used to watch her set out gamely on cold winter Saturday afternoons in her warm black coat and homemade hat, prepared to freeze on a park bench watching children ice-skate for three hours – to earn one dollar.

Next along the hall from Birdie was Florrie, a middle-aged widow living on a pension. Florrie spent her days reading the *Daily News* and

True Romances but her chief passion was the radio, which she turned on when she got up and turned off when she went to bed. Her mornings were spent with radio talk shows: Breakfast with the Fitzgeralds, then Breakfast with Dorothy and Dick, and Mary Margaret McBride for lunch. A succession of afternoon soap operas carried her up to Lowell Thomas and the six o'clock news, then the Kraft Music Hall, the Lux Radio Theatre and so to bed.

Across the hall from me was Mamselle, a spinster who taught French at a fashionable Park Avenue girls' school. Mamselle had an inflammable temper and the blackest dyed hair I ever saw. She used to get up at five in the morning one Sunday a month to have the bathroom to herself while she dyed it.

In the room between Florrie and Mamselle was Gale, a tall, dark-haired, good-looking girl from Texas. She and I were the only young ones on the floor, and a few months after I moved in, we became close friends due to an arithmetic problem posed by the community kitchen.

There were two kitchen cabinets, each with three shelves, which divided evenly into one shelf per tenant (half the shelf for your staples, half for your private kitchen equipment), leaving the sixth shelf for community property: pots, pans, an iron and a hand-operated toaster. But any way you divided it, the stove had only four burners. On nights when all five tenants were cooking dinner at the same time, we were a burner short.

Gale and I solved the problem by pooling our money and cooking and eating together every night. She cooked one week and I cooked the next. Sometimes we put our dinner under the broiler or on one of the two oven racks to save our burner for the coffee pot. On nights when one of us had dinner company, the other obligingly ate out. This was after I'd lived there for a few months and had learned to cook.

Initially, I confined myself to two dinner guests, neither to be envied. Maxine, of course, was the first guest. She came over, on my second Sunday there, to help me hang blue burlap drapes, tack a makeshift blue burlap slipcover to the armchair and cover the stained wooden floor with a fluffy white bathroom rug. As a special treat for helping me, she was invited to eat the first dinner I ever cooked: hamburger and two canned vegetables. But it was Tom Goethals, the Latin and Greek teacher I'd found through the *Saturday Review*

Personals column, who was really put through the wringer.

I decided that the least I could do was give him dinner every week before my lesson, in lieu of salary. Like most neophyte cooks, I had an unbridled imagination and a childlike faith in newspaper recipes, so every time Tom came to dinner he came braced. I remember one mess I cooked up, compounded of chicken livers, green peppers, hard-boiled eggs, scallions, and a couple of other things in a dank, livery sauce, which we both gave up on, and I went back to the kitchen and made us an omelet out of my breakfast eggs and the bologna for my lunch sandwiches. But everything else I cooked him Tom gallantly ate, and some of it was just incredible.

With five tenants living a community life in very close quarters, there were bound to be small family fights. We averaged three or four a week. They stemmed from the community kitchen, the community bathroom and the community pay phone in the hall.

The phone fights began whenever a phone call came for Gale or me after 9:45 P.M. By that time the rest of the floor was in bed. The phone would ring at quarter to ten and as Gale or I dashed for it, three doors would open and three heads pop out simultaneously. Then the caterwauling started.

Mamselle would scream that she needed her rest, she got up early and worked hard, and phone calls had got to stop coming in the middle of the night. Whereupon Florrie, who'd been all set to complain herself a moment earlier, would turn on Mamselle and bawl:

'Lissen, Queen Mary Anto-Nette, if you're so damn stuck on yourself you have to lay down the law to everybody and make a big stink because a couple nice kids get a phone call, you better go live at the Waldorf!'

Whereupon Maudiebird would quiver into the conversation with the tearful announcement that having waked her up out of a sound sleep, we had now given her a headache with all the shouting.

The kitchen fights were incessant. In the first place, who was going to clean it? Each of us cleaned up her own cooking mess, but none of us considered that this included scrubbing the entire kitchen floor, or cleaning the entire stove or the entire refrigerator of which each of us was allotted only half a shelf. In open discussion one evening as we cooked, the rest of the tenants hinted that as Gale and I were young and strong, we were chosen by Natural Selection to clean the kitchen. We spent the following Saturday morning at it and then tacked up a sign on the kitchen wall:

> Schedule for Scrubbing Kitchen Floor, Cleaning Stove, Oven and Refrigerator.
>
> First Week of Month: Gale and Helene
> Second Week of Month:
> Third Week of Month:
> Fourth Week of Month:

But nobody else filled in her name for the available weeks, and after a while the schedule got splattered with grease and we took it down and went on having open discussions, attended by all five tenants and an increasing number of cockroaches. That was a great kitchen for signs.

> I accidentally overturned the sugar bowl on the middle shelf of the right-hand cabinet.
> I cleaned it up.
> I will replace sugar if owner will see me.
>
> FLORRIE.

> Please leave this oven at 350 degrees until my casserole is done. I will take it out at five o'clock.
>
> M.E.B.

> PLEASE MOVE THIS COFFEE POT ONTO YOUR CLOSET SHELF. IT CAN NOT STAND ON THIS BURNER ALL DAY. OTHER PEOPLE ARE ENTITLED TO USE THIS BURNER.
>
> (unsigned)

Maudiebird caused a whole series of kitchen spats because her room was next to the kitchen. She ate her meager supper early and generally retired to her room with it just as the rest of us arrived in the kitchen to start our dinners. If one of us sang or laughed or spoke above a library whisper, Birdie was sure to appear in the doorway and say that we would have to stop making so much noise, she was working on her figures.

'How long can it take her,' I demanded when she'd gone back to her room, 'to add up twenty hours of companion-sitting and six hours of park-bench-sitting?'

And Florrie, when anybody laughed, would mutter:

'Be quiet: Birdie's doing her Examples.'

The bathroom crises were caused entirely by Gale and me.

I mentioned that there was a discreetly anonymous building next door to us on the corner. It was six stories high, so that our seventh-floor bathroom overlooked its roof. Gale and I, through the bathroom window, had made the acquaintance of two young men who sunbathed on the roof occasionally, after their work in the discreet building, which was a very upper-class funeral parlor. One Saturday afternoon not long after I moved in, Gale and I were washing our hair and doing our nails in the bathroom when one of the boys called up to us:

'Have you girls got dates for tonight?' For a wonder, we both did.

'Would you like some flowers to wear?' he inquired. We said we'd love some and the boy told us he'd be right back. He and his friend disappeared and came back five minutes later carrying between them a blanket of gardenias.

'Compliments of the corpse!' one of the boys said cheerily. 'They came too late for the funeral.'

They upended the gardenia blanket and hoisted it up and Gale and I leaned down and hauled it up and through the window.

Honesty compels me to admit that he did not say 'the corpse,' he told us *whose* corpse. It was the body of a distinguished statesman and if I wasn't afraid the funeral parlor would sue me I'd tell you his name. Gale and I were reluctant to steal his flowers but the boys explained that famous corpses often got flowers from total strangers, with cards reading 'An Admirer,' 'An Unknown Friend,' and so forth; and when these offerings were too ostentatious or came too late for the funeral, the family of the deceased directed that the flowers be sent to some hospital. Several hospitals having done very well by this particular corpse, the boys saw no reason to consult the family about giving us one gardenia blanket.

Thus reassured, Gale and I sat down on the bathroom floor to detach ourselves a pair of corsages. Let me tell you it was no easy trick. Each flower was wired to the greenery with heavy wire and you nearly ripped your fingers off detaching a corsage spray. It therefore took us some time – and of course, while we were working, there was an importunate knock on the bathroom door.

'Let's carry it to my room,' I said to Gale.

'I am not,' she said in her Texas drawl, 'paradin' through the hall with a funeral blanket on my head.'

Instead, she turned on the bath faucets to indicate we'd be in there for some time. This brought a stream of French invective from Mamselle, so as soon as I heard her door slam, I tiptoed out of the bathroom with the blanket in my arms, and when I'd made it safely to my room, Gale called loudly to the rest of the hall:

'Bathroom's free!'

and we finished our corsages in my room.

During the single season the two boys worked next door, we had perfectly glorious flowers to wear and bowls of lilies as centerpieces for our dinette tables. We also got mildly ghoulish. I'd read in the *Times* that a certain famous actress had died and was on view at our parlor, and I'd hurry down the hall, knock on Gale's door and when she opened it cry: 'Guess who's next door!'

All in all, it was garret living at its best, and it was a sad day for all of us when we received notice that the building was to be renovated and we'd have to move.

This was 1948, and there was a severe postwar housing shortage in New York. Gale and I each found a friend willing to take us in temporarily; Florrie moved in with her recently widowed sister; Mamselle's school found her a room in a residence club; and Maudiebird, after three months of searching, finally found a fourth-floor walk-up. It gave me a pang to think of her thin old legs climbing four flights several times a day, but she told me wistfully that a room in an elevator building was too expensive for anybody.

We bade each other farewell and went our separate ways. My way took me into the sharp teeth of the housing shortage. The friend who took me in had barely helped me get settled in her apartment when it was completely gutted by fire. The next day I was out on the street with my salvageable clothes in a suitcase in one hand and my portable typewriter in the other, looking for a place to live.

Whole families were living in their cars that year. I met them on Saturday nights when all of us who were homeless gathered at the *New York Times* office to get the earliest edition of the Sunday real estate section. During the next eighteen months I had eleven addresses, most of them two-week and one-month sublets from people going on winter or summer vacations. When there was no sublet I slept at Maxine's – she had twin beds in her room – until I became so acutely embarrassed at seeming to move in on her that I couldn't bring myself to do it one more night and paid a doorman to let me sleep on two lobby chairs instead.

So you'll understand that when, after eighteen homeless months, I finally found a 'converted apartment' available, I was past caring that the rent was twice what I could afford.

The building was a five-story greystone on East Ninety-fifth Street and had formerly been a private home. Its larger rooms had been 'converted' to apartments by installing ancient kitchen and bathroom equipment in adjoining smaller rooms. The ground-floor apartment I looked at was a large, dark room-in-the-back, its one window looking out on a courtyard below and a stone wall opposite. Beyond it, the kitchen with its ancient stove and leaky refrigerator was all mine, and the adjoining bare room with its iron tub and a chain toilet in a former closet was the first private bathroom of my life. And no mansion could have seemed more beautiful to me than that three-room hovel when I was told it might be mine.

It wasn't mine for certain. The tenant who was moving out told me his lease had only a month to run and he couldn't guarantee the rental agency would give me a new lease. I wanted to go directly to the building's owner but of course that wasn't possible. When I went down to see the rental agent, he explained that the owner owned several similar buildings and had nothing to do with the running of any of them. Everything was handled by the agency. But the rental agent was kind and said that if my references were satisfactory he saw no reason why I shouldn't count on a lease. I had to be content with that.

I moved in forthwith and plunged into the job of furnishing and decorating. I furnished the room in what New Yorkers called Early Orange Crate. The super helped me make a bookcase out of wooden planks he found in the cellar, and a dressing table for the bathroom out of an orange crate. One of my brothers donated a dresser his little girls had outgrown, and I bought a secondhand dropleaf table and chairs and a secondhand studio bed. Add white enamel paint to cover everything, my old white rug, and yards of red burlap which Maxine draped across the top of the window and down over the rusty living-room pipes in an opulent swag – and in our objective opinion the room was simply stunning.

Two thorny problems remained. The kitchen and bathroom floors were covered with stained, faded and cracked linoleum, which clearly had to be replaced. I bought two bright rolls of linoleum at Woolworth's, brought them home – and wondered what to do with them. What did I know about cutting linoleum and running it around the kitchen pipes and bathroom pipes and under the elderly stove and bathtub? I phoned Maxine.

'How much would it cost me,' I asked, 'to hire a man to cut and lay new linoleum for me?'

'A fortune,' said Maxine positively.

'Well, I don't know what to do!' I said. 'I bought all this linoleum and I bought a knife and a ruler they said I'd need, and I'm paralyzed. I don't know where to start!'

There was a thoughtful pause at the other end.

'What night,' asked Maxine, 'is Tom coming for your lesson?'

Oh.

So when Tom came for my Latin lesson he spent four exhausting hours stretched out on the kitchen and bathroom floors – neither long enough to accommodate all of him, but the rooms fortunately having no door between. Armed with ruler, knife, hammer, a box of tacks and the disposition of a saint, he measured, cut and tacked my new kitchen and bathroom linoleum while I read him the Gospel According to St. Matthew out of a Latin Bible borrowed from him.

The bathroom floor looked so bright and new it called attention to the dirty, faded wallpaper. So a week later, when Tom arrived for my lesson, he found the bathtub full of water and two rolls of do-it-yourself wallpaper waiting for him, and he put in another active recreational evening wallpapering the bathroom while I read to him out of my Catullus.

The last remaining problem concerned kitchen equipment; and it was in her solution to this one that Maxine pulled off her greatest financial coup.

Never having owned a kitchen before, I made the appalling discovery that except for a coffee pot and a few plates left over from the seventh-floor garret, I had nothing whatsoever to put in it. I mean I didn't own a strainer, a kitchen fork or spoon, a pot holder, a can opener, a pot or a pan. Nothing. I sat down and made a list of bare kitchen essentials and when I totted up the approximate cost the total came to roughly fifty dollars.

If I have to add this, I didn't have fifty dollars.

Maxine and I were going to theatre that night and we met at a nearby drugstore for our watch-and-wait cup of coffee.

'Do we have a problem!' I said as we ordered the coffee. I gave her my kitchen list, with the total cost at the bottom ringed round with exclamation points.

Our coffee came and Maxine sipped hers absently as she studied the list.

'What you need,' she said finally, 'is a kitchen shower.'

'I'm not getting married,' I said.

'You're marrying New York,' said Maxine. 'You'll have to write a cute invitation. We'll have the shower at my house. A luncheon. A Saturday luncheon.'

'I couldn't!' I said. 'I can't send out invitations asking people to furnish my kitchen!'

'You're not sending the invitations. I'm sending them. You don't know anything about the luncheon,' said Maxine. 'It's a surprise. Showers are always surprises. You're just coming to my house for lunch. When you get there, be surprised.'

We drew up the invitation in the theatre lobby during intermission. We drew up a list of guests, including my two out-of-town sisters-in-law who, said Maxine, wouldn't come but wouldn't-have-the-nerve-not-to-send-something. And to avoid duplication, Maxine had me draw up an alphabetical list of essential items, a copy of which she enclosed with each invitation, together with a request that the recipient check off the item she was bringing.

And so on the appointed Saturday I wandered into Maxine's parents' apartment for lunch – and there was my sister-in-law come all the way in from Garden City and a simple host of friends. And sitting in the middle of the floor in a large wicker basket, each item brightly wrapped and tied with flossy ribbon, were frying pans and double boilers and mixing bowls and kitchen knives and pot holders and dish towels and a roasting pan and a Revere Ware teakettle that sang.

By the end of the month I had as warm and bright and well-equipped a home as any penniless writer ever had. And none of it securely mine until I signed a lease.

On the day the old lease ran out, I went down to the rental office ready to do battle but inwardly terrified, with the eighteen-month nightmare fresh in my memory.

To my relief, the agent smiled warmly at me when I walked into his office. He told me that my references had been approved and that my lease was ready for signing. I sat down, suddenly weak. The agent pushed the lease toward me and handed me a pen. I didn't even read the lease, I'd have signed anything that guaranteed a roof over my head. I went straight to the bottom of the page, where the two lines for signatures were: the bottom line marked OWNER, the top line marked TENANT. I signed my name along the line marked TENANT.

Then the pen slipped out of my hand and rolled to the floor and I stared at the lease, dumbfounded. Because on the line marked OWNER, a signature had been written just below my own. In a thin spidery hand, it read:

'Maude E. Bird.'

9

Outside Hollywood

To be young and trying to crash the theatre in the forties was to resign yourself to the chronic problem of how to earn enough money to keep alive till you became famous on Broadway. You learned to avoid nine-to-five jobs and look instead for part-time work which, though it paid a meager wage, would leave you free most of the day to pursue what you liked to think of as your real profession.

The jobs actors took in those days ran a gamut considerably longer than this book. An actor, for instance, might work as a bellhop, bartender, bus driver, barker on a sightseeing bus, bonded messenger, bouncer, or butcher's delivery boy, and that's only the B's.

Actresses were more limited, as Maxine discovered, even though when she filled out an Employment Agency Questionnaire and came to the question: 'Kind of Position Wanted: _____ ' she wrote simply: 'I'll do anything.' In addition to taking street-corner and door-to-door surveys, Maxine drove a school bus, was a saleslady at Lord & Taylor during the pre-Christmas rush, and taught elocution in a convent.

Maxine's trouble was that when she was out of work she got impetuous and she'd seize any job that came along without a careful enough consideration of the hours involved. There was the winter she drove the school bus, for instance. Like most actresses, she was used to going to bed very late and sleeping half the morning. Even when she wasn't in a play, she was generally up half the night working on some big project like drying her hair.

Since Maxine's hair was shoulder-length and as thick as a mop, just washing it took most of the evening. And for reasons known to nobody, she decided that the way to dry it was to turn on the oven, sit on the kitchen floor and spread her hair out on an oven rack to dry. She put the oven on at the lowest possible heat so as not to set her hair on fire, and as a result it took her half the night to dry it. She washed it once a week, sat with her hair in the oven till two or three in the morning and as a result slept through the alarm clock five hours later.

So during the season when she drove the school bus, she overslept regularly one morning a week, thereby leaving twenty-five children standing around under twenty-five apartment-house canopies waiting for the school bus. And at least one afternoon a week she was summoned to a two o'clock audition which invariably started an hour late and ran longer than anticipated, causing her to leave twenty-five children standing on the school steps for a couple of hours waiting for the bus to take them home. So Maxine and the school parted company by mutual consent after three months, freeing her in time for the Christmas rush at Lord & Taylor.

Ideally, of course, she found what might be called grey-area acting jobs, like appearing in that U.S. government-sponsored documentary on gonorrhea which enabled her to be seen by thousands of American GIs during World War II.

But the best part-time job for an actress was a running part in a radio soap opera, which was acting of a sort and the easiest imaginable (you didn't have to memorize lines, you just read them), and which paid handsomely. Maxine hit this jackpot only once. For a halcyon thirteen weeks she was Caroline, the female menace in The Romance of Helen Trent. Unfortunately, by the end of thirteen weeks Maxine had had radio, and radio, she was frank to admit, had had her.

'I'm standing there in front of the mike,' she reported to me over coffee at the Astor drugstore after her first broadcast, 'I'm enunciating beautifully and giving a magnificently bitchy performance, as called for – when I notice that the idiot director is staring at me and making little-bitty circles with his thumbs, both thumbs going round and round and round. I tried to ignore him but he went on staring at me, making more and more little-bitty circles in the air with his thumbs. And I said to myself: "That man is getting on my nerves."

'So as soon as I had a ten-second pause, I turned to him and mouthed silently: "Stop doing that." And I shook the script at him for emphasis, only the script accidentally hit the microphone causing a needle to fly up to the top which meant that on millions of radios across the country, The Romance of Helen Trent was instantly drowned out by static.'

After the broadcast she learned that the little circles were radio sign language for 'Speed it up.' It was some weeks before she learned the sign for 'Slow down.'

'Can they write "Slow down" on a piece of paper and hand it to you?' she demanded of me as we sat on stools in Sardi's bar, where she was putting her radio profits to good use by being Seen. 'No! When they want you to slow down, the director stares at you with his fists close together against his chest and then slowly pulls his fists away from each other – like a Stanislavski improvisation of a taffy-pull. This means s-t-r-e-t-c-h in radio, but nobody tells you this, you have to guess it! I'm standing there trying to give a performance and I see him step in front of me and start pulling his fists apart and I think: "In the middle of a radio broadcast, he has to start playing The Game!"' (The Game is what theatre people call Charades.)

So what with one thing and another, Maxine wasn't greatly surprised one day, just before the expiration of her thirteen-week contract, to read in the script that Caroline's headaches had definitely been diagnosed as an obscure form of Rocky Mountain fever which she could cure only by moving to Switzerland for several years. Her contract was not renewed, the party was over and a week later she was back at her old post in front of Radio City Music Hall, taking surveys on the average woman's opinion of hormone creams and what a man looks for in a razor blade.

Playwrights, of course, hunted for writing jobs. For a while I thought I had the best of these, writing publicity in the Theatre Guild press department. But the Guild job took the whole day and occasional evenings, leaving me no time to write in. So eventually I left the Guild and began looking for part-time jobs instead. Fortunately, back in the forties, there was one part-time job for which would-be playwrights and novelists were in demand.

This was the era when Hollywood was in its heyday, and the best of all part-time writing jobs was to be had in the New York offices of Hollywood studios. Warner's, 20th Century-Fox, M-G-M, Columbia,

Paramount, Selznick, Universal, all had New York story departments which became a positive Mecca for unemployed, undiscovered writers.

I got to Mecca through a letter from the story editor at one of the studios. He wrote to say he'd read my play and had recommended me to the West Coast office as a writer the studio might want at some future date. I wrote back and said How about a part-time job with the East Coast office now instead? Two days later I was an outside reader for a studio we'll call Monograph.

There were inside readers and outside readers and I'll explain the whole thing to you in a minute, but first I would like you to appreciate what people with that job title had to contend with. Some tax expert or friend of your family would ask:

'What do you do for a living?'

and you'd say:

'I'm an outside reader for a film studio.'

and the questioner would give you the blankest look ever seen on a human face and say:

'You're a what?'

and you knew it would take you twenty minutes to explain it, and there was no way you could avoid explaining it, and in four or five years you got so *tired* explaining it.

Most Hollywood movies were adapted from novels, plays and short stories which the studios bought by the ton. To find this material, every studio hired inside readers, who worked nine-to-five in the studio offices; and outside readers, who worked part-time and at home. We didn't go out and look for the material, you understand; we read what was submitted to the studio by producers and publishers, playbrokers and literary agents, magazines and newspapers. The submissions included plays, novels, short stories, science fiction, and westerns and whodunits by the gross. Every reader had a specialty – mine was plays – but when your specialty wasn't available you read whatever was. Sooner or later, you read everything imaginable and a lot that wasn't.

The studios were supposed to accept manuscripts only from professional sources but it never worked out that way. If the story editor's mother's janitor wrote a play, Monograph covered it. If your landlady or your Aunt Clara thought her life would make a book and wrote the book in six hundred pages, as long as the pages were typed she could submit it and Monograph would cover it. It didn't have to be literate, it didn't have to be sane, it just had to be typed.

We went to Monograph at four each afternoon, got a play or novel, took it home and read it, wrote a two-page Summary and a Comment and brought the work in at four the next afternoon. I can't print a two-page Summary here but a friend of mine still at Monograph dug a couple of my old Comments out of the files as samples for you, to indicate the extent of what Monograph covered. Comments were readers' opinions of the work covered and looked like this:

TITLE:	Hope Is Eternal
AUTHOR:	John Malan
FORM:	Playscript

COMMENT:

Crackpot illiterate fantasy about an unsuccessful play-wright who throws himself under a subway train, wakes up in Heaven and finds himself posthumously famous on Broadway. (I've tried everything else; next year I may try this.)

TITLE:	Cappy Meets the Test
AUTHOR:	Frances Eager Dawes
FORM:	Juvenile (8–12 age group)

COMMENT:

If Cappy doesn't straighten out and pass his algebra test, Hilldale High is going to lose the championship football game. Listen, this is my second Eager Dawes this week, next week it's somebody else's turn, O.K.?

For reading and summarizing a play or novel you got $6 (in 1947 when I started reading). The next year they raised it to $8 and by the early fifties (when I quit) it had got up to $10. You read one a day and two or three over a weekend. You weren't supposed to read for two studios at once – it was like working for both Macy's and Gimbel's – but when the bills piled up you bootlegged a little reading from a second studio. And you went babysitting, evenings, and read Monograph's scripts on the baby's family's electric bill, and they also had to give you dinner half the time, and one way or another if you didn't exactly make a living you somehow made out. Once you learned the technique of professional reading, you had the whole day free to write in. I could read a long novel in an evening, write the summary of it after breakfast and at nine-thirty be free to write until four, when I took the work in to Monograph. I keep hearing about these expensive courses that will teach you how to read faster. Don't take them; I'll give you the whole course right here, free. The technique is never to be applied to books you want to read, you understand; it's only for books you don't want to read but have to.

Open to page one of a long novel you don't want to read, and run your eye down the left-hand side of the page, noting the first sentence in each paragraph. Say a paragraph begins:

'*The house was set well back, in . . .*'

Skip the whole paragraph; it's going to describe the house and grounds and you're not reading the book for the architecture. Run your eye on down to the paragraph beginning:

'*Her eyes were a pale water blue. Her skin, which had once . . .*' Skip that paragraph too; she's getting old and unattractive. You've learned this in a sentence-and-a-half, why read twelve?

Skip the paragraph beginning:

'*He strode toward the moors. In the darkening light, the moors . . .*' unless you're just crazy about moors.

Keep running your eye down past all such paragraphs until you come to a paragraph in which something *happens*. Say you come to a murder or a rape on page 250. You can count on the author spending at least thirty pages on this event. The facts will be set forth on pages 250–251, the outcome will be found on pages 279–280. Skip the pages in between; the studio that hired you only wants the facts and you only want to get to bed before dawn.

When reading plays, skip the parentheses.

'(*Large, well-appointed living-room. At left . . .*)' It goes on for ten or twenty lines and you've read the only one the set designer will pay any attention to.

'(JANE *enters through French windows. SHE is a tall, rather . . .*)' She's tall unless the director happens to cast a short actress for the part.

After the first scene, the parentheses will include all the emotions the playwright couldn't manage to convey in the dialogue. It's easier, for instance, to write '*(angrily)*' than it is to write an angry line. Skip all those, too; the audience won't see them and every actor and actress I ever knew found them distracting and blacked them out before learning the part.

Of course, when we got a new Steinbeck or Hemingway novel, or a Williams or Miller play, we didn't write a two-page summary, we wrote a ten-to-twenty-page synopsis, including all the minor characters and large hunks of dialogue; but long synopses paid a dollar a page so they were worth the time they took.

Every afternoon at four o'clock, the outside readers took their completed assignments down to the Broadway theatre district (where most studios had their offices) and up to the Monograph story department, which occupied half a floor in an office building and was just jumping with personnel.

There was the story editor, in charge of novels; the play editor, in charge of plays; their assistant, who assigned work to the readers; Jean, in charge of cataloguing and returning all material submitted; Lilian, who sent copies of all readers' reports to Monograph's Hollywood office; and Evelyn, who got out a news bulletin on what everybody else was doing. Not forgetting two private secretaries, an at-large stenographer and Miriam, the file clerk. And way down at the end of a hall, in a private dungeon of their own, were the inside readers who read all day long. We never saw them; they never came out.

The outside readers sat in a row on a bench outside the assistant's office, each of us waiting our turn to go in. All of us were starving writers except Dolly. And my God, how we resented Dolly.

Dolly was a fashionable young matron who came to Monograph looking and behaving as if she were at a glamorous cocktail party. Her husband was a successful businessman and Dolly didn't need the reading job. She read for fun – she told us with entire innocence that she thought reading was 'a fun job.' And wouldn't you know Dolly's specialty was the easiest and best-paid of all reading work? She read the empty little romances in women's magazines – *Ladies' Home Journal*, *Woman's Home Companion*, *Good Housekeeping* – which in those days published only creampuff fiction. Six stories to a magazine, Dolly got $2 per story and only had to write one-paragraph summaries on little file cards.

Dolly would sit on that bench with a fur stole across her lap and say chattily to all us hungry writers:

'I didn't feel like taking any work last night. But yesterday morning I saw a pair of alligator pumps at Saks and I looked at the price tag and it was only two magazines! So when they asked if I wanted any work last night I said to myself: 'Dolly, you take it! You can get those alligator shoes! So I took it.'

Out of our mouths, you understand, she took it. She was a very pleasant woman, friendly and sociable; but I'd sit on that bench watching one of her two-magazine alligator pumps dangle from a nylon toe – I wore pants to Monograph myself because with pants you could wear thirty-five-cent ankle socks instead of $1.35 nylons – and wish I could hate her.

But the fact that she didn't need the job was only (a). (b) Dolly wasn't a writer. Not being a writer, she used to utter the most loathsome of all amateur literary clichés. She'd leaf through the *Ladies' Home Journal* she'd just read and she'd say:

'I could write better stories than these.'

If she said it once she said it three times a week.

Understand, none of us had a high opinion of women's magazine fiction. But being writers, we knew that any kind of specialized writing demanded technical skill, at the very least. What infuriated us was that Dolly didn't know how fiendishly difficult it was to write *anything*, especially anything salable. So every time she said: 'I could write better stories than these,' there'd be a highly charged pause and I'd wonder if this was the day one of the male readers was finally going to go berserk and stomp her to death.

The other readers were the standard types to be found in every studio reading department. If standard is the word.

There was middle-aged Miss Manheimer, who was large and stout and addicted to garden hats with bunches of fruit on them and lived with her mother. There was Jason, a failed actor who had decided to be a playwright instead. And there was Wide-Margin Wirtz, who was bald and fat and the reading department thief.

Readers were permitted to do a long synopsis (which paid ten to twenty dollars) whenever they considered a manuscript warranted it. Wide-Margin thought everything he read warranted it. But he didn't exactly write a ten-page synopsis. What he did was set three-inch margins at both ends of the typewriter so that his synopsis ran like a wide ribbon down the center of the paper, stretching two or three pages of copy to ten. Now and then the editors would complain and Wide-Margin would sulk along on six-dollar summaries until the fuss died down. Then he'd start again. But that's not what I meant by 'thief.'

I ran out of paper in the middle of a long synopsis one morning and since Wide-Margin lived closer to me than any of the other readers I phoned to ask him if he had any extra 'setups' – paper with carbon attached – and he said he had plenty so I went over to his apartment to get them. He was typing when I got there, and he waved toward a closet and said:

'Help yourself.'

I opened the closet door and what met my eyes was a writer's dream of Christmas morning. On shelves from floor to ceiling were reams of Monograph typing paper and setups, boxes of carbon paper, type-writer ribbons, pens, pencils, rubber bands, paper clips and two stapling machines. Monograph eventually caught him raiding the supply room and fired him and he moved on to another studio.

But our prize character was Winston Atterbury. Winston was Monograph's disappearing reader.

Every studio had for its sins one reader to whom it gave the galleys of, say, *The Rise and Fall of the Third Reich*. That is, it was always a big book, six or seven hundred pages long, it was always a widely heralded work by an important writer, it was still in printer's galleys and no other studio had yet seen it. The galleys had been stolen from the publisher's office by bribing a stenographer or office boy, and rushed to the studio late on a Friday afternoon. The reader was summoned, taken into the story editor's private office, told about the property and exhorted to read the book over the weekend taking copious notes, do a long synopsis later for double money, but rush the galleys back to Monograph early Monday morning so they could be whipped over to the publisher's office before they were missed. The reader would nod eagerly, hurry home with the galleys and disappear from the face of the earth for two weeks.

That's a disappearing reader. And I have to say that during four or five years of reading for a living, almost every reader was tempted to disappear at least once. Including me.

I've never liked novels and there were weeks when I had to read one a night for Monograph. But I was usually spared what I regarded as the ultimate professional-reading horror: the seven-hundred-page, three-generation family saga that always had more subplots than a soap opera and more characters than Dickens, and forced you to make pages and pages of notes. Anything worse was simply beyond my imagination.

Well, on the blackest Friday I ever want to see, I was summoned to Monograph and handed three outsized paperback volumes of an English book which was about to be published here. I was to read all three volumes over the weekend, and since each volume was double the length of the usual novel I was invited to charge double money for each. I hurried home with the three volumes and after dinner began to read Volume 1. And if Monograph's office had been open at that hour, I'd have phoned and quit my job.

What I had to read, during that nightmare weekend – taking notes on all place names, characters' names and events therein – was fifteen hundred stupefying pages of the sticky mythology of J.R.R. Tolkein. (I hope I'm spelling his name wrong.) I remember opening one volume to a first line which read

Mr. Bilbo Baggins of Bag End announced that he would shortly be celebrating his eleventy-first birthday. . . .

and phoning several friends to say good-bye because suicide seemed so obviously preferable to five hundred more pages of that.

I also remember the bill I turned in:

For Reading and Summarizing:	
TITLE: Lord of the Rings	
AUTHOR: J.R.R. Tolkien	
Volume I	$ 20
Volume II	20
Volume III	20
Mental Torture	40
TOTAL	$100

They paid it. I think they knew how close I'd come to disappearing; and one disappearing reader per season was all any studio could cope with. We had three of them during the years I was at Monograph. Each had his own technique for evading studio attempts to find him during his disappearance. First there was Howie, who hid out in the flophouse movie theatres lining Forty-second Street; then there was Elwood, who got friends in Chicago or Pittsburgh to send bogus telegrams to the studio reading CALLED AWAY BY DEATH IN FAMILY GALLEYS WITH LANDLADY ELWOOD, which Monograph appreciated because they could send somebody up to the Bronx to get the galleys back. Lastly, there was Winston Atterbury.

Winston had bleached blond curls with bleached blond sideburns and he was a very dapper dresser, he favored pearl-grey ties to match his pearl-grey suede shoes. As long as I knew him he was working on a novel about plantation days in the Old South. We'd assumed he was born Willie Smith or Joe Potts and renamed himself Winston Atterbury, but during his disappearance his mother phoned from Omaha to ask if Monograph knew 'where my son is,' and damned if she wasn't Mrs Atterbury.

Winston was a professional pauper. Every day, he borrowed six cents from Miriam, the file clerk. Miriam was a willowy, dark-haired girl with great sympathetic brown eyes and a heart that melted and bled for Monograph's underpaid outside readers. Her voice shook when she spoke of us because we had no union and no minimum wage and no unemployment insurance and no consideration from Monograph and we were all so nice and so talented and so pathetic.

So naturally it was Miriam Winston turned to when he first decided to borrow six cents. She listened with brimming eyes as he explained he only had nine cents and if he couldn't borrow six he'd have to walk to Washington Heights, where his rooming house was; it took a bus and a subway to get there.

Miriam begged him, she entreated him, to take at least a quarter. But no, six cents was all he would take. After that, Miriam lent him six or eight cents a day – he varied the amount but it never went above nine – and on Friday, payday, he paid her back. Then one Friday I walked into the office in time to hear Miriam tell Winston in a low, passionate voice that she would absolutely not take his thirty-one cents, he was to use it toward a good big lamb chop.

'Why didn't you take it?' I asked her when Winston had gone. 'He just got paid and we've had a good week.'

Miriam turned on me, trembling with compassionate fury.

'Would you like to know,' she demanded, quivering, 'what that boy did for his dinner last night?'

'What did he do for his dinner last night?' I asked obligingly.

'He ate cat food!' said Miriam and burst into tears.

I couldn't say so to the mother of us all, but Winston's poverty stories never inspired much confidence in me. They were too interesting by half.

He was there quite awhile before we discovered Winston was a disappearer. He disappeared with *The Wall* by John Hersey.

The Wall was not only the hottest advance property of the year, it was also the longest. It came into the office in three hundred and thirty galleys, each galley nine feet long if it was an inch. Winston was summoned into the inner office late on a Friday afternoon and told to take copious notes on the book over the weekend and do a long synopsis at his leisure, just so he got the galleys back early Monday morning. Winston nodded eagerly, hurried home to Washington Heights and disappeared.

When he didn't show Monday morning, Monograph phoned the stationery store on the corner next to his rooming house (the rooming house had no phone) and asked the owner to call Winston to the phone. The owner sent somebody up to Winston's room but Winston wasn't there. All morning, the story editor's secretary kept on phoning without success. In the afternoon she sent Winston a telegram.

On Tuesday, two secretaries were assigned the job of locating Winston. Every hour they phoned the stationery store and got somebody to run up and knock on Winston's door and all day long he wasn't home. On Wednesday, Jason, one of the other readers, offered to go up to Washington Heights and ask the landlady to let him into Winston's room so he could get *The Wall* out of it. Off Jason went to Washington Heights and the landlady let him into Winston's room. *The Wall* wasn't there. Wherever he'd gone, Winston had taken the longest galleys of the decade with him.

Which is probably what caused the secretary who knew him best to start phoning the bars in Winston's neighborhood. He'd once told her that 'like writers in Paris,' he enjoyed reading and writing 'in the local cafes.' She phoned the bar on the opposite corner from the stationery store, which Winston had said was his favorite. When the proprietor of the bar said he'd never heard of Winston Atterbury, the two secretaries got the phone book and looked up all the Washington Heights bars and began phoning each in turn. No Winston. Finally, late on Thursday afternoon, one of them phoned the bar on the corner again.

'I told you before, lady, I never heard of the guy!' said the bartender.

'Now don't tell me that!' snapped the secretary, whose nerves were pretty frayed by then. 'He lives on your block and we're told he's in your bar regularly.'

'I don't know him by name,' said the bartender. 'If you want to tell me what he looks like, maybe I seen him.'

'He's tall, with blond hair and sideburns,' said the secretary, 'and he dresses –'

'Oh, you mean *Douglas!*' said the bartender. 'Just a second. Hey, Douglas! Lady on the phone for you!'

So Winston-alias-Douglas got on the phone and said, Hello, there! How were we all? . . . The what? . . . Oh, *The Wall!* Sure, he had it. Had it right there with him. Hadn't got too far into it yet, he'd been busy with his own writing, but it looked to be a pretty fair book, he thought . . .

That was the last we saw of Winston. He moved on to another studio before Monograph had a chance to fire him.

In a business which depended on the Winston Atterburys and Wide-Margin Wirtzes, the turnover was fairly heavy. Along with whose who were fired, there was the occasional reader who blossomed into a successful writer (Ayn Rand was once an outside reader) and there was the occasional Dolly who didn't need the job and quit when she got bored with it.

We missed Dolly after she left. As I said, she was a sociable, friendly soul and much as we resented her, we all liked her. Jason, who inherited her specialty, mentioned her affectionately one afternoon as he came out of the story editor's office with the new *Ladies' Home Journal.*

'Poor old Dolly,' he said, 'I wonder if she misses –' And then he stopped cold.

There on the cover of the *Ladies' Home Journal*, streaming across the bottom like a banner, was Dolly's name and the announcement that a story by this gifted new *Journal* writer would be found within.

Dolly'd not only thought she could write better stories than those: she'd gone home and done it.

And I mean to tell you the Monograph Studio outside reading department was fit to be TIED.

10

Owl and Piglet on Broadway

All I did was answer a call from Warner Brothers' story department and wander over to Warner's prepared to bootleg a little extra reading – and the sky fell on me.

The state of mind known as 'stagestruck' has never been confined to the hopeful young who think they have a creative or performing talent. There are hundreds of men and women who lay no claim to such talents, but who have wangled permanent niches for themselves in the theatre purely because they're incurably stagestruck.

First are the theatrical agents, whose skill at selling and negotiating might have made them richer – and would certainly have given them more security – in any of a dozen mundane industries.

Then there are the backers. They range from the pants manu-facturer – whose few thousand dollars invested in a half-million-dollar production gives him the illusion of being In The Theatre – to Howard Cullman, former chairman of the New York Port Authority, who throughout an impressive business career has invested most of his money in Broadway plays.

Third are the theatrical lawyers who take only theatre people as clients, invest their legal fees in their clients' productions and attend preproduction conferences and auditions as assiduously as the producers they wish they were and sometimes become.

In a category all his own was a singular gentleman who died before

this book was written, but who is alive and cherished in my memory
and will be as long as I live. He is the Owl in this story; and all I knew
about him when I wandered over to Warner's that day was that his
name was Jacob Wilk and that, publicly, he was the eastern story
editor for Warner Brothers Pictures. Privately, Jake Wilk was
Broadway's foremost, if not its only, secret producer. This is how he
secretly produced plays:

Some reader would cover a novel that seemed a likely vehicle for
one of Warner's stars and would recommend the novel to Jake. Jake
would read it and decide it would make a fine Broadway play. (Movies
didn't interest him.) He'd go over in his mind the names of all
Broadway playwrights until he came to the one who was exactly right
for this particular book. Then he'd phone the playwright.

'I want you to read this book,' he'd say. 'I'll send it over to you. I
think you ought to adapt it for Broadway.'

'I'm tied up right now, Mr Wilk,' the playwright would say with
innocent tact, 'but as soon as I get time I'll certainly read it.'

Jake would send him the book that afternoon and phone the
playwright next morning.

'Have you read it yet?' he'd ask.

The playwright in some surprise would repeat that he was 'tied up.'

'All right,' Jake would say agreeably, 'I'll be in touch with you.'

The next day he'd phone again.

'Have you read it yet?'

He'd keep this up day after day until finally, to get Jake off his back,
the playwright would sit down and read the bloody book. And the
next day when Jake phoned, the playwright could say heartily:

'Jake, I've read it and you're right, it would make a very funny play.
But I'm all tied up this season. Why don't you get somebody else?'

'That's all right,' Jake would say. 'I'll wait till you're free.'

He'd give the playwright a week and then he'd phone him:

'Are you free yet?'

And from then on he'd phone the playwright every day with 'Are
you free yet?' until finally the playwright would explode at him over
the phone:

'Look, Jake, even if I were free, we don't have the rights to the
damn book, we don't have the money and we don't have a producer!'
And he'd hang up before Jake could answer.

For a month or so, the playwright would hear nothing further. And just as he'd forgotton all about Jake and his book, Jake would phone him and say:

'We've got the rights to the book, I have a producer and two thirds of the backing, and I can get the final third from Warner's on a preproduction deal as soon as they've seen your script. Are you free yet?'

And so the dazed playwright would sit down and write the play and in due time it would open on Broadway. Some of the plays he secretly produced were smash hits; sometimes, as Jake's daughter put it, there'd be 'a string of flops that opened and shut like clams.'

But whatever the outcome, from the moment one of his plays went into production, Jake would exhort everybody involved not to mention his name in connection with it. He didn't want Warner's to know he was messing with another Broadway play (though some of Warner's most successful films were made from Jake's Broadway plays).

'Keep my name out of it,' he'd say. And they'd keep his name out of it. But they couldn't keep Jake himself out of it. During rehearsals of one of his secret productions he was so incessantly underfoot that the producer and playwright threw him out of the theatre with enough force to break his arm. It didn't stop him. Nothing stopped him. Because when Jake got a Broadway brainstorm it became an obsession. If you thwarted him the obsession intensified.

How I know is, the last of Jake Wilk's obsessions – and the one totally and permanently thwarted by Broadway – was me. You may know what it's like to have an obsession. You've got no idea what it's like to be one.

As I said, it began with a phone call.

'This is Warner Brothers' story department,' a secretary said. 'Can you stop in and see Mr Jacob Wilk, our story editor, this afternoon?'

I assumed that Gene Burr, Jake's assistant, had recommended me as a reader. Gene Burr had bought me a drink a few weeks earlier to tell me how much he liked my new play, and he knew I was struggling to make ends meet on Monograph's pittance. I went over to Warner's and up to the story department and was ushered, all unsuspecting, into the office of Mr Wilk.

He sat behind a cluttered desk, the walls around him covered with framed posters of Broadway hits which I assumed he had purchased for Warner's. He had, but of course that's not why they were on the wall. He'd secretly produced all of them.

He looked up when I entered and glared at me from behind rimless spectacles. He had greying sandy hair and a strong, unremarkable sixty-year-old face.

'Hello,' he barked. 'Sit down!'

I sat, quaking. I didn't know then that Jake never spoke, he barked, and he never smiled, he glared, and he never had the slightest idea that that's what he did.

On his desk was the familiar blue-bound copy of my play which Gene Burr had liked and had given him to read, and Jake now glared at that.

'This is a good play,' he snapped. 'Who's seen it?'

I gave him the names of the four producers who had so far turned it down.

'Who's your agent?' he barked. I told him. He reached for the phone and called my agent and demanded to know who else had seen the play.

'Has Leland seen it?' he rapped into the phone. 'Irene?' He listened a moment and said impatiently, 'All right. I'll be in touch with you,' and hung up. Then he looked past me and bawled out of the open office door like a train conductor:

'Where's Leland Hayward?'

Jake had a secretary and two assistants and he never addressed any one of them by name in my hearing. When he wanted something, he just bawled into empty space and whoever was within earshot came running. This time both the secretary and Gene Burr came running.

'Leland Hayward's in Rome on his honeymoon,' said Gene.

'Take a note to him,' barked Jake, and as this was clearly meant for the secretary, Gene withdrew. 'Dear Leland. Let me know what you think of this script as soon as possible. Regards, Jake.' He handed the secretary the blue-bound script and said: 'Get his address in Rome. Send it airmail.'

It passed through my mind that Leland Hayward might be less than eager to spend his honeymoon reading my play. Such an extraneous thought never passed through Jake Wilk's mind. He glared at me and said:

'Get me some scripts. Irene hasn't seen it, Guthrie hasn't seen it, nobody's seen it!'

Believe me, everybody was going to.

During the next few weeks, the play was airmailed to Leland Hayward on his honeymoon and sent by messenger to Irene Selznick, who was in the hospital recovering from surgery. It went to Guthrie McClintic and Gilbert Miller and Kermit Bloomgarden and then on down the line of lesser producers. Within a couple of months, every producer on Broadway had read it and for assorted reasons turned it down. Jake spent an afternoon tabulating the reasons. The next morning my phone rang. When I said hello, a voice at the other end, like a voice barking the final order to a firing squad, rapped:

'Wilk!'

I jumped slightly and said how-was-he and Jake said:

'I've found out what's the matter with this play. You'll have to rewrite it.

'I generally do,' I said.

'All right, we'd better have lunch,' he snapped. 'Sardi's! One o'clock!'

I walked into Sardi's five minutes early but Jake was there ahead of me, sitting at a large round table for five at the back of the room. This was his table. Whether he ate alone or had six guests, that's where he sat. The two of us lunched with the width of the table between us, most of the width taken up by letters from producers telling Jake what was wrong with the play. We discussed the play's faults, and over coffee we mapped out an entirely new plot.

(The play's characters and setting appealed to everybody; the play's plot appealed to nobody. I mention this to keep you from wondering what was the matter with my plays. That's what was the matter with all of them. I'd never liked fiction and fiction was getting back at me: I never could invent a story worth a damn.)

The coffee came in a silver pot and as we talked, Jake tapped the pot absently with a finger to see if it was hot – then with two fingers, then three. As soon as he could press four fingers against it without pain, he bawled at any waiter going past:

'Coffee's not hot!'

and the waiter carried off the old pot and brought a fresh one. During our two-hour conference we ran through four pots.

(What paralyzes me about this finger-tapping procedure is that Jake bequeathed it to me. Sitting over my breakfast or dinner coffee to this day, I tap the pot to see if it's hot. Thanks to a long association with Jake Wilk, if the coffee's not scalding I can't drink it.)

When we left Sardi's, he asked how long I thought the revisions would take and I said I hoped to do them in six weeks.

'Fine,' he said. 'I'll be in touch with you.'

I started work on the revisions at nine o'clock the next morning. At ten o'clock the phone rang.

'Wilk!' barked the firing squad. 'How's it coming?'

I thought How - the - hell - do - you - think - it's - coming - I - only - started - an - hour - ago. I said it was coming fine.

'Good,' said Jake. 'I'll be in touch with you.'

Next morning at ten he phoned again. He phoned the morning after that and the morning following. He phoned every day for a month, as regularly as he brushed his teeth, and the conversation never varied.

'Wilk! How's it coming?'

'Fine.'

'Good. I'll be in touch with you.'

At the beginning of the sixth week, the password changed. When the phone rang at ten and I said hello, he didn't ask how it was coming, he didn't even rap 'Wilk!' He just barked:

'Well, where is it?'

And for the rest of the week it was Where is it? which drove me on Friday to promise him I'd finish it over the weekend. That Saturday, in the dirty apartment I normally cleaned on Saturday, I typed from 9 A.M. to midnight, breaking my back to meet Jake Wilk's mythical deadline. I crawled beaten into bed at 1 A.M., slept late on Sunday and was nearly halfway through breakfast before he called and said Where was it?

'I still have the last scene to type, and then I have to separate the carbons and bind the copies,' I said. 'I'll drop it at your office tomorrow,'

'I'll be home tonight,' he said. 'Drop it off here with the doorman. I'll read it before I go to bed.'

I worked all day Sunday. I finished binding one copy of the script at six o'clock, and without stopping to wash my face I tore out of the house (Maudiebird's little hovel on Ninety-fifth Street) and down to Sixty-eighth Street to the plush Fifth Avenue apartment house where Jake lived, and left the script with the doorman. Then I went home and collapsed. Lying on the studio couch staring up at the ceiling, I lectured myself bitterly.

'Why,' I asked myself, 'are you ruining your health for this madman? He could have waited till tomorrow. He could have waited till Adelaide's wedding day in *Guys and Dolls*, which if I remember was the Twelfth of Never!'

Joy came in the morning: no phone call. It was the producers' turn for a while.

None of the producers who read the new version wanted any part of it. (If you can't invent plots you can't invent plots.) But, as I said, Jake Wilk's obsession was not that particular play, it was me. During the weeks I had worked on the revisions, he had read his readers' reports on several of my old plays and he now wanted to read the plays for himself. I'd thrown away most of them but there were two I'd kept and I sent them to him. He liked both of them. And having failed to get my Play No. 14 produced, he now went to work on Nos. 9 and 11.

For a solid winter, he tried to sell them. Not until he had exhausted – and I mean exhausted – the last producer and backer on Broadway did he admit defeat.

He sat in his office with me at twilight of a March afternoon, holding in his hands the last script which had just come back from the last possible producer. He put the script down and stared at it. Then his eyes moved to No. 14, which was his favorite and which it seemed to me was always on his desk. He picked it up in both hands and hefted it gently.

'Just can't crack the ice,' he muttered. It was the first time I ever heard him sound tired. 'So much talent, it's all here...' And he barked fiercely again: 'We just have to crack the ice!'

I wanted to speak and I couldn't. He was an eminently successful man with a massive list of achievements, both public and *sub rosa* and there he sat, glaring at No. 14 and mumbling tiredly again: '... just can't crack the ice...' I wanted to comfort him for my failure to write a good play. But of course, to Jake it wasn't my failure at all, it was Broadway's failure. Broadway was blind, and with all his driving force he couldn't make Broadway see.

It took him a month to bounce back. It was actually a pleasure, when the phone rang one April morning, to hear 'Wilk!' barked at me from the other end.

'Have you got an idea for a new play yet?' he asked.

'No,' I said. 'I wish I had.'

'What do you do all day besides read for Monograph?' he demanded. I could have said, 'I'm trying to memorize my Greek middle voice endings' but I didn't.

'Nothing much,' I said.

'You don't get ideas sitting around waiting for them,' he said. 'I'll find you some work to do. Then you'll get an idea. All right, I'll be in touch with you.'

A few days later he phoned back.

'I have a very talented boy here,' he announced. 'He's a songwriter. He has a musical he wants the studios to buy but the book's not very good. He doesn't want to submit the book, he needs a good presentation. You want to write him a presentation? He'll pay you for it.'

I said I'd love to.

'Sardi's!' snapped Jake. 'One o'clock!'

He was there ahead of me again. When I threaded my way to his back table he was already sitting at it.

Sitting next to him, talking nonstop in a joyous bellow, was the 'very talented boy,' a round, beaming Mr Five-by-Five who had written the lyrics to *No, No, Nanette* thirty years earlier.

'This is Irving Caesar,' rapped Jake. 'He's a very talented boy.'

'How do you do,' I said.

'Hello, dolling!' Irving bellowed, beaming.

They were insane opposites. Where Jake was lean and unsmiling, Irving was completely round and had a beaming smile which never left his face for an instant. Where Jake said little and barked it, Irving talked continuously and hollered it. But who wants to sit at the quietest table in Sardi's?

A 'presentation' was a long synopsis written as a press agent or the show's producer might write it, the object being to persuade the studio that the script was sensational. If you had to redesign the plot, misrepresent some characters and add or delete a few, nobody minded

– least of all the studio, which, if it bought the script, would turn it over to five or six new writers anyway.

But the musical comedy Irving wanted a presentation of was called *My Dear Public*. It had been a flop on Broadway, and a bore to me when I'd read it for Monograph. I thought it only fair to tell Irving this.

'What the hell, dolling, you'll make it look sensational!' he beamed, and I was hired.

I did an outline of the presentation and mailed it to Irving for his approval. He phoned me as soon as he read it.

'Dolling, you're a genius, I don't know how you do it!' he said. 'I'll buy you a steak at Gallagher's to celebrate. Nine o'clock, can you wait to eat till nine o'clock? I can't stand to eat early, the waiters got no time to pay attention. Nine o'clock, all right, dolling?'

So we met for dinner at Gallagher's Steak House at nine o'clock.

'Bring her a thick one!' Irving bellowed, beaming at the waiter. 'She's my genius, she lives in a tenement!' He hadn't seen my apartment but he'd seen the address on the envelope I mailed him. Tenement.

While we waited for the steaks, Irving told me about himself. In addition to *No, No, Nanette* he'd written the lyrics to 'Swanee' way back when, he wrote musical scores for the Ringling Brothers' Circus and he'd written a couple of hundred Safety Songs and Friendship Songs for schoolchildren across the country. The Friendship Songs, he told me, had been translated into ten languages. He was a member of the board of ASCAP and an occasional Broadway producer. He was currently at work on songs for a new musical to be called *Kisses and Knishes*, and he would sing me the score as soon as it was finished.

'I'm a bachelor,' he told me as the steaks came, beaming benevolently at mine when he saw it was thick enough, and benevolently at the sliced cucumbers and tomatoes when he saw they were thick enough because usually they were too thin. 'Marriage is all right, I got nothing against it, but why should I restrict myself to one woman? But so all right, so that's how I am, so I got this suite at the Park Central – Lissen, whaddaya think it costs me every morning to get *The New York Times*? A dollar ninety-five. Because how can you phone down every morning and say, "Send me up a *New York Times*"? You can't, you gotta phone down and order breakfast, I don't eat breakfast but every day I phone down and order breakfast and then I say casually' – he tossed his head and waved a fat arm airily to show me how casually he did it – ' "Oh, by the way, send me up a *New York Times.*" The breakfast is a dollar fifty-five, you gotta tip the kid and pay him for the *Times* so the *New York Times* costs me a dollar ninety-five every day. I should write and tell them that. Should I?'

At which moment, the headwaiter came over to our table.

'Irving, how's the steak?' he asked.

When I said that Irving's face never lost its beaming smile I meant that he not only beamed happily, he could also beam sadly. He now beamed very sadly at the waiter and said:

'I wish I could say it was great! I wish I could!' And he shook his head, still beaming sadly.

'How's the lady's steak?' the waiter asked me.

'What're you asking *her*?' Irving beamed with a snort attached. 'What would she know, she's a starving writer, she lives in a tenement, where would she get a steak unless I buy it for her? To her it tastes good!'

And don't think it didn't.

After dinner, he put me in a cab, paid the driver and said, 'Sweet dreams, dolling, I'll call you,' before departing off down Broadway in a round, rolling, eager gait that would have done both Milne and Piglet proud.

Irving was – and I hope still is – the happiest man I ever knew. He loved everybody and everything, but most especially he loved Broadway – where he lived, ate, worked and spent his evenings-out. He loved all of it, from the marquees and big neon signs to the honky-tonk gift shops and shooting galleries. Broadway was his ocean and he bounced around on top of it like a cork, on intimate terms with every wave, every piece of seaweed and every shark. ('Frank's a very nice fella!' he told me earnestly, speaking of the notorious gangster Frank Costello. 'He gives big to the Heart Fund!')

He called me one day, when I'd nearly finished the presentation, and told me to meet him for lunch at Dinty Moore's and he'd sing me the score of *Kisses and Knishes*. But he didn't sing it to me at Dinty Moore's. He waited, and sang the score to me as we walked down Broadway afterward, he on his way to his office and I on my way to Monograph.

Walking down Broadway on a spring afternoon with Irving Caesar singing to you at the top of his stentorian lungs is what they call an Experience.

He'd finish a chorus of a song, and I'd say:

'That's a very pretty –'

'NOW WAIT!' he'd holler, seizing my arm to halt me in my tracks in case I wasn't planning to wait, and keeping a firm grip on me as he sang the second verse and another round of the chorus. Then he'd let my arm go and we'd walk on a few more steps while he set the scene for the next song for me.

People were going by in a steady stream as we walked, and at every step we took, somebody coming along would wave or tip his hat or nod, and say, 'Hello, Irving' or 'Hi, Irving,' or 'Hiya, Mr Caesar.' Everybody who went by seemed to know him: cops and song pluggers, actors and fight promoters and prostitutes, bookies and Broadway producers and winos and panhandlers. Everybody spoke to him and Irving beamed back and waved and said How-ya-doin'? and Call-me-I'll-buya-a-drink, and never lost a beat of the song he was singing from *Kisses and Knishes*.

I finished the presentation and Irving pronounced it magnificent and predicted we'd both get rich on the sale of *My Dear Public* to some movie studio. He hurried off to sell it and I took a week to pick up my scattered wits and straighten them out.

He phoned a few weeks later to tell me that all the studios had rejected *My Dear Public*. I said I was sorry.

'Don't worry about it! Forget it!' Irving advised me on the phone, his tone of voice as enthusiastic as if he'd just made a million dollars on the sale. 'It didn't work, that's yesterday! Forget it, I forgot it already! I got a million projects, get yourself a project, dolling! Write a play, I'll put money in it.'

'It's funny you should say that,' I told him, 'because just this morning, for the first time in a year, I got an idea for one.'

'See, dolling?' he said triumphantly. 'So who needs the presentation? Write a funny play, I'll put money in it.'

That was on a Friday. The new play wouldn't take form enough for me to start writing for several weeks and it would be one more unproducible dog when I did write it. But if you're a writer and you've got an idea for something solid to write, you're happy as

Christmas morning. On Saturday night, therefore, I stayed out late, celebrating. One of the male readers at Monograph bought us a lavish pair of standing-room tickets to a Broadway musical and we went on to a party afterward. When I finally crawled into bed shortly before dawn it was with the secure knowledge that I could sleep till noon on Sunday.

And I would have, if the phone hadn't wakened me at ten. Without opening my eyes I sent an exploratory arm out toward the night table, located the phone and pulled the receiver onto my pillow. Still with my eyes closed I mumbled:

'Hello?'

'Wilk!' snapped my guardian angel at the other end. 'Irving says you have a new play. How's it coming?'

11

'Lhude Sing Cuccu'

'I've had summer theatres,' I said to Maxine one spring day in the early fifties. 'I'm going to apply to the MacDowell Colony this year instead.'

'The what?' said Maxine.

'It's an artists' colony,' I said.

She threw me a dubious look.

'What's it like?' she asked.

'Now how would I know?' I said. 'Ask me when I come home.'

When I wrote to the Colony's New York office for an application blank, all I knew about the place was what I'd read in magazine articles: that it was in the pine woods of New Hampshire and had been founded (in 1906) by Mrs Edward MacDowell, widow of the American composer. She had built it as a haven where composers, painters and writers could come for a few summer weeks, to work in absolute peace, free of the pressures of having to earn a living.

The application blank arrived in the mail, along with a glossy brochure containing photos of a few of the twenty-five studios. You could apply for a studio for one of three six-week periods between May and September. On the application blank, you had to list your 'Creative Achievements' and describe the work you wanted to do at the Colony. (I-won-a-fellowship-once, I-was-a-Theatre-Guild-protegée, I-have-a-play-under-option-and-the-producer-wants-it-re-written.) You had to enclose with your application two letters of recommendation from 'Persons Eminent in Your Profession' and I got Terry Helburn and Jake Wilk to write glowing testimonials for me.

On the day the letter came telling me I'd been accepted, I wished I hadn't applied. In spite of the brochure's description of happy working days in solitary studios and long, cozy evenings with your fellow-artists, I set out nervously for Peterborough, New Hampshire, with a mammoth suitcase, my portable typewriter and no idea what to expect. (Unless you count my gloomy conviction that I was going to be surrounded for six weeks by Genuine Creative Artists who would look down on me.)

I reached the Colony in time for dinner. And the odd thing was that even when I'd been there an evening and had seen all the main buildings, I still didn't know what to expect.

The main buildings were clustered together in a clearing in a six-hundred-acre pine forest. The chief building, Colony Hall, was a large white clapboard house with a big, old-fashioned living-room, a dining-room with half a dozen tables each seating four or five and a big kitchen where they locked up everything at night. (How I found this out is, five of us got hungry one midnight and spent half an hour ransacking kitchen cabinets looking for anything edible that wasn't locked away in high cupboards. Nothing.)

Next to Colony Hall was an old rambling frame house where the women slept, next to that was the library and way off down the road out of sight was the Men's Lodge where the men slept, built good and far from the women's building to discourage That Sort of Thing. (Mrs MacDowell had overseen the construction of the buildings in 1906.)

Those buildings were all I saw of the Colony that evening and all tourists ever see of it. You learn what the Colony is like on your first day – and from then on all days are miraculously the same.

If you're an early riser you're up and dressed in a bathing suit with heavy wool sweater and pants over it at 7:30 A.M., when a teenaged waitress comes out of Colony Hall, stations herself on the lawn and clangs a cowbell enthusiastically. First call to breakfast.

You race over to the dining-room and join the other early risers. There are only five or six colonists up that early and you all squeeze together at one table, known as the Early Table and so famous for its high good humor that now and then a late-riser would stagger into the dining room in time for the conversation at the Early Table and then go back to bed.

You eat an enormous breakfast. (This is particularly true of the men, for reasons which will become apparent at lunchtime. From a masculine point of view, lunch at the MacDowell Colony simply passes belief.) At 8:45, you bid a reluctant farewell to human society and go down to your studio. If you can find it.

You enter the surrounding pine forest by one of four main roads leading to the studios. But the studios have been scattered so far apart through the six-hundred-acre woods that the painter in one studio can hear neither the piano to his east nor the typewriter to his west. So each main studio road has several forks, each branching into a narrow dirt path leading to a single studio. The problem, as you trudge down your main studio road, is to remember whether you take the second fork to your northeast or the third fork southwest, always providing you know which way is north, which I personally don't.

And since the cardinal Colony rule is that no one may enter anyone else's studio at any time without invitation, you cannot stop in at the Omicron, say, if you happen to arrive there by mistake, and ask the composer inside if he knows where the Veltin is. Instead, you go back to Colony Hall – if you can find that – and say to the manager:

'Cousin, I've lost it again.'

And the manager takes you down to your studio in the Colony truck.

You're probably wondering how a studio came to be called the Omicron. Any patron generous enough to donate a studio to the Colony may name it anything he, she or it likes. (Omicron was donated by some sorority, I think. I've no idea who, or what, Veltin was.) The patron is also entitled to build it any way he, she or it likes, so the studios run a gamut in nomenclature from the Alexander to the Monday Music, and in architecture from Italian Palazzo to Backwoods Monastic. Whatever its style, each studio seems to have one demented feature all its own.

Take my favorite studio, the Veltin, which is the one I had that first summer. It's a perfect example of Backwoods Monastic architecture: a plain wooden shack with a bare wooden floor, bare wooden work tables, two straight chairs, an old rocker and a big fireplace. Out back on the porch is what in Thomas Jefferson's day was called a Necessary and that's about all that can be said for it.

Well, in the middle of the floor of this bare hut is a glossy, white-enameled staircase complete with newel posts, its five or six steps leading up to a landing, big enough for you to stand on with your head just clearing the ceiling (if you're short). After you've stood there awhile you come back down because there's nowhere else to go. The steps don't go anywhere. Over lunch I used to speculate endlessly on what the architect had in mind.

But whether you're writing in the Veltin or painting in the Alexander (a replica of a seventeenth-century Swiss chapel, reproduced stone for stone and stained-glass window for stained-glass window), once you've walked in and shut the door, all studios are magically alike. All your life you've worked in dark rooms above noisy streets, with the phone ringing, the radio overhead blaring, the baby next door crying. Here in your studio you will work, for the first time, in absolute quiet and inviolable privacy through a long uninterrupted day. And you offer up a prayer for the soul of Mrs Edward MacDowell, who gave it to you.

As soon as you come in in the morning, you build a fire in your fireplace. Then you either nod to your tombstone or studiously avoid it. Your tombstone stands on the mantel over the fireplace. It's a wooden plaque shaped like an old-fashioned headstone, on which you'll find the signature of every colonist who worked in that studio before you. If your tombstone has a line reading:

Thornton Wilder – Playwright – 1937

which tells you that Thornton Wilder wrote *Our Town* sitting where you're getting ready to sit, it can put you off your aim – till you notice that his name is followed by a long list of writers you never heard of, which makes you feel better.

Having made the fire, you sharpen your pencils, clean your typewriter, stack your typing paper neatly and put your cigarettes and ashtray within reach. Then you stare out the window at the trees. And then, having completely run out of dodges, you get to work. By one o'clock you've finished two days' work. The sun is high and hot and you've let the fire go out and peeled down to your bathing suit. You go out to the back porch and splash your face and wash your hands and discover you're so hungry you could eat anything. And you're about to.

You go out to the front step of your studio and take in the wicker basket which has been left there for you. You clear off a work table and take out of the lunch basket and arrange on the table: three little cellophane bags, four sealed paper cups, two thermos bottles, two plastic-wrapped sandwiches – one of which is known to colonists as 'the Other sandwich' – and a rolled-up paper napkin containing cutlery. Bouncing around by itself at the bottom of the basket is probably an apple. For later.

Cellophane bag No. 1 contains a carrot, a scallion, a radish and a stick of celery. This is salad. Bag No. 2 has whole-wheat crackers to eat with your soup, which is in thermos No. 1. Bag No. 3 is sugar for the coffee in thermos No. 2. Paper cup No. 1 contains half a stewed peach. This is not dessert, this is compote. How you know is, paper cup No. 3 has the dessert: last night's cake doused with sauce (which is why they locked up last night's cake after dinner). Paper cup No. 2 is mayonnaise for sandwich No. 1. Paper cup No. 4 is cream for the coffee.

One sandwich contains meat. The Other sandwich may contain absolutely anything. Whatever's in it is smooth, soft, a pretty color and hard to identify. You taste it, you smell it, you carry it to the window and peer closely at it – and still, you eat it without the slightest idea of what you're eating. When you get back up to Colony Hall that night, you ask the cook what you ate. One, for instance, was a bright pale mauve and turned out to be cream cheese and apple butter beaten up together. Another was just plain mashed figs.

('They ask you,' a young composer said to me earnestly at dinner that night, 'to write down on your basket all the things you don't like. I wrote "liverwurst and sardines." Who thinks to put down "I don't like mashed fig sandwiches"?')

After lunch guilt drives you back to the typewriter and you work till five or five-thirty, when you quit and survey the shambles. The floor is strewn with fireplace ashes and balled-up paper discards, your apple and one shoe are on the mantel, your sweater's on the newel post, your pants are on the landing and you can't find your other shoe. (It's out back by the Necessary.) You're hot, tired and dirty, but you burn the trash, sweep the floor and fireplace and stack the finished pages of your manuscript neatly before trudging back up to Colony Hall to shower and dress before the dinner cowbell.

At dinner you meet your fellow-artists. Five or six, at least, are college professors – who, with their steady salaries, their tenure, their sabbaticals, Fulbrights and pension plans, are the Colony's filthy rich. The rest are full-time working artists with an uncertain income and half the time no income at all.

For the first few evenings you're so mellowed by your Utopian days you love everybody. After that, you find the four or five colonists most congenial to you and you spend your evenings with them – especially when, as happens at least once a week, the evening begins with a cultural crisis precipitated at dinner.

Either Wanda, a wispy poetess, taps her water glass for attention during dessert, and announces that on Tuesday evening the Colony poets will give a Reading of their poems in Colony Hall for their fellow-colonists; or Alfred, a painter, announces that he will give a lecture on Nonrepresentational Trends in the library on Friday evening and he's going to serve sherry afterward (if the kitchen lets him have the glasses). Or Professor Kimmel, composer, aged seventy-two, lets it be known through a disciple that he can be prevailed upon to play a recording of his twelve-tone symphony this evening and his studio is large enough to accommodate everybody.

When one of these gruesome offerings is advertised, you go off after dinner to huddle under a tree with your gang and have a heated argument about whether you *have* to go to this thing or not. (*Pro:* 'We can't insult our fellow-artists! Everybody's sensitive, we can't hurt Wanda's feelings.' *Con:* 'I worked hard all day, I'm damned if I'm going to spend the evening listening to Alfred run off at the mouth for two hours!' Or more simply: 'I had Alfred for dinner; that's enough.') When two of these entertainments were advertised for two different evenings of the same week, we compromised: we went to the Poetry Reading on Tuesday; and on Friday, the night of Nonrepresentational Trends, we snuck off to Peterborough to see Joel McCrea in a horse opera. Alfred wasn't speaking to us on Saturday, of course, but he got over it.

You're there for six weeks, and for five of them you're blissfully happy. And then abruptly, early in the sixth week, you become violently sick of the place and you want to go home. It happens without warning when the Colony's one zombie – in dyed orange beard and purple shorts – praises Ezra Pound's political views once too often, or a mousy woman you're fond of turns out to be a solitary drinker. Or a letter from home may do it.

It happened to me when I came up from the studio one hazy afternoon to find a thick letter waiting for me, addressed in Maxine's lavish, all-over-the-envelope handwriting. It was postmarked Washington, D.C., and written on Hotel Willard stationery, several pages of it, and after I bathed and dressed I parked myself under a tree to read it before dinner.

'I just want you to know,' wrote Maxine, 'that while you've been rubbing noses with the Intelligentsia, I have been making my singing debut. Of course, they only let me sing on opening night and I am a *little* put out about that.

'I got back from the Cape on a Sunday night and there was a message to call Eddie at home the minute I got in. He'd left his home phone number – and when an agent wants you to call him at home on a Sunday night, you *must* be right for the part.

'I called him and he said a new show was getting ready to try out in Washington, they needed a last-minute replacement for the ingenue, and I should fly down to Washington Monday morning. I flew down and gave my usual superb audition and Bobby, the director, said: "Fine, dear. We open Friday, take the script home and study it and come back after lunch and we'll get to work."

'So I got a hotel room and locked myself in with the script and read the first act where I didn't have much to do, and then I read the second act where I had a big scene, and in the middle of the big scene it said in the script: "*She drapes herself over the piano and sings.*" Sings? Maxine Stuart sings??

'So when I went to the theatre I said to Bobby: "Lissen, I think you better hear me sing," and he said: "Sure, baby, I want to, now let's get to work." And we rehearsed the first act. On Tuesday morning we started the second act, and we got to where I was supposed to drape myself over the piano and sing "He Ain't Got Rhythm" and Bobby called out: "We'll get you the sheet music later. Skip the song for now."

'Wednesday they gave me the sheet music which I couldn't read. On my dinner hour I went around to a music store and played a record of "He Ain't Got Rhythm" and learned the tune in my fashion. But on Thursday, when dress rehearsal started, I still hadn't sung for anybody so I went over to Bobby and said: "Lissen, I think you better hear me sing," and he said: "Just speak the words today; save your voice for the opening."

'On opening night, Don, who plays the piano in the scene, stopped by my dressing room and said: "How did the key sound to you? Can you manage that A all right?" And I said: "Well, I can certainly try!" I felt so educated, knowing there was an A in it.

'The first act went by like a breeze, and in the second act I made my entrance in my black-lace-over-pink-net-with-flounce evening gown and on cue, Don started to play and I draped myself over the top of the piano and began to sing "He Ain't Got Rhythm" in my one note. I sang about four bars – making a great important message out of the words so nobody'd notice there wasn't much tune – when I heard the piano getting very loud. I pushed my resonance all the way up and gave it my full projection and I still couldn't top the piano. And I thought: "That scene-hog has got to be made to take his foot off the pedal. Nobody can hear me." Well, I finished triumphantly – by which I mean the note I finished on was very close to the note the piano finished on – and I said to myself: "You see? There's nothing to it."

'After the show, we were all standing around on stage waiting for the management's criticisms and cuts and so forth, and Bobby came over and put his arm around me and said: "Maxine, honey, you're great in the part, now-lemme-ask-you-something. How are you at pantomime?" So of course I said I was great at that, too, and Bobby said: "Fine, baby, fine, now why don't we get a record of some blues singer singing 'He Ain't Got Rhythm' and you can just drape over the piano and pantomime the words and you won't have to bother singing."

'The show got appalling notices so it's closing after Washington, and I'll be home in two weeks. Trust you'll be the same. Arty studios in New England are all very well for the summer but it'll be coming on Fall soon and you should be just panting to get back to the big wide world of unemployment and telephones and trucks clanking down Second Avenue.'

And just as suddenly as that, I was panting to get back to it.

12

A Round Trip through the Annex
or
Sarah Wants to Do Something Greek and Other Stories

On a spring day in 1952, a worried young dentist named Joey lifted his melting brown eyes from my X rays to me and said sadly:

'It's staggering. There's no room left for any more fillings.' Like George Washington, I had bad teeth.

I was faced, he said, with a choice: I could have all my teeth capped, for roughly $2,500; or I could have all my teeth out and replaced with false ones, for roughly $2,500.

Since I was earning $50 a week at Monograph and had $92 in the bank, I went home and suggested to the Lord that this was an ideal moment for a miracle. What I had in mind, of course, was that if He really felt like it, the Lord could get one of my plays produced on Broadway and have it run long enough to make me $2,500. What the Lord had in mind, of course, was Flanagan's Law.

Literally ten minutes after I discussed miracles with my Creator, the telephone rang and Gene Burr said Hi, how was I, and I said Fine, where was he? I knew he'd left Jake Wilk's office at Warner's but I didn't know where he'd gone.

'That's what I'm calling about,' said Gene. 'How would you like to write for television?'

Television was barely four years old and I knew nothing whatever about it. Before I could say this, Gene added carelessly:

'It's only two bills.'

'Two what?' I asked.

'Two hundred dollars for a half-hour script.'

Two hundred dollars would buy two porcelain tooth-jackets. If I wrote a script a month for a year, Joey could live on the television money and I could live on the Monograph money.

'You're sent from Heaven,' I told Gene Burr. 'What show is it?'

'The Adventures of Ellery Queen,' he said. 'It's a low-budget show on a little network called DuMont. I'm the story editor. Come on down to my office tomorrow afternoon and we'll talk.'

The next afternoon, driven every inch of the way by the simple desire to have teeth, I became a writer of television murders.

A few weeks later, Maxine dropped in one morning for a cup of coffee. After two seasons of unemployment she was grimly pleased to report that she was working at last. She could be seen nightly, she informed me, on all the better TV channels.

'What show are you in?' I asked.

'I am not in a show. I do a solo act,' said Maxine acidly. 'I am the Blue Cheer girl.' Blue Cheer, she explained to me, was a detergent. She was selling it on television.

This is not just how Maxine and I got into television in the fifties, it's how everybody got into television in the fifties. Unable to get rid of us any other way, the theatre had built an Annex and flogged us into it.

(Gene Burr, who had wanted to be a Broadway producer and whose Ellery Queen writers were all failed playwrights, put it more brutally but defined it for all of us with deadly precision. 'Television,' he said, 'is the asshole of the theatre.')

The budget for Ellery Queen was so small that the cast of each script was limited to five characters. Since two of them had to be Ellery and his father, it left you only three characters for the murder plot: the character who got murdered (known as the corpse) and two suspects, one innocent and one guilty. But in addition to the five full parts, we were allowed two 'five-liners' – actors who, for the pittance they were paid, were permitted by Actors' Equity to speak five lines and no more. These five-liners were very useful to the writer; you kept them standing around looking silent and villainous.

I myself brought a unique extra dimension to Ellery's adventures. Until I came on the scene, the show's scripts had been evenly divided between low-brow and middle-brow murders. In prizefight and racetrack murders, the suspects and corpses spoke uneducated English and were therefore low-brow, while murders involving politicians or businessmen were middle-brow. What the show lacked was a group of distinctly high-brow murders in which the suspects and corpses were all cultured. That was my contribution. I became Ellery Queen's special writer of arty murders. I wrote six: murder in the art gallery, murder at the opera, murder in the concert hall, murder at the Shakespeare festival and two murders at the ballet. And we were just getting round to the rare-book business when the show went off the air.

Nobody outside the industry would have believed the physical restrictions of live television. Ellery Queen was televised in a large rehearsal hall, a bare room blocked off into the three separate stage sets which were all the budget allowed. Well, in 'Murder at the Opera,' if Ellery played one scene in an opera star's dressing room and the next scene in his own living-room, you couldn't give him the last few lines in the dressing-room scene or the first few lines in the living-room scene because he needed ten seconds off-camera to walk from the dressing-room set to the living-room set. And if he wore white tie and tails in the opera scene, you put him in his living-room in the next scene, so that during his ten-second walk he could slip a long dressing gown over his evening clothes. I mean, you didn't take him from the opera scene and put him on a beach in the next scene because there was never time for costume changes, there was only time to slip one costume over another.

But the technical restrictions were easy to learn. What made writing this nonsense the hardest work I'd ever done was the appalling economy imposed by the clock and the small budget. Out of five characters and two five-liners, you had to create the illusion of an entire opera company or a full symphony orchestra. And the economy of background was nothing compared with the economy of words demanded by the clock, which ordered you to tell a complete story in twenty-six minutes. You were constantly forced to compress eight or ten rambling lines of dialogue into one succinct one – to say nothing of having to create a believable character in five lines.

The result was that in a year of grinding out shabby murder stories of which I was ashamed, I learned more about dramatic writing than Aristotle, Stanislavski and Terry Helburn had ever been able to teach me. This didn't infuriate me at the time because I didn't know it. All I knew was that to avoid being toothless, I had sunk to the depths of literary depravity.

This view oppressed me less when I graduated from Ellery Queen to more respectable dramatic shows. But then as now, American television was controlled by the large corporations who 'sponsored' – paid for – every show, and not only interrupted each play several times to sell soap or cars or underarm deodorants, but also dictated what the writer might, and might not, say in a script. Because of this – and in spite of the fact that I enjoyed writing TV scripts – I never overcame my conviction that writing for commercial television was a kind of prostitution.

How I know this is that between 1952 and 1959 I must have written at least fifty television scripts, but through those years I steadily refused to buy a TV set, and I never saw a single show I wrote.

Maxine insisted that the Annex had no such traumatic effect on her, but I maintain that anyone who could send the Blue Cheer ad agency executive the Christmas present Maxine sent was expressing an obvious death wish. Maxine insisted she wasn't jeopardizing her job because her career as the Blue Cheer girl was doomed anyway.

Blue Cheer detergent came in fine powdery crystals in a blue box. The way the commercial was written, Maxine was supposed to hold out her cupped hands while some unseen spirit poured Blue Cheer into them from a mammoth box overhead. Then the camera moved in for a close-up of Maxine's cupped hands full of Blue Cheer while she rattled away about the fine quality of the granules. But Maxine turned out to have peculiar fingers. No matter how tightly she cupped her hands, there was a narrow space between all of her fingers. So while she was enthusiastically describing the fine granules, the said granules were sifting through her fingers in a messy cloud which spilled all over the floor and loused up the whole commercial.

Well, the hell with it, the Blue Cheer people must have said to themselves, because they rewrote the script so that all Maxine had to do was hold a big box of Blue Cheer in both hands while she talked about the product. She did this so well that after the filming, five Blue Cheer ad agency and company executives converged on her with congratulations.

'Wonderful!' one of them exclaimed. 'You held the box absolutely straight!'

Carried away by this praise, Maxine informed me one day that she was shopping for a Christmas gift for the account executive.

'It's done,' she assured me blandly. 'I've asked around and I'm told you *always* give the account executive a Christmas present.'

It took her two weeks to find the right gift and she phoned to tell me about it.

'I sent him a red-and-white Blab-Off,' she said. 'They come in all colors. I sent him the prettiest.'

'What,' I inquired, 'is a Blab-Off?'

'It's a little gadget you hook onto your TV set,' said Maxine.

It has a sign on it that says STOP THOSE ANNOYING TV COMMERCIALS. As soon as a commercial comes on, you push the button on your Blab-Off and the set goes dead for two minutes.'

Like me, Maxine later graduated to dramatic shows and, like me, she got over the Shame of it. She has since spent most of her life acting on television and enjoying it thoroughly. And as I said, I had a very good time myself in the Annex, despite a few incidents that might be described as unsettling. The first of these happened on The Hallmark Hall of Fame.

This was in 1953, after the demise of Ellery Queen. I was having lunch with another Monograph reader when I happened to see Ethel Frank, an old acquaintance, having lunch at a nearby table. When she learned I'd been writing for television, she said:

'I'm story editor on The Hallmark Hall of Fame. You ought to write for us. It's a historical show and you like history. Call me tonight and I'll tell you what kind of outline to submit.'

I called her for instructions and then submitted an outline on the love story of John Donne. Ethel bought the outline, Albert

McCleery, the Hallmark producer, liked the finished script and from then on I was one of seven or eight writers who wrote steadily for the show.

The Hallmark Hall of Fame dramatized incidents in the lives of great men and women. We could select our subjects from any country, any century, any area of greatness, ranging theoretically from Cleopatra to Dickens, from Boadicea to Gershwin. We were restricted only by the taboos imposed on us by the peculiar morality of television in the fifties.

I say 'peculiar' because you'll have gathered from Ellery Queen that murder was never considered immoral by American television. Murder was pure entertainment as long as the murderer went to prison or died in the end. The only immorality – the only Sin – was Sex. Every sponsor kept a hawk eye out for any suggestion of this sin in his writers' scripts. And on the outside chance that something sinful might slip past the sponsor's eye, every network maintained its own censorship office to which a copy of every television script had to be submitted.

Well, Hallmark was a biographical show – and you just wouldn't believe how many of the world's great heroes and heroines failed to live up to the moral standards of American television. Boadicea might have got by, but you couldn't possibly write a script about Cleopatra, Dickens or Gershwin without cleaning up their sex lives first.

Plus which, Mr Joyce C. Hall, owner of the Hallmark Greeting Card Company, sponsor of The Hallmark Hall of Fame, imposed two fascinating taboos of his own. Mr Hall, whose home and headquarters were in Kansas City, Missouri, was a gentleman of the Old South. Which meant that while we could dramatize the love story of Jefferson Davis, we were forbidden to write scripts about Abraham Lincoln. Or Harriet Beecher Stowe or General Grant or Walt Whitman-who-was-immoral-anyway.

Mr Hall's second taboo was in deference to the star of The Hallmark Hall of Fame. I've often wondered if she knew about it; I have a feeling it amused her vastly if she did. The mistress of ceremonies on The Hallmark Hall of Fame, and the star of one weekly show in every four, was Sarah Churchill. And Mr Hall forbade all scripts dealing with heroes of the American Revolution because he wouldn't insult the British Prime Minister's daughter by suggesting the British had lost it.

We submitted our Hallmark outlines on special paper with a printed legend across the top:

We nominate .... for
The Hallmark Hall of Fame *because*:
....
....

After 'nominate' you filled in the name of the great man or woman; after '*because*' you stated his-or-her chief claim to fame. On the rest of the page you outlined the particular incident or event in the nominee's life which you wanted to dramatize.

But in actual practice, 'We nominate . . . *because*' was likely to mean a phone call from Ethel Frank:

'Listen, we need something for the Jewish holidays, you want to do Joseph and his coat-of-many-colors or some damn thing?'

Or:

'Hon, dig up somebody for Sarah for Valentine's Day and call me back on it, will you?'

Since Sarah starred in one show a month we were constantly beating the bushes for heroines she could play. So it was a help when Sarah herself came up with a suggestion, which one day she did.

Though all the scripts were written in New York, the Hallmark show was produced in Hollywood and there were daily trans-continental phone calls between Ethel in New York and Albert McCleery in Hollywood. It was after one such phone call that Ethel phoned me.

'Sarah,' she announced, 'wants to do something Greek.'

Greek?

'Ethel,' I said, 'except for an occasional queen who murdered her family, Greek women did not go out and get famous. Of course,' I added tentatively, 'there's Sappho.'

'Sappho's out,' said Ethel. 'Mr Hall knows she was a lesbian.'

'Well, I don't know what Sarah wants from me,' I said. 'I'm not Euripides.'

'You'll find somebody,' said Ethel briskly. 'Call me back.' And she hung up.

I went over to my bookshelves. My books provided me with most of my Hallmark nominees but this time, as I studied them, my mind kept cracking jokes:

'We nominate Persephone for The Hallmark Hall of Fame *because*: she was the first woman to go to hell and back for her man.

'We nominate Jocasta for The Hallmark Hall of Fame *because*: she was Oedipus' mother and Freud's inspiration.'

And then suddenly a book on the top shelf leaned out and waved to me. 'Eureka,' I said, feeling very Greek, and took the book down and kissed it.

The book was *Imaginary Conversations* by Walter Savage Landor and the conversation in it I loved best was a lyric dialogue between Aesop and a young slave girl named Rhodope (pronounced Rah-do-pay. I think). The dialogue contained no incident or event I could dramatize, but I decided that Aesop and his fables would make a fine nominee and that Sarah would enjoy playing Landor's gentle slave girl. And it was a sunny day on which to walk down through Central Park and on to the Forty-second Street main library to do a little research.

Strolling down through the park, I tried to remember where else I'd read about Rhodope. It seemed to me that somebody else had written about her, but I couldn't remember who it was. Since it was Aesop I was nominating, I stopped trying to place Rhodope and concentrated instead on Aesop's fables. By the time I reached the library I knew just which fables I wanted to use and how I wanted to use them, and I ran up to the third floor and hurried over to the card file marked A and made out library slips for all the books on Aesop.

In an hour I'd read all the library could tell me about Aesop's life because the fact is that nothing at all is known about him for certain. A few books described him as a humpbacked beggar, a few backed Landor's theory that he was a slave and an equal number stated that no such person as Aesop ever lived and that the fables were the work of anonymous writers.

None of the books on Aesop mentioned a slave girl named Rhodope.

Hallmark scripts were supposed to be factual. I had no facts. I found a library phone booth and called Ethel and gave her a digest of my findings.

'Based on Landor's dialogue,' I said, 'I could write a story about Aesop with a lovely part for Sarah – but I'd have to make it all up.'

There was a pause while Ethel studied the problem.

'Here's what you do,' she said. 'In Sarah's mistress-of-ceremonies introduction, write a line saying that nobody knows anything about Aesop's life. And then add, 'Some say he was a hunchback, some say he never lived – and some say it happened like this. WE say it.' That way, you're not lying but you're not claiming it's factual and you can make up your own story.'

'Like a fable!' I cried, carried away.

I hung up, left the booth, hurried past the card catalogue, down the steps and out of the library. And since I'd learned nothing about Aesop and was writing the script for Sarah anyway, I can't tell you why it didn't even cross my mind to stop at the card catalogue marked R and look up Rhodope. All I know is it didn't. I hurried home to reread Landor's dialogue and get to work on the script.

I was positively inspired as I wrote it. I was inspired by Landor's lovely lines, Aesop's fables, the evils of slavery, the glory that was Greece and the fact that I could make up what I needed as I went along. I finished it late one afternoon, proofread it after dinner and then took it over to Ethel Frank's house that evening; she liked working on scripts at home in the evening when it was quiet. Ethel's mother let me in and told me Ethel was in her bedroom talking on the phone to Albert in Hollywood. I went down the hall and walked into her bedroom just in time to hear Ethel tell Albert, in a tone of high tragedy:

'Helene just quit the show.'

'Oh, she couldn't have,' I said. 'Her teeth aren't paid for.'

Ethel waved at me furiously to be quiet. Her face wore the dignified, persecuted look it always wore when she was bawling out Albert. She had an arresting face, with angular cheekbones and wide eyes. Her hair, which was whatever shade Arden's was featuring in any given season, was pale brown with gold streaks that spring.

'I have told you before, Albert, to keep your grubby hands off my writers' scripts,' she went on with wounded dignity. 'The last time Helene walked off the show I talked her into coming back. This time I don't know whether I can or not.'

Albert had a habit of tinkering with dialogue to give it a soap-opera touch. Since I never saw the show, I never knew when he'd got his itchy fingers on one of my scripts until Ethel told me about it afterward, and to avoid getting ulcers over it I refused to read his rewrites. I loved writing for Hallmark, but once a script was finished and out of my hands, the show was over and I went on to the next one. It was Ethel who got the ulcers. She was fiercely protective of her writers.

I sat down on the bed, pushing aside a litter of TV scripts, to wait out the fight, which was the last, and always the longest, of her three daily fights with Albert. The fights had begun a year earlier when the Hallmark show had moved to Hollywood. Albert, of course, had ordered Ethel to move out there with it. Ethel had declined; she didn't like Hollywood.

'I can't produce a show in California with my story editor in New York!' Albert had shouted.

'Fire me,' Ethel had advised him sympathetically. But they'd worked together a long time, and since Ethel was the best story editor in the business Albert hadn't been able to bring himself to fire her. So the show was produced in Hollywood with scripts written in New York, necessitating an open telephone line coast-to-coast, on which Ethel conducted her three daily fights. The first took place at 1 P.M. our time and 10 A.M. Albert's time and got him out of bed. (He rehearsed at night and slept late.) The second took place at 4 P.M. our time and 1 P.M. Albert's and took him away from his lunch. And the third began at 10 P.M. our time and disposed of Albert's dinner hour.

'That Albert,' Ethel remarked conversationally when she finally hung up. 'He's ruining my entire nervous system.' She took a tranquilizer – she took one after most evening fights with Albert – and then pointed eagerly to the script in my lap.

'How'd it come out?' she asked.

'Great,' I said modestly. Ethel read the script aloud with a stopwatch, and agreed that it was the best little television script in the whole wide world, and we mailed it to Hollywood. A few days later Sarah phoned from Hollywood to tell me how much she liked it, and Albert got on the phone to congratulate me and everybody was happy.

The Hallmark Hall of Fame went on the air at 5 P.M. New York time (2 P.M. Hollywood time) on Sunday afternoons. On the Sunday on which 'Aesop and Rhodope' was to be broadcast I was up early and dawdled over breakfast with the *Sunday Times*. As always, I read the theatre section and the front page over breakfast; and with my second cup of coffee I turned to the *Book Review* section. I scanned the review on the front page and then opened the section to pages 2 and 3.

The entire upper half of page 3 was occupied by a review of a book entitled *A House Is Not a Home* by Polly Adler. A headline indicated that Polly Adler was a madam and that her book concerned houses of prostitution. Under the headline was a photograph of the sculptured head of a young girl. Under the photograph, the caption read simply, in neat black italics:

Rhodope, the most famous prostitute in Greece.

Well, there we were. Or rather, since I couldn't wake up Ethel at nine-thirty on a Sunday morning, there I was.

Sitting there spilling coffee all over myself, I remembered (*now* I remembered) where I'd read about Rhodope. I'd come upon her in sketchy accounts of the life of Sappho and in the two or three lines of Sappho's Greek I'd ever been able to read. But in Greek, the spelling of a noun changes with every case, so Rhodope was Rhodope when you talked to her and Rhodopis when you talked about her. Sappho had talked about her. Not flatteringly.

To while away the time till I could break the news to Ethel, I got down a couple of books to see exactly what it was Sappho had said about her. According to the only accounts I had in the house, Rhodope had been a slave until she was thirteen years old, at which age she was set up in business as a prostitute by her owner. Sappho's brother met her, fell in love with her, bought her freedom and took her to live with him. And Rhodope (according to Sappho) took Sappho's brother for every drachma he had and then left him for richer men.

Where Landor got his version of Rhodope as a gentle, innocent maiden I didn't know and still don't.

At ten o'clock it occurred to me that Mr Joyce C. Hall out in Kansas City, Missouri, subscribed to the *Sunday Times* (he was a TV sponsor and all TV sponsors subscribed to it for the theatre section, which contained TV news, reviews and commentary), and I woke up Ethel.

'What's the matter?' she demanded sleepily on the phone.

'It says on page three of the *Times Book Review* section,' I said, 'that Rhodope was the most famous prostitute in Greece.'

'The most famous what?' said Ethel, wide awake.

'Prostitute,' I said. 'Her picture's in the paper. They wait two thousand five hundred years and then pick today to put her picture in the paper, surrounded by a review of a book on whore-houses.'

Ethel enjoyed crises; they stimulated her.

'Now don't panic,' she said briskly. 'Let me get the *Book Review* section.'

She was gone from the phone for a couple of minutes. Then she came back and said:

'Hang up, let me call Ed in Kansas City, I'll call you back.' Ed was the Hallmark account executive. I gathered she had to wake him up, too — it was an hour earlier in Kansas City — because it was some time before she phoned me back.

'Okay,' she said. 'Ed's driving out to Hall's place, he thinks the *Times* will still be on Hall's front porch and he'll take the *Book Review* section out of it. If they've already taken the *Times* in, he'll ring the bell and ask to borrow the *Book Review* section for his kid.'

'What about Albert and Sarah?' I asked.

'They haven't time to read anything on a Sunday, are you kidding?' said Ethel. 'They'll be rehearsing clear to air time and then they go out and eat.'

'Well, just tell Ed to keep an eye out for the mail,' I said. 'We're going to be getting letters from college professors —'

'Nobody in this country ever heard of Rhodope but you and Polly Adler,' said Ethel. 'And even if they have, it's one thing to see the name in print and another thing to hear it pronounced. Who knows how Sarah'll pronounce it? We won't get letters from anybody.'

We got two. From two prep-school English teachers who wrote to request copies of the script for their classes and to express the hope that Hallmark would continue to do interesting educational shows of this kind.

By the time Hallmark went off the air, my teeth were capped and paid for and I had two thousand dollars in the bank, making me richer than I'd ever been in my life. But I was also unemployed. And when, one early summer day, notice arrived that Maudiebird's building was to be renovated and we were all to be evicted, I had no way of knowing what rent I could afford on my next hovel. I had three months to find a place and I was room-hunting in a half-hearted fashion when, one morning Rosemary phoned. Rosemary was a friend of Ethel's and a former Hollywood writer.

'Ethel and Albert have a new show,' she announced.

'I knew they could do it,' I said. 'What is it?'

'Well,' said Rosemary, 'are you sitting down? It's to be called Matinee Theatre and it's going to be an hour dramatic show, produced live and in color from Hollywood, every day.'

'You mean every week,' I said.

'Every week day,' said Rosemary. 'Five a week. Albert's the executive producer, Ethel's the associate producer, I'm the chief story editor and you're the chief writer.'

'Are you sure, Rosemary?' I asked.

'I'm sure,' said Rosemary.

'Hang up,' I said. 'I have to think.'

The chief writer of such a show would be writing a script a month – more, if she could write them faster than that. Pay-checks floated before my eyes in heady profusion. The time had come which I'd begun to believe would never come: I was finally through with garrets. I was going to get myself a home.

One week later I signed a three-year lease on an apartment in a brand-new luxury building. It had a large living-room, a small alcove big enough for bookshelves, a desk and my typewriter, a flossy new kitchen and a shiny new tile bath. I blew my entire savings on furniture and drapes and wall-to-wall carpet, and on a day in October I moved in. A big, good-natured guy named Herbie arrived early in the morning to lay the carpet, and when he finished that afternoon, he insisted on uncrating the new furniture for me and distributing it around at my direction. And as long as I live I will never forget the moment when he shoved the last end table and lamp into place, and I stood in the middle of my own home and looked around and said:

'It's beautiful.'

And I didn't even know I was crying till Herbie said:

'Well, it's nothin' to bawl about, honey!'

Two days later, Rosemary moved into a flat on the floor above mine, and you have no idea what having her overhead meant to me in the three wild and woolly years of Matinee Theatre. All the other Matinee writers had to run down to Radio City to Ethel's office all the time. I never had to leave the house. Rosemary would come home at six, bringing me a book or play to adapt. I'd write the first draft and when it was finished leave it in her mailbox. She'd read it the next day, leave the office an hour early and come to my apartment for cocktails and a story conference. I'd write the revisions and then run up the back stairs to her apartment with the final version, and she'd take it to the office the next morning and bring home a new assignment for me that evening.

I say 'that evening' because nobody connected with the show ever got a day off. Matinee Theatre was the most frenzied operation in the history of television.

Out in Hollywood, under Albert McCleery, were two assistant producers, ten directors, two story editors and twenty writers. In New York, under Ethel, were three readers, two story editors and fifty to sixty writers. There were five plays in rehearsal in Hollywood at all times. On a given Sunday, Monday's show would be in its sixth and last day of rehearsal, Tuesday's in its fifth day, Wednesday's in its fourth – and so on, with Albert overseeing (presumably by bicycle) all five. In New York, all Ethel Frank had to do was find twenty properties a month, clear the literary rights, assign the scripts, read and approve the final edited versions and mail them to Hollywood at a rate which ensured a backlog of a month's scripts.

With so many scripts to assign, Ethel was frequently forced to gamble on new and untried writers, and every few months one of them turned in an unusable script. Since there was no money in the budget for a new script, the crisis might have been acute. Thanks to me – Miss Big-Mouth – Matinee Theatre found a simple solution to the problem.

The first day an unproducible script was turned in, Rosemary read it and left it on Ethel's desk with a note:

'Ethel: This is a dog. What do we do now?'

It happened that on that day I finished a script just before lunch. I took advantage of the rare, free afternoon to stroll down through the park and on to Rockefeller Center to pay a social call on my friends in the Matinee Theatre office. I wandered into Ethel's private office and found her sunk in gloom. She showed me Rosemary's note and then invited me to read the first page of the 'dog.' The script was not just unproducible, it was illiterate.

'What do you do when this happens?' I asked.

'What can I do?' Ethel demanded. 'We've got a hundred dollars left in the budget! I can't get a script written on that!'

Ethel was my friend, wasn't she? Thanks to her, I was making piles of money and living in a breathtaking one-and-a-half-room palace, wasn't I?

'I'll do it over for you, Ethel,' I said.

'We could only pay you a hundred bucks for it!' cried Ethel. (An hour script paid a thousand.)

'That's all right, Ethel,' I said.

'You'd have to write a whole new script!' cried Ethel.

'That's all right, Ethel,' I said.

'We need it in a week!' cried Ethel. (An hour script normally took four weeks or five.)

'That's all right, Ethel,' I said.

I hurried home with the crisis assignment, I slaved for seven days and seven evenings and managed to turn in the script on time. Ethel and Rosemary read it and liked it and showered me with praise and gratitude and admiration, and what the two of them did to me from then on I have trouble believing, even now. As Rosemary had the nerve to reconstruct one of their typical crisis conversations for me, it went like this:

I'd be hard at work trying to reduce *Pride and Prejudice* to eight characters and fifty minutes, while down at the Matinee office Rosemary was hurrying into Ethel's office with an illiterate script and the dread pronouncement: 'It's a dog!'

'It can't be!' Ethel would snarl. 'Albert's hired a star for it! It goes into rehearsal next Monday!'

'Well, you're going to have to get a new script written in three days, then!' Rosemary would say. And she and Ethel would eye each other.

'How,' Ethel would inquire delicately, 'is she feeling?'

'I could ask her,' Rosemary would offer nervously.

'I'll do it,' Ethel would say. 'She can hold up on *Pride and Prejudice* till the weekend and still finish on time; she's fast.'

A minute later my phone would ring and Ethel would ask brightly: 'How do you feel, hon? Do you feel strong?'

Occasionally it was Rosemary who phoned and, in a voice dripping with catastrophe, said:

'Dear, we're in a *terrible jam*, I know how tired you are, but –'

I resurrected so many dead dogs for Matinee that after a while, when the phone rang, a sixth sense told me Ethel or Rosemary was at the other end with another dog and I'd pick up the phone and say briskly:

'City Pound.'

I couldn't sign my name to those scripts, of course. The only person who could legally rewrite unusable scripts without being paid for it was the story editor. So each time, I was put on the show's payroll as a story editor. But since story editors were not entitled to screen credit for the rewriting they did, it was necessary for me to have a pseudonym. If you ever run across a television script by Herman Knight, I wrote it. Herman wasn't great but he was dirt-cheap and fast as the wind.

Herman and I were both worn out by the beginning of Matinee's third year. I was working on the adaptation of a disorganized Chinese fantasy called *The Carefree Tree*, when the phone rang and a secretary said: 'Ethel Frank calling.'

'Hon,' said Ethel. 'Drop *The Carefree Tree*, you can go back to it later. Come on down, I have a special assignment for you.'

'No,' I said.

'It's not a dog, it's a big assignment!' said Ethel, and added solemnly: 'We have a new sponsor. You're going to do their first show.'

This so thoroughly baffled me I left *The Carefree Tree* in the typewriter and went down to the Matinee office out of sheer curiosity.

The cost of producing Matinee five days a week, live and in color, meant that the show was shared by four or five sponsors. This multiple sponsorship kept the show, and the writers, beyond the reach of corporation or ad agency interference, since no sponsor could hope to control a show of which he owned only one fifth. Plus which, sponsors were constantly signing on and dropping off the Matinee roster the way you'd hop on or off a bus. I couldn't imagine any sponsor whose arrival Ethel would announce with such solemnity.

She and Rosemary were in a huddle over a list of names when I walked in.

Ethel looked up.

'We're going to produce a series of special plays,' she said, 'for the United Lutheran Church in America.'

It shook me. It shook all three of us.

'You're going to write the first script,' said Ethel. 'We're buying that Ozark play you liked, if the Lutherans okay it.'

'Ethel,' I said, 'do you think I'm the ideal writer for the United Lutheran Church?'

Ethel looked pious.

'The Lutherans,' she intoned, 'are remarkable men. They told me they do not have the slightest interest in the religious denomination of the writer.'

'That may very well be,' I said, 'but I doubt if they had Reform Judaism in mind.'

Rosemary laughed.

'All I need on this show is to run around trying to find six Lutheran writers,' said Ethel bitterly.

'Well, we ought to find them a Lutheran story editor, dear!' said Rosemary. Rosemary had a Catholic father and a Methodist mother, the other story editor was Jewish, and neither of them had time to take on additional scripts.

It was several days later that Ethel phoned to say she'd found a story editor for the Lutherans and I went down to the office and met Katherine, a gentle, blonde Episcopalian. (Said Ethel morosely: 'In this town they're lucky I found them a Protestant.')

In a simple black dress with a white collar and a retiring violet lipstick, Katherine was pronounced very holy-looking, and she trotted off to meet the Lutherans with the Ozark play under her arm. The play was the story of a fifteen-year-old girl in the backwoods of Arkansas, all of whose yearnings were focused on a red dress in a mail-order catalogue. Neglected by ignorant parents and ignored by a preoccupied schoolteacher, the girl allowed a boy to make love to her in return for money to buy the red dress; she became pregnant and was driven to a fatal, self-inflicted abortion. I had read the play a few years earlier for Monograph and had recommended it to Ethel as one we might somehow sanitize for television.

The Lutherans liked the play, and they didn't want it sanitized. They wanted plays that dealt with the problems confronting all mid-twentieth-century churches, and the teenager's tragedy was grimly familiar to them. They approved the script and directed that it be produced as their Easter show.

Katherine and I worked hard on the script, and when it was finished copies were sent to the six Lutherans in charge of the project. All six read the script and then invited Katherine and me to a dinner conference to discuss revisions. They were charming hosts and it wasn't till coffee was served that the six copies of the script were passed to Katherine and me, each with notes in the margins suggesting revisions. All the revisions were minor. But one particular margin note appeared prominently on every script: 'WHERE EASTER?' My heritage had caught up with me; I'd gone and left Easter out of the Easter script.

We assured the Lutherans that Easter would be prominently featured in the final version, the conference ended and I went home to do the revisions. A week later, the final revised script was approved by the Lutherans and airmailed to Albert in Hollywood. It went into rehearsal on a Thursday.

On Friday, the NBC censorship office telephoned Albert and ordered him to cancel the show. NBC censorship was sent a copy of every Matinee script as a matter of form, and the only one it ever ordered off the air as too immoral for the television industry was the first script sponsored by the Lutheran Church.

Ethel, Rosemary and Katherine sat in the East Coast Matinee office that afternoon in a kind of paralysis, wondering how to tell the Lutherans they were too sinful for television. But out in Hollywood, Albert McCleery was phoning NBC, beginning with the censorship office and working his way straight up to the top-level executives, repeating the same message to each:

'You go ahead and cancel this show,' he was shouting, 'and I'll see to it that every newspaper from New York to California carries the story of how NBC censored the Lutheran Church off the air!'

Late that afternoon, NBC backed down and rehearsals of the play were allowed to proceed.

My last unsettling experience unsettled me clear out of the Annex.

Not long after Matinee Theatre went off the air, I won a fellowship from CBS. I was given five thousand dollars on which to work for a year on TV dramatizations of American history. Sitting in the bathtub, the day after I won this contest, I made a momentous decision:

henceforth I would stop looking down on television. I would stop writing bad plays and commit myself unreservedly to television scripts. I even toyed with the possibility of buying a TV set.

Fired by this decision, I flung myself into the fellowship year. I researched for months in libraries, I wrote a ninety-minute script, rewrote it under the supervision of one of the Playhouse 90 producers and then plunged into a series of outlines for more ninety-minute scripts to come.

And all this time, behind my back, television, which had waited to do it till I'd made my great bathtub decision, now went completely to pot. First, the quiz-show scandals broke. Then the CBS executives in charge of the fellowship project were forced out of CBS. Then Playhouse 90 went off the air. Then every other dramatic show went off the air, to be replaced by Gunsmoke, Perry Mason, and fifty imitations of each. Most devastating of all, I woke up at the end of my fellowship year to discover that the entire television industry had packed up and moved to Hollywood where it was now permanently resettled.

I was unwilling (to put it mildly) to follow Gunsmoke and Perry Mason to Hollywood; westerns bored me and nothing could induce me to revert to shabby TV whodunits. No need to worry, I told myself. Ethel and Albert were bound to get a new show, produced in Hollywood and written in New York.

And sure enough, one day in the fall of 1960, Ethel phoned with the long-awaited words:

'Albert and I have a new show.'

'Hallelujah,' I said. 'What is it?'

'I just want you to realize,' said Ethel, 'that we're almost the only show that's still written on the East Coast. And East or West, dear, if you want to work in television you're going to have to write for this kind of show. It's all they're doing now.'

'Ethel,' I said, 'what's the show?'

'The Adventures of Ellery Queen,' she said.

Please Use Nearest Exit

Dec. 6? 7? '60

Now listen, Maxine —

As soon as we hung up the other night I phoned those girls you sublet to and told them about your green deck chair and your good stew pot and they are mailing the stew pot to Hollywood today by Parcel Post but they said to tell you you do not HAVE a green deck chair. They looked in the closet where you said it probably was, and the cellar storeroom where you said it would be if it wasn't in the closet, and it isn't in either place and it also isn't anywhere else, you probably hocked it.

This is not a real letter because (a) you already owe me two letters and (b) I'm late for the Unemployment Insurance office.

WRITE ME.

love

h.

Dear Heart –

I know I said on my Christmas card I'd write soon and here it is March but I've been busy making my movie debut.

First, did you know when you see '(MOS)' in a shooting script it means MidOut Sound? Comes from way back in the days of the early talkies when some German was directing a movie and at one point he shouted: 'Ve do zis next take midout sound!' So of course they've been writing (MOS) in shooting scripts ever since.

Now about my movie debut. I bumped into Joe Anthony on the street and he told me he was directing *Career* and he'd try and get me a bit in it. The next day I got a call from Paramount and would I come in and meet Hal Wallis, producer of *Career*? I went in and met him – I was very charming and commented on the chic of his office, his sweater, his tan and anything else I could see – and he said I could report to the casting director of *Career* the next day, there was a part in it for me.

So the casting director gave me a script and told me which scene to study. There were two characters in the scene – CHIC WOMAN IN HER MID-THIRTIES and MIDDLE-AGED TV DIRECTOR, both parts maybe five lines long. I started reading the CHIC WOMAN IN HER MID-THIRTIES and he said: No, you're the TV director.

Well, lemme tell you it was a blow to the ego, but I started reading the TV director till I got to a line in the business where it said the chic woman 'hands HIM a book.'

So that night I called my agent and said: 'Listen, there's been a mistake; they've got me playing a man. And if it costs Paramount Pictures half a million when they find out the mistake and have to retake the whole scene, somebody's gonna get a poker up. So you better check with Paramount.'

The next day when they got ready to shoot the scene I met both the chic woman who'd been hired to play the chic woman and the middle-aged gent who'd been hired to play the TV director. It seems Mr Wallis can't stand to see people out of work so he keeps hiring three or four people for the same bit part, regardless of sex. So they made the TV director a woman and let me play that, and they gave the nice middle-aged gentleman two lines to say someplace else, and that's how Muzzy got into the movies, kiddies.

I'm homesick. Spring has come to California and it puts me in mind of little goodies like Radio City and Bloomingdale's but let's face it, I'm working out here. I've done five TV shows in the last two months.

And that's the story of my life and please write and tell me about yours, your last letter around Christmas was very disquieting. You must have found gainful employment by now, please God?

love

m.

305 E. 72nd St. STILL!

(even though the rent just

went up again)

Doll!

I'm getting up a party of hundreds to go see *Career* and cheer and stomp when you come on.

I have mildly earthshaking news of my own which I'm sitting here celebrating with a rare and beautiful martini – You should see me, running around this opulent, wall-to-wall palace in slacks with patches in the seat and sweaters with holes in the elbow, putting quarters in a piggy-bank till they mount up to a bottle of gin. Hysterical.

Anyhow, here I was with my unemployment insurance running out and the bells ringing in a New Year and suddenly for the first time I faced the fact that I was NOT between assignments, I was NOT temporarily out of work, I was permanently out of a profession. And I thought: 'What are you DOING, sitting here waiting for television to move back East and turn respectable or somebody to buy one of your old plays? Television is not coming back East and nobody's going to buy your plays, they're all terrible. If you want to eat for the rest of your life you'd better try writing something else.'

So I got down the old play about *Oklahoma!* and decided if I deleted the junky plot and just told the straight facts it might make a magazine article. Slaved over it for three weeks and sent it to *Harper's* and damned if *Harper's* didn't buy it. Sent me a letter of acceptance and $200. Before-taxes-and-agent's-commission but think of the presTIGE, *Harper's* kept telling me.

Carried away by this success, I got down the old play about Stokowski and turned it into what I hoped was a *New Yorker* story and sent it off to *The New Yorker* and a week later one of their editors phoned to say he liked it and *The New Yorker* was buying it.

Well, I like to fall down dead with joy. Every day for the next week I hurried down for the mail, looking for the check and the letter-of-acceptance or whatever they called their contract. It didn't come. So I wrote to the gent who'd phoned, saying Would he please send me a contract; and I added: 'You didn't say on the phone how much *The New Yorker* is paying me. Is it a secret?'

It was a secret. He didn't answer my letter. And he didn't send a contract.

Two weeks later the galleys arrived – which is how I knew they'd 'bought' the story. A week after that, the story appeared in print. On the day the issue of *The New Yorker* with my story in it turned up on the newsstands, a check came in the mail from *The New Yorker* for $400.

I tore up the street to the bank with it, and standing at the teller's window I turned the check over, to endorse it.

On the back of the check, rubber-stamped and bleeding off the edge of the paper, was the contract.

When I endorsed the check, I automatically signed the contract – which then went back to *The New Yorker* as a canceled check.

So cancel your *New Yorker* subscription and rush RIGHT out and subscribe to the *Readers Digest*. They don't believe in contracts either – but they picked up the *Harper's* story for reprint and paid me more for it than *Harper's* and *The New Yorker* put together. The check just came this morning – along with a letter from an editor at Harper & Row, Book Publishers, saying she liked the *Oklahoma!* story in *Harper's* and Do I have a book in mind? No, I do not have a book in mind but the letter made my day, who else ever asked me such a high-brow question?

I think my potroast is burning.

love

h.

MISS MAXINE STUART
1105 MERILLON AVENUE
LOS ANGELES CALIFORNIA

HARPERS WANTS ME TO WRITE MY AUTOBIOGRAPHY HOW TO
GET NOWHERE IN THE THEATRE YOU'RE COSTARRING SEND
REMINISCENCES IT TURNS OUT I SPENT ALL THOSE YEARS TRYING
TO WRITE PLAYS JUST SO I COULD WRITE A BOOK ABOUT IT
AFTERWARDS IS THAT THE LIVING END LOVE

                                                    HELENE

MISS HELENE HANFF
305 EAST 72ND STREET
NEW YORK CITY

   DARLING AM HYSTERICAL WITH EXCITEMENT ITS NOT THE
LIVING END ITS FLANAGANS LAW LOVE AND CHEERS

                                                    MAXINE

84, Charing Cross Road

F.P.D. In Memoriam

14 East 95th St.
New York City

OCTOBER 5, 1949

Marks & Co.
84, Charing Cross Road
London, W.C. 2
England

Gentlemen:

Your ad in the *Saturday Review of Literature* says that you specialize in out-of-print books. The phrase 'antiquarian book-sellers' scares me somewhat, as I equate 'antique' with expensive. I am a poor writer with an antiquarian taste in books and all the things I want are impossible to get over here except in very expensive rare editions, or in Barnes & Noble's grimy, marked-up schoolboy copies.

I enclose a list of my most pressing problems. If you have clean secondhand copies of any of the books on the list, for no more than $5.00 each, will you consider this a purchase order and send them to me?

Very truly yours,

Helene Hanff
(Miss) Helene Hanff

MARKS & CO., Booksellers
84, Charing Cross Road
London, W.C. 2

25TH OCTOBER, 1949

Miss Helene Hanff
14 East 95th Street
New York 28, New York
U.S.A.

Dear Madam,

In reply to your letter of October 5th, we have managed to clear up two thirds of your problem. The three Hazlitt essays you want are contained in the Nonesuch Press edition of his *Selected Essays* and the Stevenson is found in *Virginibus Puerisque*. We are sending nice copies of both these by Book Post and we trust they will arrive safely in due course and that you will be pleased with them. Our invoice is enclosed with the books.

The Leigh Hunt essays are not going to be so easy but we will see if we can find an attractive volume with them all in. We haven't the Latin Bible you describe but we have a Latin New Testament, also a Greek New Testament, ordinary modern editions in cloth binding. Would you like these?

Yours faithfully,

FPD
For MARKS & CO.

14 East 95th St.
New York City

NOVEMBER 3, 1949

Marks & Co.
84, Charing Cross Road
London, W.C. 2
England

Gentlemen:

The books arrived safely, the Stevenson is so fine it embarrasses my orange-crate bookshelves, I'm almost afraid to handle such soft vellum and heavy cream-colored pages. Being used to the dead-white paper and stiff cardboardy covers of American books, I never knew a book could be such a joy to the touch.

A Britisher whose girl lives upstairs translated the £1/17/6 for me and says I owe you $5.30 for the two books. I hope he got it right. I enclose a $5 bill and a single, please use the 70c toward the price of the New Testaments, both of which I want.

Will you please translate your prices hereafter? I don't add too well in plain American, I haven't a prayer of ever mastering bilingual arithmetic.

Yours,

Helene Hanff

I hope 'madam' doesn't mean over there what it does here.

MARKS & CO., Booksellers
84, Charing Cross Road
London, W.C. 2

9TH NOVEMBER, 1949

Miss Helene Hanff
14 East 95th Street
New York 28, New York
U.S.A.

Dear Miss Hanff,

Your six dollars arrived safely, but we should feel very much easier if you would send your remittances by postal money order in future, as this would be quite a bit safer for you than entrusting dollar bills to the mails.

We are very happy you liked the Stevenson so much. We have sent off the New Testaments, with an invoice listing the amount due in both pounds and dollars, and we hope you will be pleased with them.

Yours faithfully,

FPD
For MARKS & CO.

14 East 95th St.

NOVEMBER 18, 1949

WHAT KIND OF A BLACK PROTESTANT BIBLE IS THIS?

Kindly inform the Church of England they have loused up the most beautiful prose ever written, whoever told them to tinker with the Vulgate Latin? They'll burn for it, you mark my words.

It's nothing to me, I'm Jewish myself. But I have a Catholic sister-in-law, a Methodist sister-in-law, a whole raft of Presbyterian cousins (through my Great-Uncle Abraham who converted) and an aunt who's a Christian Science healer, and I like to think *none* of them would countenance this Anglican Latin Bible if they knew it existed. (As it happens, they don't know Latin existed.)

Well, the hell with it. I've been using my Latin teacher's Vulgate, what I imagine I'll do is just not give it back till you find me one of my own.

I enclose $4 to cover the $3.88 due you, buy yourself a cup of coffee with the 12c. There's no post office near here and I am not running all the way down to Rockfeller Plaza to stand in line for a $3.88 money order. If I wait till I get down there for something else, I won't have the $3.88 any more. I have implicit faith in the U.S. Airmail and His Majesty's Postal Service.

Have you got a copy of Landor's *Imaginary Conversations*? I think there are several volumes, the one I want is the one with the Greek conversations. If it contains a dialogue between Aesop and Rhodope, that'll be the volume I want.

Helene Hanff

MARKS & CO., Booksellers
84, Charing Cross Road
London, W.C. 2

26TH NOVEMBER, 1949

Miss Helene Hanff
14 East 95th Street
New York 28, New York
U.S.A.

Dear Miss Hanff,

Your four dollars arrived safely and we have credited the 12 cents to your account.

We happen to have in stock Volume II of the Works & Life of Walter Savage Landor which contains the Greek dialogues including the one mentioned in your letter, as well as the Roman dialogues. It is an old edition published in 1876, not very handsome but well bound and a good clean copy, and we are sending it off to you today with invoice enclosed.

I am sorry we made the mistake with the Latin Bible and will try to find a Vulgate for you. Not forgetting Leigh Hunt.

Yours faithfully,

FPD
For MARKS & CO.

14 East 95th St.
New York City

DECEMBER 8, 1949

Sir:

(It feels witless to keep writing 'Gentlemen' when the same solitary soul is obviously taking care of everything for me.)

Savage Landor arrived safely and promptly fell open to a Roman dialogue where two cities had just been destroyed by war and everybody was being crucified and begging passing Roman soldiers to run them through and end the agony. It'll be a relief to turn to Aesop and Rhodope where all you have to worry about is a famine. I do love secondhand books that open to the page some previous owner read oftenest. The day Hazlitt came he opened to 'I hate to read new books,' and I hollered 'Comrade!' to whoever owned it before me.

I enclose a dollar which Brian (British boy friend of Kay upstairs) says will cover the /8/ I owe you, you forgot to translate it.

Now then. Brian told me you are all rationed to 2 ounces of meat per family per week and one egg per person per month and I am simply appalled. He has a catalogue from a British firm here which flies food from Denmark to his mother, so I am sending a small Christmas present to Marks & Co. I hope there will be enough to go round, he says the Charing Cross Road bookshops are 'all quite small.'

I'm sending it c/o you, FPD, whoever you are.

Noel.

Helene Hanff

14 East 95th St.

DECEMBER 9, 1949

FPD! CRISIS!

I sent that package off. The chief item in it was a 6-pound ham, I figured you could take it to a butcher and get it sliced up so everybody would have some to take home.

But I just noticed on your last invoice it says. 'B. Marks, M. Cohen,' Props.

ARE THEY KOSHER? I could rush a tongue over.
ADVISE PLEASE!

Helene Hanff

MARKS & CO., Booksellers
84, Charing Cross Road
London, W.C. 2

20TH DECEMBER, 1949

Miss Helene Hanff
14 East 95th Street
New York 28, New York
U.S.A.

Dear Miss Hanff,

Just a note to let you know that your gift parcel arrived safely today and the contents have been shared out between the staff. Mr. Marks and Mr. Cohen insisted that we divide it up among ourselves and not include 'the bosses.' I should just like to add that everything in the parcel was something that we either never see or can only be had through the black market. It was extremely kind and generous of you to think of us in this way and we are all extremely grateful.

We all wish to express our thanks and send our greetings and best wishes for 1950.

Yours faithfully,

Frank Doel
For MARKS & CO.

14 East 95th St.

MARCH 25, 1950

Frank Doel, what are you DOING over there, you are not doing ANYthing, you are just sitting AROUND.

Where is Leigh Hunt? Where is the *Oxford Verse*? Where is the Vulgate and dear goofy John Henry, I thought they'd be such nice uplifting reading for Lent and NOTHING do you send me.

you leave me sitting here writing long margin notes in library books that don't belong to me, some day they'll find out i did it and take my library card away.

I have made arrangements with the Easter bunny to bring you an Egg, he will get over there and find you have died of Inertia.

I require a book of love poems with spring coming on. *No Keats or Shelley*, send me poets who can make love without slobbering – Wyatt or Jonson or somebody, use your own judgment. Just a nice book preferably small enough to stick in a slacks pocket and take to Central Park.

Well, don't just sit there! Go find it! i swear i don't know how that shop keeps going.

MARKS & CO., Booksellers
84, Charing Cross Road
London, W.C. 2

7TH APRIL, 1950

Miss Helene Hanff
14 East 95th Street
New York 28, New York
U.S.A.

Dear Miss Hanff,

I have to thank you for the very welcome Easter parcel which arrived safely yesterday. We were all delighted to see the tins and the box of shell eggs, and the rest of the staff joins me in thanking you for your very kind and generous thought of us.

I am sorry we haven't been able to send you any of the books you want. About the book of love poems, now and then we do get such a volume as you describe. We have none in stock at the moment but shall look out for one for you.

Again, many thanks for the parcel.

Faithfully yours,

Frank Doel
For MARKS & CO.

MARKS & CO., Booksellers
84, Charing Cross Road
London, W.C. 2

7TH APRIL, 1950

Dear Miss Hanff,

Please don't let Frank know I'm writing this but every time I send you a bill I've been dying to slip in a little note and he might not think it quite proper of me. That sounds stuffy and he's not, he's quite nice really, very nice in fact, it's just that he does rather look on you as his private correspondent as all your letters and parcels are addressed to him. But I just thought I would write to you on my own.

We all love your letters and try to imagine what you must be like. I've decided you're young and very sophisticated and smart-looking. Old Mr. Martin thinks you must be quite studious-looking in spite of your wonderful sense of humor. Why don't you send us a snapshot? We should love to have it.

If you're curious about Frank, he's in his late thirties, quite nice-looking, married to a very sweet Irish girl, I believe she's his second wife.

Everyone was so grateful for the parcel. My little ones (girl 5, boy 4) were in Heaven — with the raisins and egg I was actually able to make them a cake!

I do hope you don't mind my writing. Please don't mention it when you write to Frank.

With best wishes,

Cecily Farr

P.S. I shall put my home address on the back of this in case you should ever want anything sent you from London.

C.F.

14 East 95th St.

APRIL 10, 1950

Dear Cecily —

And a *very* bad cess to Old Mr. Martin, tell him I'm so unstudious I never even went to college. I just happen to have peculiar taste in books, thanks to a Cambridge professor named Quiller-Couch, known as Q, whom I fell over in a library when I was 17. And I'm about as smart-looking as a Broadway panhandler. I live in moth-eaten sweaters and wool slacks, they don't give us any heat here in the daytime. It's a 5-story brownstone and all the other tenants go out to work at 9 A.M. and don't come home till 6 — and why should the landlord heat the building for one small script-reader/writer working at home on the ground floor?

Poor Frank, I give him such a hard time, I'm always bawling him out for something. I'm only teasing, but I know he'll take me seriously. I keep trying to puncture that proper British reserve, if he gets ulcers I did it.

Please write and tell me about London, I live for the day when I step off the boat-train and feel its dirty sidewalks under my feet. I want to walk up Berkeley Square and down Wimpole Street and stand in St. Paul's where John Donne preached and sit on the step Elizabeth sat on when she refused to enter the Tower, and like that. A newspaper man I know, who was stationed in London during the war, says tourists go to England with preconceived notions, so they always find exactly what they go looking for. I told him I'd go looking for the England of English literature, and he said:

'Then it's there.'

Regards —

Helene Hanff

MARKS & CO., Booksellers
84, Charing Cross Road
London, W.C. 2

20TH SEPTEMBER, 1950

Miss Helene Hanff
14 East 95th Street
New York 28, New York
U.S.A.

Dear Miss Hanff,

It is such a long time since we wrote to you I hope you do not think we have forgotten all about your wants.

Anyway, we now have in stock the *Oxford Book of English Verse*, printed on India paper, original blue cloth binding, 1905, inscription in ink on the flyleaf but a good secondhand copy, price $2.00. We thought we had better quote before sending, in case you have already purchased a copy.

Some time ago you asked us for Newman's *Idea of a University*. Would you be interested in a copy of the first edition? We have just purchased one, particulars as follows:

NEWMAN (JOHN HENRY, D.D.) Discourses on the Scope and Nature of University Education, Addressed to the Catholics of Dublin. First edition, 8vo. calf, Dublin, 1852. A few pages a little age-stained and spotted but a good copy in a sound binding.

Price – $6.00

In case you would like them, we will put both books on one side until you have time to reply.

With kind regards,
Yours faithfully,

Frank Doel
For MARKS & CO.

14 East 95th St.

SEPTEMBER 25, 1950

he has a first edition of Newman's *University* for six bucks, do i want it, he asks innocently.

Dear Frank:

Yes, I want it. I won't be fit to live with myself. I've never cared about first editions per se, but a first edition of THAT book – !

oh my.

i can just see it.

Send the *Oxford Verse*, too, please. Never wonder if I've found something somewhere else, I don't look anywhere else any more. Why should I run all the way down to 17th St. to buy dirty, badly made books when I can buy clean, beautiful ones from you without leaving the typewriter? From where I sit, London's a lot closer than 17th Street.

Enclosed please God please find $8. Did I tell you about Brian's lawsuit? He buys physics tomes from a technical book-shop in London, he's not sloppy and haphazard like me, he bought an expensive set and went down to Rockefeller Plaza and stood in line and got a money order and cabled it or whatever you do with it, he's a businessman, he does things right.

the money order got lost in transit.

Up His Majesty's Postal Service!
HH

am sending very small parcel to celebrate first edition, Overseas Associates finally sent me my own catalogue.

MARKS & CO., Booksellers
84, Charing Cross Road
London, W.C. 2

2ND OCTOBER, 1950

Dear Helene

I brought the enclosed snapshots to the shop with me weeks ago, but we've been frightfully busy so have had no chance to send them on to you. They were taken in Norfolk where Doug (my husband) is stationed with the RAF. None of them very flattering of me, but they are the best we have of the children and the one of Doug alone is very good.

My dear, I do hope you get your wish to come to England. Why not save your pennies and come next summer? Mummy and Daddy have a house in Middlesex and would be delighted to put you up.

Megan Wells (secretary to the bosses) and I are going on a week's holiday to Jersey (Channel Islands) in July. Why don't you come with us and then you could economize the rest of the month in Middlesex?

Ben Marks is trying to see what I'm writing so shall have to close.

Sincerely,

Cecily

14 East 95th St.

OCTOBER 15, 1950

WELL!!!

All I have to say to YOU, Frank Doel, is we live in depraved, destructive and degenerate times when a bookshop – a BOOKSHOP – starts tearing up beautiful old books to use as wrapping paper. I said to John Henry when he stepped out of it:

'Would you believe a thing like that, Your Eminence?' and he said he wouldn't. You tore that book up in the middle of a major battle and I don't even know which war it was.

The Newman arrived almost a week ago and I'm just beginning to recover. I keep it on the table with me all day, every now and then I stop typing and reach over and touch it. Not because it's a first edition; I just never saw a book so beautiful. I feel vaguely guilty about owning it. All that gleaming leather and gold stamping and beautiful type belongs in the pine-panelled library of an English country home; it wants to be read by the fire in a gentleman's leather easy chair – not on a secondhand studio couch in a one-room hovel in a broken-down brownstone front.

I want the Q anthology. I'm not sure how much it was, I lost your last letter. I think it was about two bucks, I'll enclose two singles, if I owe you more let me know.

Why don't you wrap it in pages LCXII and LCXIII so I can at least find out who won the battle and what war it was?

HH

P.S. Have you got Sam Pepy's diary over there? I need him for long winter evenings.

MARKS & CO., Booksellers
84, Charing Cross Road
London, W.C. 2

1ST NOVEMBER, 1950

Miss Helene Hanff
14 East 95th Street
New York 28, New York
U.S.A.

Dear Miss Hanff,

I am sorry for the delay in answering your letter but I have been away out of town for a week or so and am now busy trying to catch up on my correspondence.

First of all, please don't worry about us using old books such as Clarendon's Rebellion for wrapping. In this particular case they were just two odd volumes with the covers detached and nobody in their right senses would have given us a shilling for them.

The Quiller-Couch anthology, *The Pilgrim's Way*, has been sent to you by Book Post. The balance due was $1.85 so your $2 more than covered it. We haven't a copy of Pepys' *Diary* in stock at the moment but shall look out for one for you.

With best wishes,
Yours faithfully,

F. Doel
For MARKS & CO.

MARKS & CO., Booksellers
84, Charing Cross Road
London, W.C. 2

2ND FEBRUARY, 1951

Miss Helene Hanff
14 East 95th Street
New York 28, New York
U.S.A.

Dear Miss Hanff,

We are glad you liked the 'Q' anthology. We have no copy of the *Oxford Book of English Prose* in stock at the moment but will try to find one for you.

About the *Sir Roger de Coverley Papers*, we happen to have in stock a volume of eighteenth century essays which includes a good selection of them as well as essays by Chesterfield and Goldsmith. It is edited by Austin Dobson and is quite a nice edition and as it is only $1.15 we have sent it off to you by Book Post. If you want a more complete collection of Addison & Steele let me know and I will try to find one.

There are six of us in the shop, not including Mr. Marks and Mr. Cohen.

Faithfully yours,

Frank Doel
For MARKS & CO.

Eastcote
Pinner
Middlesex

20–2–51

Helene my dear –

There are many ways of doing it but Mummy and I think this is the simplest for you to try. Put a cup of flour, an egg, a half cup of milk and a good shake of salt into a large bowl and beat altogether until it is the consistency of thick cream. Put in the frig for several hours. (It's best if you make it in the morning.) When you put your roast in the oven, put in an extra pan to heat. Half an hour before your roast is done, pour a bit of the roast grease into the baking pan, just enough to cover the bottom will do. The pan must be *very hot*. Now pour the pudding in and the roast and pudding will be ready at the same time.

I don't know quite how to describe it to someone who has never seen it, but a good Yorkshire Pudding will puff up very high and brown and crisp and when you cut into it you will find that it is hollow inside.

The RAF is still keeping Doug in Norfolk and we are firmly hoarding your Christmas tins until he comes home, but my dear, what a celebration we shall have with them when he does! I do think you oughtn't to spend your money like that!

Must fly and post this if you're to have it for Brian's birthday dinner, do let me know if it's a success.

Love,

Cecily

14 East 95th St.

FEBRUARY 25, 1951

Dear Cecily –

Yorkshire Pudding out of this world, we have nothing like it, I had to describe it to somebody as a high, curved, smooth, empty waffle.

Please don't worry about what the food parcels cost, I don't know whether Overseas Asso. is non-profit or duty-free or what, but they are monstrous cheap, that whole Christmas parcel cost less than my turkey. They do have a few rich parcels with things like standing rib-roasts and legs of lamb, but even those are so cheap compared with what they cost in the butcher shops that it kills me not to be able to send them. I have such a time with the catalogue, I spread it out on the rug and debate the relative merits of Parcel 105 (includes one-dozen-eggs-and-a-tin-of-sweet-biscuits) and Parcel 217B (two-dozen-eggs-and-NO-sweet-biscuits), I hate the one-dozen egg parcels, what is two eggs for anybody to take home? But Brian says the powdered ones taste like glue. So it's a problem.

A producer who likes my plays (but not enough to produce them) just phoned. He's producing a TV series, do I want to write for television? 'Two bills,' he said carelessly, which it turned out means $200. And me a $40-a-week script-reader! I go down to see him tomorrow, keep your fingers crossed.

Best –

helene

MARKS & CO., Booksellers
84, Charing Cross Road
London, W.C. 2

4TH APRIL, 1951

Helene dear —

Your marvelous Easter parcels arrived safely and everyone is quite upset because Frank left the city on business for the firm the next morning and so hasn't written to thank you, and of course no one else quite dares to write to Frank's Miss Hanff.

My dear, the *meat!* I really don't think you should spend your money like that. It must have cost a packet! Bless you for your kind heart.

Here comes Ben Marks with work so must close.

Love,

Cecily

Earl's Terrace
Kensington High St.
London, W. 8

5TH APRIL, 1951

Dear Miss Hanff,

This is just to let you know that your Easter parcels to Marks & Co. arrived safely a few days ago but have not been acknowledged as Frank Doel is away from the office on business for the firm.

We were all quite dazzled to see the meat. And the eggs and tins were so very welcome. I did feel I must write and tell you how exceedingly grateful we all are for your kindness and generosity.

We all hope that you will be able to come to England one of these days. We should do our best to make your trip a happy one.

Sincerely,

Megan Wells

Tunbridge Road
Southend-On-Sea
Essex

5TH APRIL, 1951

Dear Miss Hanff:

For nearly two years I have been working as a cataloguer at Marks & Co, and would like to thank you very much for my share-out in the parcels which you've been sending.

I live with my great-aunt who is 75, and I think that if you had seen the look of delight on her face when I brought home the meat and the tin of tongue, you would have realized just how grateful we are. It's certainly good to know that someone so many miles away can be so kind and generous to people they haven't even seen, and I think that everyone in the firm feels the same.

If at any time you know of anything that you would like sent over from London, I will be most happy to see to it for you.

Sincerely,

Bill Humphries

MARKS & CO., Booksellers
84, Charing Cross Road
London, W.C. 2

9TH APRIL, 1951

Miss Helene Hanff
14 East 95th Street
New York 28, New York
U.S.A.

Dear Miss Hanff,

I expect you are getting a bit worried that we have not written to thank you for your parcels and are probably thinking that we are an ungrateful lot. The truth is that I have been chasing round the country in and out of various stately homes of England trying to buy a few books to fill up our sadly depleted stock. My wife was starting to call me the lodger who just went home for bed and breakfast, but of course when I arrived home with a nice piece of MEAT, to say nothing of dried eggs and ham, then she thought I was a fine fellow and all was forgiven. It is a long time since we saw so much meat all in one piece.

We should like to express our appreciation in some way or other, so we are sending by Book Post today a little book which I hope you will like. I remember you asked me for a volume of Elizabethan love poems some time ago – well, this the nearest I can get to it.

Yours faithfully,

Frank Doel
For MARKS & CO.

CARD ENCLOSED WITH *ELIZABETHAN POETS:*

To Helene Hanff, with best wishes and grateful thanks for many kindnesses, from all at 84, Charing Cross Road, London.

April, 1951

14 East 95th St.
New York City

APRIL 16, 1951

To All at 84, Charing Cross Road:

Thank you for the beautiful book. I've never owned a book before with pages edged all round in gold. Would you believe it arrived on my birthday?

I wish you hadn't been so over-courteous about putting the inscription on a card instead of on the flyleaf. It's the bookseller coming out in you all, you were afraid you'd decrease its value. You would have increased it for the present owner. (And possibly for the future owner. I love inscriptions on flyleaves and notes in margins, I like the comradely sense of turning pages someone else turned, and reading passages some one long gone has called my attention to.)

And why didn't you sign your names? I expect Frank wouldn't let you, he probably doesn't want me writing love letters to anybody but him.

I send you greetings from America — faithless friend that she is, pouring millions into rebuilding Japan and Germany while letting England starve. Some day, God willing, I'll get over there and apologize personally for my country's sins (and by the time i come home my country will certainly have to apologize for mine).

Thank you again for the beautiful book, I shall try very hard not to get gin and ashes all over it, it's really much too fine for the likes of me.

Yours,

Helene Hanff

Backstage, London
SEPTEMBER 10, 1951

Dearheart –

It is the loveliest old shop straight out of Dickens, you would go absolutely out of your mind over it.

There are stalls outside and I stopped and leafed through a few things just to establish myself as a browser before wandering in. It's dim inside, you smell the shop before you see it, it's a lovely smell. I can't articulate it easily, but it combines must and dust and age, and walls of wood and floors of wood. Toward the back of the shop at the left there's a desk with a work-lamp on it, a man was sitting there, he was about fifty with a Hogarth nose, he looked up and said 'Good afternoon?' in a North Country accent and I said I just wanted to browse and he said please do.

The shelves go on forever. They go up to the ceiling and they're very old and kind of grey, like old oak that has absorbed so much dust over the years they no longer are their true color. There's a print section, or rather a long print table, with Cruikshank and Rackham and Spy and all those old wonderful English caricaturists and illustrators that I'm not smart enough to know a lot about, and there are some lovely old, old illustrated magazines.

I stayed for about half an hour hoping your Frank or one of the girls would turn up, but it was one-ish when I went in, I gather they were all out to lunch and I couldn't stay any longer.

As you see, the notices were not sensational but we're told they're good enough to assure us a few months' run, so I went apartment-hunting yesterday and found a nice little 'bed-sitter' in Knightsbridge, I don't have the address here, I'll send it or you can call my mother.

We have no food problems, we eat in restaurants and hotels, the best places like Claridge's get all the roast beef and chops they want. The prices are astronomical but the exchange rate is so good we can afford it. Of course if I were the English I would loathe us, instead of which they are absolutely wonderful to us, we're invited to everybody's home and everybody's club.

The only thing we can't get is sugar or sweets in any form, for which I personally thank God, I intend to lose ten pounds over here.

Write me.

Love, *Maxine*

14 East 95th St.

SEPTEMBER 15, 1951

Maxine, bless your golden heart, what a peachy description, you write better than I do.

I called your mother for your address, she said to tell you the sugar cubes and Nestle bars are on the way, I thought you were dieting?

I don't like to sound bitter, but I would like to know what YOU ever did that the good Lord lets YOU browse around my bookshop while I'm stuck on 95th St. writing the TV 'Adventures of Ellery Queen.' Did I tell you we're not allowed to use a lipstick-stained cigarette for a clue? We're sponsored by the Bayuk Cigar Co. and we're not allowed to mention the word 'cigarette.' We can have ashtrays on the set but they can't have any cigarette butts in them. They can't have cigar butts either, they're not pretty. All an ashtray can have in it is a wrapped, unsmoked Bayuk cigar.

And you hobnobbing with Gieguld at Claridge's.

Write me about London – the tube, the Inns of Court, Mayfair, the corner where the Globe Theatre stood, anything, I'm not fussy. Write me about Knightbridge, it sounds green and gracious in Eric Coates' London Suite. Or London Again Suite.

xxxx

hh

14 East 95th St.
OCTOBER 15, 1951

WHAT KIND OF A PEPYS' DIARY DO YOU CALL THIS?

this is not pepys' diary, this is some busybody editor's miserable collection of EXCERPTS from pepys' diary may he rot.

i could just spit.

where is jan. 12, 1668, where his wife chased him out of bed and round the bedroom with a red-hot poker?

where is sir w. pen's son that was giving everybody so much trouble with his Quaker notions? ONE mention does he get in this whole pseudo-book, and me from philadelphia.

i enclose two limp singles, i will make do with this thing till you find me a real Pepys. THEN i will rip up this ersatz book, page by page, AND WRAP THINGS IN IT.

HH

P.S. Fresh eggs or powdered for Xmas? I know the powdered last longer but 'fresh farm eggs flown from Denmark' have got to taste better, you want to take a vote on it?

MARKS & CO., Booksellers
84, Charing Cross Road
London, W.C. 2

20TH OCTOBER, 1951

Miss Helene Hanff
14 East 95th Street
New York 28, New York
U.S.A.

Dear Miss Hanff,

First of all, let me apologize for the Pepys. I was honestly under the impression that it was the complete Braybrooke edition and I can understand how you must have felt when you found your favourite passages missing. I promise to look at the next reasonably priced copy that comes along, and if it contains the passage you mention in your letter I will send it along.

I am glad to say I have managed to dig out a few books for you from a private library that we have just bought. There is a Leigh Hunt which includes most of the essays you like, also a Vulgate New Testament which I hope will be O.K. I have also included a Dictionary to the Vulgate which you might find useful. There is also a volume of 20th century English essays, though it contains only one by Hilaire Belloc and nothing to do with bathrooms. Enclosed is our invoice for 17s 6d. or approximately $2.50, all that is due us on the books as you had a credit balance with us of nearly $2.00.

About the eggs – I have talked to the rest of the inmates here and we all seem to think that the fresh ones would be nicer. As you say, they would not last so long but they would taste so much better.

We are all hoping for better times after the Election. If Churchill and Company get in, as I think and hope they will, it will cheer everyone up immensely.

With best wishes,
Yours sincerely,

Frank Doel
For MARKS & CO.

14 East 95th St.
New York City

NOVEMBER 2, 1951

Dear Speed —

You dizzy me, rushing Leigh Hunt and the Vulgate over here whizbang like that. You probably don't realize it, but it's hardly more than two years since I ordered them. You keep going at this rate you're gonna give yourself a heart attack.

that's mean. You go to so much trouble for me and i never even thank you, i just needle you, it's mean. I really am grateful for all the pains you take for me. I enclose three dollars, I'm sorry about the top one, I spilled coffee on it and it wouldn't sponge off but I think it's still good, you can still read it.

Do you carry hard-cover vocal scores, by any chance? Like Bach's St. Matthew Passion and Handel's Messiah? I could probably get them here at Schirmer's, but they're 50 cold blocks from where I live so I thought I'd ask you first.

Congratulations on Churchill & Co., hope he loosens up your rations a little.

Is your name Welsh?

HH

MARKS & CO., Booksellers
84, Charing Cross Road
London, W.C. 2

7TH DECEMBER, 1951

Miss Helene Hanff
14 East 95th Street
New York 28, New York

Dear Miss Hanff,

You will be glad to know that the two boxes of eggs and the tins of tongue have all arrived safely and once again we all wish to thank you most sincerely for your extreme generosity. Mr. Martin, one of the older members of our staff, has been on the sick list for some time and we therefore let him have the lion's share of the eggs, one whole boxful in fact, and of course he was delighted to get them. The tins of tongue look very inviting and will be a welcome addition to our larders, and in my case will be put on one side for a special occasion.

I enquired at all the local music shops but was unable to get the *Messiah* or Bach's *St. Matthew Passion* in stiff covers in clean, secondhand copies, and then I found they were available from the publisher in new editions. Their prices seemed a bit high, but I thought I had better get them and they have been sent by Book Post a few days ago, so should arrive any day now. Our invoice, total £1/10/ = ($4.20) is enclosed with the books.

We are sending you a little gift for Christmas. It is linen and we do hope you will not have to pay any duty on it. We will mark it 'Christmas Gift' and keep our fingers crossed. Anyway, we hope you will like it and accept it with our sincere best wishes for Christmas and the coming year.

My name is certainly not of Welsh origin. As it is pronounced to rhyme with the French word 'Noel,' I think there may be a possibility that it originated in France.

Yours sincerely,

Frank Doel
For MARKS & CO.

[CARD ENCLOSED WITH HEAVILY WORKED,
HAND-EMBROIDERED IRISH LINEN
TABLECLOTH]:

Christmas Greetings
and
All Good Wishes for the
New Year
from

| *Geo. Martin* | *Megan Wells* | *W. Humphries* |
| *Cecily Farr* | *Frank Doel* | *J. Pemberton* |

MARKS & CO., Booksellers
84, Charing Cross Road
London, W.C. 2

15TH JANUARY, 1952

Miss Helene Hanff
14 East 95th Street
New York 28, New York
U.S.A.

Dear Miss Hanff,

First of all, we were all so glad that you liked the cloth. It gave us a lot of pleasure to send it and it was one little way of thanking you for all your kind gifts over the last few years. You may be interested to know that it was embroidered, quite recently, by an old lady of over eighty who lives in the flat (apartment) next door to me. She lives all by herself and does quite a lot of needlework as a hobby. She does not often part with any of her work, but my wife managed to persuade her to sell this cloth, and I think she also made her a present of some of the dried egg you sent us which helped a lot.

If you must clean your Grolier Bible, we should advise ordinary soap and water. Put a teaspoonful of soda in a pint of warm water and use a soapy sponge. I think you will find this will remove the dirt and you can then polish it with a little lanolin.

J. Pemberton is a lady and the J. is for Janet.

With best wishes from all of us for the coming year.

Faithfully yours,

Frank Doel

37 Oakfield Court
Haslemere Road
Crouch End
London, N. 8

20–1–52

Dear Miss Hanff:

For a long time I have wanted to write to you to thank you for my family's share in the wonderful food parcels you've been sending to Marks & Co. Now I have an excuse as Frank tells me you want to know the name and address of the old lady who embroidered your cloth. It was beautiful, wasn't it?

Her name is Mrs. Boulton and she lives next door at No. 36 Oakfield Court. She was thrilled to know that her cloth had crossed the Atlantic and I know she would be delighted to hear how much you admired it.

Thank you for wanting to send us more dried egg, but we still have a bit left to see us through until spring. Some time between April and September we usually manage all right for eggs, as they go off ration for a time and then we do a bit of trading with the tins, as once for a special occasion I traded a tin of dried egg for a pair of nylons. Not quite legal but it does help us to get by!

I will send you snaps of my happy family one of these days. Our oldest girl was twelve last August, by name Sheila, who by the way is my ready-made daughter, as Frank lost his first wife during the war. Our youngest, Mary, was four last week. Last May, Sheila announced at school that she was sending Mummy and Daddy an anniversary card and told the nuns (it's a convent) that we had been married four years. It took a bit of explaining as you can imagine.

I will close this with all good wishes for the New Year and especially a wish that we may see you in England one of these days.

Sincerely,

Nora Doel

36 Oakfield Court
Haslemere Road
Crouch End
London, N. 8

JAN. 29TH, 1952

Dear Miss Hanff:

Thank you very much for your letter, I appreciate your kindness in telling me the cloth I worked has given you so much pleasure. I only wish I could do more. I expect Mrs. Doel has told you I am getting on in years so I am unable to do as much as I used to. It is always a joy to me when my work gets into the hands of someone who appreciates it.

I see Mrs. Doel most days, she often speaks of you. Perhaps I may see you if you come to England.

Again thanking you,

Yours very sincerely,

Mary Boulton

14 East 95th St.

FEBRUARY 9, 1952

Now listen, Maxine —

I just talked to your mother, she says you don't think the show will run another month and she says you took two dozen pairs of nylons over there, so do me a favor. As soon as the closing notice goes up take four pairs of nylons around to the bookshop for me, give them to Frank Doel, tell him they're for the three girls and Nora (his wife).

Your mother says I am NOT to enclose any money for them, she got them last summer at a close-out sale at Saks, they were very cheap and she'll donate them to the shop, she's feeling pro-British.

Wait'll you see what the shop sent me for Christmas. It's an Irish linen tablecloth, the color of thick cream, hand-embroidered in an old-fashioned pattern of leaves and flowers, every flower worked in a different colour and shaded from very pale to very deep, you never saw anything like it. My junk-shop drop-leaf table CERTainly never saw anything like it, i get this urge to shake out my flowing Victorian sleeve and lift a graceful arm to pour tea from an imaginary Georgian teapot, we're gonna play Stanislavski with it the minute you get home.

Ellery raised me to $250 a script, if it keeps up till June *I* may get to England and browse around my bookshop myself. If I have the nerve. I write them the most outrageous letters from a safe 3,000 miles away. i'll probably walk in there one day and walk right out again without telling them who i am.

I fail to see why you did not understand that groceryman, he did *not* call it 'ground ground nuts,' he called it ground ground-nuts' which is the only really SENSible thing to call it. Peanuts grow in the GROUND and are therefore GROUND-nuts, and after you take them out of the ground you grind them up and you have *ground* ground-nuts, which is a much more accurate name than peanut butter, you just don't understand English.

XXX

h. hanff
girl etymologist

P.S. Your mother is setting out bravely this morning to look at an apartment for you on 8th Avenue in the 50's because you told her to look in the theatre district. Maxine you know perfectly well your mother is not equipped to look at ANYTHING on 8th Avenue.

14 East 95th St.

FEBRUARY 9, 1952

SLOTH:

i could ROT over here before you'd send me anything to read. i oughta run straight down to brentano's which i would if anything i wanted was in print.

You may add Walton's Lives to the list of books you aren't sending me. It's against my principles to buy a book I haven't read, it's like buying a dress you haven't tried on, but you can't even get Walton's Lives in a library over here.

You can look at it. They have it down at the 42nd street branch. But not to take *home*! the lady said to me, shocked. eat it here, just sit right down in room 315 and read the whole book without a cup of coffee, a cigarette or air.

Doesn't matter, Q quoted enough of it so i know i'll like it. anything he liked i'll like except if it's fiction. i never can get interested in things that didn't happen to people who never lived.

what do you do with yourself all day, sit in the back of the store and read? why don't you try selling a book to somebody?

> *MISS Hanff to you.*
> (I'm helene only to my
> FRIENDS)

p.s. tell the girls and nora if all goes well they're getting nylons for Lent.

MARKS & CO., Booksellers
84, Charing Cross Road
London, W.C. 2

14TH FEBRUARY, 1952

Miss Helene Hanff
14 East 95th Street
New York 28, New York
U.S.A.

Dear Helene

I quite agree it is time we dropped the 'Miss' when writing to you. I am not really so stand–offish as you may have been led to believe, but as copies of letters I have written to you go into the office files the formal address seemed more appropriate. But as this letter has nothing to do with books, there will be no copy.

We are quite at a loss to know how you managed the nylons which appeared this noon as if by magic. All I can tell you is that when I came back from lunch they were on my desk with a note reading: 'From Helene Hanff.' No one seems to know how or when they arrived. The girls are very thrilled and I believe they are planning to write to you themselves.

I am sorry to say that our friend Mr. George Martin who has been so ill for some time passed away in hospital last week. He was with the firm a great number of years, so with that loss and the King dying so suddenly as well, we are rather a mournful crowd at the moment.

I don't see how we can ever repay you for your many kind gifts. All I can say is, if you ever decide to make the trip to England, there will be a bed for you at 37 Oakfield Court for as long as you care to stay.

With best wishes from us all,

Frank Doel

14 East 95th St.
New York City

MARCH 3, 1952

Oh my, i do bless you for that Walton's *Lives*. It's incredible that a book published in 1840 can be in such perfect condition more than a hundred years later. Such beautiful, mellow rough-cut pages they are, I do feel for poor William T. Gordon who wrote his name in it in 1841, what a crummy lot of descendants he must have – to sell it to you casually for nothing. Boy, I'd like to have run barefoot through THEIR library before they sold it.

fascinating book to read, did you know John Donne eloped with the boss's highborn daughter and landed in the Tower for it and starved and starved and THEN got religion, my word.

Now listen, I'm enclosing a $5 bill, that *Lives* makes me very dissatisfied with my *Angler* which I bought before I met you. It's one of those hard-faced American Classics-for-the-Masses editions, Izaak just hates it, he says he's not going around looking like THAT for the rest of my life, so use the extra $2.50 for a nice English *Angler*, please.

you better watch out, i'm coming over there in 53 if ellery is renewed. i'm gonna climb up that victorian book-ladder and disturb the dust on the top shelves and everybody's decorum. Or didn't I ever tell you I write arty murders for Ellery Queen on television? All my scripts have artistic backgrounds – ballet, concert hall, opera – and all the suspects and corpses are cultured, maybe I'll do one about the rare book business in your honor, you want to be the murderer or the corpse?

hh

36 Oakfield Court
Haslemere Road
Crouch End
London, N. 8

MARCH 24TH, 1952

Dear Miss Hanff:

I hardly know how to express my thanks and feelings for the lovely box of everything to eat which you have sent me which arrived today. I have never been sent a parcel before. I really don't think you should have done it. I can only say Thank you very much, I certainly will enjoy everything.

It was very kind of you to think of me in this way. I showed them all to Mrs. Doel, she thought they were lovely.

Again Thanking you very much, and best wishes,

Yours very sincerely,

Mary Boulton

MARKS & CO., Booksellers
84, Charing Cross Road
London, W.C. 2

17TH APRIL, 1952

Miss Helene Hanff
14 East 95th Street
New York 28, New York
U.S.A.

Dear Helene (you see I don't care about the files any more),

You will be pleased to know we have just purchased a private library which includes a very nice copy of Walton's *Compleat Angler* and hope to have it to send you next week, price approximately $2.25 and your credit balance with us is more than enough to cover it.

Your Ellery Queen scripts sound rather fun. I wish we could have the chance of seeing some of them on our TV over here – it wants livening up a bit (our TV I mean, not your script).

Nora and all here join me in sending our best wishes,

Yours faithfully,

Frank Doel

37 Oakfield Court
Haslemere Road
Crouch End
London, N. 8

SUNDAY, MAY 4TH, 1952

Dear Helene,

Thanks for the parcel of dried egg received on Friday and I was very glad for same, I did mention something about eggs coming off the ration, well it just hasn't happened so the powder was a godsend for our weekend cakes, etc. Frank is taking some to the shop to send to Cecily, as he keeps forgetting to bring home her address. I expect you know she has left the shop and is waiting to join her husband in the East.

I am enclosing a few snaps, Frank says none of them do him justice, he is much better-looking; but we just let him dream.

Sheila was home for a month's break and we have been gadding about a bit to the seaside for day trips and sight-seeing and must now pull in our horns a bit, as the cost of transport here is terrific. It is our ambition to have a car but they are so expensive and a decent secondhand one is dearer than a new one. The new ones are being exported and there are so few for the home market some of my friends have been waiting 5 to 7 years for a new car.

Sheila is going to say a 'jolly good prayer' for you so you may get your wish to come to England because the tin of bacon we had from you on Easter Monday was such a treat. So if 'jolly good prayers' are answered you might have a windfall and be able to come and see us soon.

Well, so long for now and thanks once again.

Nora

14 East 95th St.
New York City

MAY 11, 1952

Dear Frank:

Meant to write you the day the *Angler* arrived, just to thank you, the woodcuts alone are worth ten times the price of the book. What a weird world we live in when so beautiful a thing can be owned for life – for the price of a ticket to a Broadway movie palace, or 1/50th the cost of having one tooth capped.

Well, if your books cost what they're worth I couldn't afford them!

You'll be fascinated to learn (from me that hates novels) that I finally got round to Jane Austen and went out of my mind over *Pride & Prejudice* which I can't bring myself to take back to the library till you find me a copy of my own.

Regards to Nora and the wage-slaves.

HH

37 Oakfield Court
Haslemere Road
Crouch End
London, N. 8

24–8–52

Dear Helene:

Here I am again to thank you most gratefully for our share in the wonderful parcels you so kindly sent to Marks & Co. I wish I could send you something in return.

By the way, Helene, this week we have become the proud possessors of a car, not a new one, mind you, but it goes and that's what matters isn't it? Now maybe you will tell us you're paying us a call?

Mrs. Boulton put up two cousins of mine who came down from Scotland for a couple of weeks and they were very comfortable. She bedded them and I fed them. Now if by any chance you can manage the fare to England next year for the Coronation, Mrs. Boulton will see that you have a bed.

Well, I'll say so long for now and send you our best wishes and thanks once again for the meat and eggs.

Yours sincerely,

Nora

MARKS & CO., Booksellers
84, Charing Cross Road
London, W.C. 2

26TH AUGUST, 1952

Miss Helene Hanff
14 East 95th Street
New York 28, New York
U.S.A.

Dear Helene,

I am writing once again to thank you on behalf of all here for your three very exciting parcels which arrived a few days ago. It is really too good of you to spend your hard-earned cash on us in this way and I can assure you that we do appreciate your kind thoughts of us.

We had about thirty volumes of Loeb Classics come in a few days ago but alas, no Horace, Sappho or Catullus.

I am taking a couple of weeks' holiday commencing September 1, but as I have just bought a car we are completely 'broke' so will have to take things easy. Nora has a sister who lives by the sea so we are hoping she will take pity on us and invite us to stay with her. It is my first car so we are all very thrilled with it – even though it is an old 1939 model. So long as it gets us to places without breaking down too often we shall be quite happy.

With all good wishes,

Frank Doel

14 East 95th St.
New York City

September 18, 1952

Frankie, guess who came while you were away on vacation? SAM PEPYS! Please thank whoever mailed him for me, he came a week ago, stepped out of four pages of some tabloid, three honest navy-blue volumes of him; I read the tabloid over lunch and started Sam after dinner.

He says to tell you he's overJOYED to be here, he was previously owned by a slob who never even bothered to cut the pages. I'm wrecking them, it's the thinnest India paper I ever saw. We call it 'onion skin' over here and it's a good name for it. But heavier paper would have taken up six or seven volumes so I'm grateful for the India. I only have three bookshelves and very few books left to throw out.

I houseclean my books every spring and throw out those I'm never going to read again like I throw out old clothes I'm never going to wear again. It shocks everybody. My friends are peculiar about books. They read all the best sellers, they get through them as fast as possible, I think they skip a lot. And they NEVER read anything a second time so they don't remember a word of it a year later. But they are profoundly shocked to see me drop a book in the wastebasket or give it away. The way they look at it, you buy a book, you read it, you put it on the shelf, you never open it again for the rest of your life but YOU DON'T THROW IT OUT! NOT IF IT HAS A HARD COVER ON IT! Why not? I personally can't think of anything less sancrosanct than a bad book or even a mediocre book.

Trust you and Nora had a fine holiday. Mine was spent in Central Park, I had a month's vacation from joey, my dear little dentist, he went on his honeymoon. i financed the honeymoon. Did I tell you he told me last spring I had to have all my teeth capped or all my teeth out? I decided to have them capped as I have got used to having teeth. But the cost is simply astronomical. So Elizabeth will have to ascend the throne without me, teeth are all I'm going to see crowned for the next couple of years.

i do NOT intend to stop buying books, however, you have to have

SOMEthing. Will you see if you can find me Shaw's dramatic criticism please? and also his music criticism? I think there are several volumes, just send whatever you can find, now listen, Frankie, it's going to be a long cold winter and I baby-sit in the evenings AND I NEED READING MATTER, NOW DON'T START SITTING AROUND, GO FIND ME SOME BOOKS.

hh

14 East 95th St.
New York City

DECEMBER 12, 1952

To 'her friends at 84, Charing Cross Road':

The Book-Lovers' Anthology stepped out of its wrappings, all gold-embossed leather and gold-tipped pages, easily the most beautiful book I own including the Newman first edition. It looks too new and pristine ever to have been read by anyone else, but it has been: it keeps falling open at the most delightful places as the ghost of its former owner points me to things I've never read before. Like Tristram Shandy's description of his father's remarkable library which 'contains every book and treatise which had ever been wrote upon the subject of great noses.' (Frank! Go find me *Tristram Shandy*!)

I do think it's a very uneven exchange of Christmas presents. You'll eat yours up in a week and have nothing left to show for it by New Year's Day. I'll have mine till the day I die — and die happy in the knowledge that I'm leaving it behind for someone else to love. I shall sprinkle pale pencil marks through it pointing out the best passages to some book-lover yet unborn.

Thank you all. Happy New Year.

Helene

37 Oakfield Court
Haslemere Road
Crouch End
London, N. 8

17–12–52

Dear Helene:

So sorry I have been so long in dropping you a line. I hope you haven't taken it too badly about Adlai. Maybe he will have better luck next time.

Mrs. Boulton says she will gladly put you up next summer if she is still alive, she says, but I don't know of anyone of her age who is more so, I feel sure she will live to be a hundred. Anyway, we can always fix you up somewhere.

Thanks for the good things you sent us for Christmas, you are much too kind, Helene! – and if those bodies at Marks & Co. don't give you a banquet when you come over next year, well, they deserve to be shot.

I hope you have a lovely Christmas. Cheerio for now and all our best wishes and thanks.

God bless!

Nora

14 East 95th St.

MAY 3, 1953

Frankie, you'll DIE when I tell you —

First, enclosed find $3, P-and-P arrived looking exactly as Jane ought to look, soft leather, slim and impeccable.

Now then. Ellery went off the air and I was shuffling around piling up dentist bills and feeling pale when I was invited to write an outline for a TV show which dramatizes incidents from the lives of famous people. So I rushed home and did an outline of an incident from-the-life-of-a-famous-person and sent it in and they bought it and I wrote the script and they liked it and they're gonna give me more work in the fall.

And whaddaya think I dramatized? JOHN DONNE ELOPING WITH THE BOSS'S DAUGHTER out of Walton's Lives. Nobody who watches television has the slightest idea who John Donne was, but thanks to Hemingway *everybody* knows No Man Is An Island, all I had to do was work that in and it was sold.

So that's how John Donne made the 'Hallmark Hall of Fame' and paid for all the books you ever sent me and five teeth.

I plan to crawl out of bed before dawn on Coronation Day to attend the ceremony by radio. Will be thinking of you all.

cheers

hh

MARKS & CO., Booksellers
84, Charing Cross Road
London, W.C. 2

11TH JUNE, 1953

Miss Helene Hanff
14 East 95th Street
New York 28, New York
U.S.A.

Dear Helene,

Just a note to let you know that your parcel arrived safely on June 1, just in time for our Coronation Day celebrations. We had a number of friends at home to watch TV on the day, and so the ham was most welcome to provide them with something to eat. It was delicious, and we all drank your health as well as the Queen's.

It was most kind of you to spend your hard-earned money on us like this, and the rest of the staff join me in saying thanks a lot.

With very best wishes,
Yours sincerely,

Frank Doel

Boldmere Road
Eastcote
Pinner
Middlesex

23–9–53

Helene dear,

Am dashing this off to say you must send *nothing at all* to the shop for Christmas, everything is now off rations and even nylons are available in all the better shops. Please save your money as the most important thing after your dentist is your trip to England. Only don't come in '54 as I shall be out of the country, come in '55 when we shall be back and you can stay with us.

Doug writes that our 'call' may come at any moment as we are next in line for married quarters. The children and I are hoping to join him before Christmas. He is well and happy on Bahrein Island in the middle of the Persian Gulf (if you've got an atlas) but will return to the RAF base at Habbaniya in Iraq when our quarters are available and we will join him there, all being well.

Write again soon. Even if I do 'pop off' Mother will forward your letter.

Love and best wishes –

Cecily

14 East 95th St.

SEPTEMBER 2, 1955

DO YOU MEAN TO SIT THERE AND TELL ME YOU'VE
BEEN PUBLISHING THESE MAMMOTH CATALOGUES ALL
THESE YEARS AND THIS IS THE FIRST TIME YOU EVER
BOTHERED TO SEND ME ONE? THOU VARLET?

Don't remember which restoration playwright called everybody a
Varlet, i always wanted to use it in a sentence.

As it happens, the only thing which MIGHT interest me is the
Catullus, it's not the Loeb Classics but it sounds like it'll do. If you still
have it, mail it and I'll send you the −/6s/2d as soon as you translate
it, Kay and Brian moved to the suburbs and left me without a
translator.

I shall be obliged if you will send Nora and the girls to church
every Sunday for the next month to pray for the continued health and
strength of the messrs. gilliam, reese, snider, campanella, robinson,
hodges, furillo, podres, newcombe and labine, collectively known as
The Brooklyn Dodgers. If they lose this World Series I shall Do
Myself In and then where will you be?

Have you got De Tocqueville's Journey to America? Somebody
borrowed mine and never gave it back. Why is it that people who
wouldn't dream of stealing anything else think it's perfectly all right to
steal books?

Regards to Megan if she's still there. And what's become of Cecily,
is she back from Iraq?

hh

MARKS & CO., Booksellers
84, Charing Cross Road
London, W.C. 2

13TH DECEMBER, 1955

Miss Helene Hanff
14 East 95th Street
New York 28, N.Y.
U.S.A.

Dear Helene,

I feel very guilty about not writing to you before this, but you can put it down to a dose of 'flu which kept me away from the shop for a couple of weeks and a sudden rush of work since I came back.

About the Catullus in our catalogue. This was already sold before we received your letter but I have sent you an edition which contains the Latin text with a verse translation by Sir Richard Burton and also a prose translation by Leonard Smithers, printed in large type, and all for $3.78. The bind is not very handsome but it's a good clean copy. We have no edition of De Toqueville but will keep looking for one for you.

Megan is still here but planning to go to South Africa to live, we are all trying to talk her out of it. We have heard nothing from Cecily Farr since she went out to the East to join her husband, though they were only to be gone a year.

I shall be only too pleased to root for the Brooklyn Dodgers if you will reciprocate with a few cheers for THE SPURS (the Tottenham Hotspur Football Club to the uninitiated), who are at present languishing next to the bottom of the League. However, the season does not finish until next April so they have plenty of time to get themselves out of the mess.

Nora and all here join me in sending our best wishes for Christmas and the New Year.

Sincerely,

Frank Doel

14 e. 95th st.
nyc

JAN. 4, 1956

i write you from under the bed where that catullus drove me.

i mean it PASSETH understanding.

Up till now, the only Richard Burton I ever heard of is a handsome young actor I've seen in a couple of British movies and I wish I'd kept it that way. This one got knighted for turning Catullus – caTULLus – into Victorian hearts-and-flowers.

and poor little mr. smithers must have been afraid his mother was going to read it, he likes to KILL himself cleaning it all up.

all right, let's just you go find me a nice plain Latin Catullus, I bought myself a Cassell's dictionary, I'll work out the hard passages by myself.

WILL YOU TELL MEGAN WELLS SHE IS OUT OF HER COTTONPICKING MIND? if she's that bored with civilization why doesn't she just move to a siberian salt mine?

certainly, certainly, glad to root for anything with Hotspur in it.

Have been socking money in the savings bank for next summer, if TV keeps feeding me till then I'm finally coming over, I want to see the shop and St. Paul's and Parliament and the Tower and Covent Garden and the Old Vic and Old Mrs. Boulton.

i enclose a sawbuck for that thing, that catullus, bound in white Limp – mit-white-silk-bookmark-yet, frankie, where do you FIND these things?!

hh

MARKS & CO., Booksellers
84, Charing Cross Road
London, W.C. 2

16TH MARCH, 1956

Miss Helene Hanff
14 East 95th Street
New York 28, N.Y.
U.S.A.

Dear Helene

I am sorry to have been so long in writing, but until today we have had nothing to send you and I thought it best to wait a decent interval after the Catullus incident before writing.

We have finally managed to find a very nice edition of *Tristram Shandy* with the Robb illustrations, price approximatedly $2.75. We have also acquired a copy of Plato's *Four Socratic Dialogues*, translated by Benjamin Jowett, Oxford, 1903. Would you like this for $1.00? You have a $1.22 credit with us so the balance due on the two books would be $2.53.

We are waiting to hear whether you are finally coming to England this summer. Both the girls are away at school so you will have your choice of beds at 37 Oakfield Court. I am sorry to say that Mrs. Boulton has been taken to a home, it was rather a sad day but at least she will be looked after there.

Sincerely

Frank Doel

14 East 95th St.
New York City

JUNE 1, 1956

Dear Frank:

Brian introduced me to Kenneth Grahame's *Wind in the Willows* and I have to have this – with the Shepard illustrations please – but DON'T MAIL IT, JUST HOLD IT FOR ME TILL SEPTEMBER and then mail it to the new address.

The sky fell on us in this cozy brownstone, we got eviction notices last month, they're renovating the building. I decided the time had come to get me a real apartment with real furniture, and in my right mind and shaking all over I went around to the construction site of a new building going up over on 2nd Avenue and signed a lease on a $2\frac{1}{2}$ ('bed-sitter') apartment that isn't even there yet. I am now racing around buying furniture and bookshelves and wall-to-wall carpet with all my England money, but all my life I've been stuck in dilapidated furnished rooms and cockroachy kitchens and I want to live like a lady even if it means putting off England till it's paid for.

Meanwhile the landlord thinks we're not moving out fast enough and is encouraging us by firing the super, leaving nobody to give us hot water or take the garbage out, and also by ripping out the mailboxes, the hall light fixtures and (as of this week) the wall between my kitchen and bathroom. all this and the dodgers disintegrating before my very eyes, nobody-knows-the-trouble-i-see.

Oh, the new address:

AFTER SEPTEMBER 1:
305 E. 72nd St., New York, N.Y. 21

MARKS & CO., Booksellers
84, Charing Cross Road
London, W.C. 2

3RD MAY, 1957

Miss Helene Hanff
305 East 72nd Street
New York 21, N.Y.
U.S.A.

Dear Helene,

Prepare yourself for a shock. ALL THREE of the books you requested in your last letter are on the way to you and should arrive in a week or so. Don't ask how we managed it – it's just a part of the Marks service. Our bill is enclosed herewith showing balance due of $5.00.

Two of your friends dropped in to see us a few days ago and now I have forgotten their names – a young married couple and very charming. Unfortunately they only had time to stop and smoke a cigarette as they were off again on their travels next morning.

We seem to have had more American visitors than ever this year, including hundreds of lawyers who march around with a large card pinned to their clothes stating their home town and name. They all seem to be enjoying their trip so you will have to manage it next year.

With best wishes from us all,

Frank

POSTCARD MAILED FROM STRATFORD-UPON-AVON, MAY 6, 1957

You might have warned us! We walked into your bookstore and said we were friends of yours and were nearly mobbed. Your Frank wanted to take us home for the weekend. Mr. Marks came out from the back of the store just to shake hands with friends-of-Miss-Hanff, everybody in the place wanted to wine and dine us, we barely got out alive.

Thought you'd like to see the house where your Sweet-William was born.

On to Paris, then Copenhagen, home on the 23rd.

Love,

Ginny and Ed

Helene Hanff   *305 East 72nd Street, New York 21, N.Y.*

JANUARY 10, 1958

Hey, Frankie –

Tell Nora to bring her address book up to date, your Christmas card just got here, she sent it to 14 e 95th. st.

Don't know whether I ever told you how dearly I love that *Tristram Shandy*, the Robb illustrations are enchanting, Uncle Toby would have been pleased. Now then. In the back, there's a list of other Macdonald Illustrated Classics which includes the Essays of Elia. I'd love to have this in the Macdonald edition – or any nice edition. If it's Reasonable, of course. Nothing's cheap any more, it's 'reasonable.' Or 'sensibly priced.' There's a building going up across the street, the sign over it says:

> 'One and Two Bedroom Apartments
> At Rents That Make Sense.'

Rents do NOT make sense. And prices do not sit around being reasonable about anything, no matter what it says in the ad – which isn't an ad any more, it's A Commercial.

i go through life watching the english language being raped before me face. like miniver cheevy, i was born too late.

and like miniver cheevy i cough and call it fate and go on drinking.

hh

p.s. whatever became of plato's minor dialogues?

MARKS & CO., Booksellers
84, Charing Cross Road
London, W.C. 2

11TH MARCH, 1958

Miss Helene Hanff
305 East 72nd Street
New York 21, New York
U.S.A.

Dear Helene,

I must apologize for having taken so long to answer your last letter but we have had rather a hectic time. Nora has been in hospital for the past several months and I have had my hands full at home. She is almost fully recovered and will be coming home in a week or so. It has been a trying time for us but thanks to our National Health Service it hasn't cost us a penny.

About the Macdonald Classics, we do get a few from time to time but have none at the moment. We had several copies of Lamb's *Essays of Elia* earlier on but they were snapped up during the holiday rush. I am off on a buying trip next week and will look out for one for you. Not forgetting the Plato.

We all hope you had a good holiday season and the girls apologize for sending your Christmas card to the old address.

Faithfully yours,

Frank

37 Oakfield Court
Haslemere Road
Crouch End
London, N. 8

MAY 7TH, 1958

Dear Helene,

I have to thank you for your two letters, thanks for the offer, Helene, but there is really nothing we need. I wish we had our own bookshop, then we would be able to repay your kindness by sending you a few books.

I am enclosing a few recent snaps of my happy family, I wish they were better but we seem to have given all the best ones to relatives. You will probably notice how very much alike Sheila and Mary are. It is rather noticeable. Frank says that Mary, as she has been growing up, is exactly like Sheila was at the same age. Sheila's mother was Welsh and I hail from the Emerald Isles so they both must resemble Frank but they are better-looking than he is, though of course he won't admit this!

If you knew how much I hate writing you would feel sorry for me. Frank says for one who talks so much I put up a very bad show on paper.

Again thanks for the letters and good wishes.

God bless!

Nora

MARKS & CO., Booksellers
84, Charing Cross Road
London, W.C. 2

18TH MARCH, 1959

Miss Helene Hanff
305 East 72nd Street
New York 21, New York
U.S.A.

Dear Helene,

I don't know how to break the bad news, but two days after offering you the *Shorter Oxford Dictionary* for your friend, a man came in and bought it when my back was turned. I have delayed replying to your letter in the hope that another one would come along, but no luck yet. I am terribly sorry to disappoint your friend but you can blame it all on me as I really ought to have reserved it.

We are sending off by Book Post today the Johnson on Shakespeare, which we happened to have in stock in the Oxford Press edition with introduction by Walter Raleigh. It is only $1.05 and your balance with us was more than enough to cover it.

We are all sorry to hear that your television shows have moved to Hollywood and that one more summer will bring us every American tourist but the one we want to see. I can quite understand your refusal to leave New York for Southern California. We have our fingers crossed for you and hope that some sort of work will turn up soon.

Sincerely,

Frank

Helene Hanff   *305 East 72nd Street, New York 21, N.Y.*

___

AUGUST 15, 1959

sir:

i write to say i have got work.

i won it, i won a $5,000 Grant-in-Aid off CBS, it's supposed to support me for a year while I write American History dramatizations. I am starting with a script about New York under seven years of British Occupation and i MARVEL at how i rise above it to address you in friendly and forgiving fashion, your behavior over here from 1776 to 1783 was simply FILTHY.

Is there such a thing as a modern-English version of the Canterbury Tales? I have these guilts about never having read Chaucer but I was talked out of learning Early Anglo-Saxon/Middle English by a friend who had to take it for her Ph.D. They told her to write an essay in Early Anglo-Saxon on any-subject-of-her-own-choosing. 'Which is all very well,' she said bitterly, 'but the only essay subject you can find enough Early Anglo-Saxon words for is "How to Slaughter a Thousand Men in a Mead Hall."'

She also filled me in on Beowulf and his illegitimate son Sidwith – or is it Widsith? she says it's not worth reading so that killed my interest in the entire subject, just send me a modern Chaucer.

love to nora.

hh

MARKS & CO., Booksellers
84, Charing Cross Road
London, W.C. 2

2ND SEPTEMBER, 1959

Miss Helene Hanff
305 East 72nd Street
New York 21, New York
U.S.A.

Dear Helene,

We were all delighted to hear that you've won a Grant-in-Aid and are working again. We are prepared to be broad-minded about your choice of subject matter, but I must tell you that one of the young inmates here confessed that until he read your letter he never knew that England had ever owned 'the States'.

With regard to Chaucer, the best scholars seem to have fought shy of putting him into modern English, but there was an edition put out by Longmans in 1934, the *Canterbury Tales* only, a modernized version by Hill, which I believe is quite good. It is (of course!) out of print and I am trying to find a nice clean secondhand copy.

Sincerely,

Frank

sunday night and a hell of a
way to start 1960.

i don't know, frankie –

Somebody gave me this book for Christmas. It's a Giant Modern Library book. Did you ever see one of those? It's less attractively bound than the Proceedings of the New York State Assembly and it weighs more. It was given to me by a gent who knows I'm fond of John Donne. The title of this book is:

The Complete Poetry
&
Selected Prose
of
JOHN DONNE
&
The Complete Poetry
of
WILLIAM BLAKE?

The question mark is mine. Will you please tell me what those two boys have in common? – except they were both English and they both Wrote? I tried reading the Introduction figuring that might explain it. The Introduction is in four parts. Parts I and II include a Professor's life of Donne mit-illustrations-from-the-author's-works-also-criticism. Part III begins – and God knows I quote – :

When, as a little boy, William Blake saw the prophet Ezekiel under
a tree amid a summer field, he was soundly trounced by his
mother.

I'm with his mother. I mean, the back of the Lord God or the face of the Virgin Mary, all right – but why the hell would anybody want to see the prophet Ezekiel?

I don't like Blake anyway, he swoons too much, it's Donne I'm writing about, I am being driven clear up the wall, Frankie, you have GOT to help me.

Here I was, curled up in my airmchair so at peace with the world, with something old and serene on the radio – Corelli or somebody – and this thing on the table. This Giant Modern Library thing. So I thought:

'I will read the three standard passages from Sermon XV aloud,' you have to read Donne aloud, it's like a Bach fugue.

Would you like to know what I went through in an innocent attempt to read three contiguous uncut passages from Sermon XV aloud?

You start with the Giant Modern Library version, you locate Sermon XV and there they are: Excerpts I, II and III – only when you get to the end of Excerpt I you discover they have deleted Jezebel off it. So you get down Donne's *Sermons*, Selected Passages (Logan Pearsall Smith) where you spend twenty minutes locating Sermon XV, Excerpt I, because by Logan Pearsall Smith it isn't Sermon XV, Excerpt I, it's Passage *126. All Must Die.* Now that you've found it, you find he also deleted Jezebel so you get down the *Complete Poetry & Selected Prose* (Nonesuch Press) but they didn't happen to Select Jezebel either, so you get down the *Oxford Book of English Prose* where you spend another twenty minutes locating it because in the *Oxford English Prose* it isn't Sermon XV, Excerpt I nor yet *126. All Must Die,* it's Passage *113. Death the Leveller.* Jezebel is there, and you read it aloud but when you get to the end you find it doesn't have either Excerpt II or III so you have to switch to one of the other three books provided you had the wit to leave all three open at the right pages which I didn't.

So break it to me gently: how hard is it going to be to find me John Donne's Complete Sermons and how much is it going to cost?

i am going to bed, i will have hideous nightmares involving huge monsters in academic robes carrying long bloody butcher knives labelled Excerpt, Selection, Passage and Abridged.

yrs,

h.hffffffffffff

MARKS & CO., Booksellers
84, Charing Cross Road
London, W.C. 2

5TH MARCH, 1960

Miss Helene Hanff
305 East 72nd Street
New York 21, New York
U.S.A.

Dear Helene,

I have delayed answering your last two letters until I had some good news to report. I have managed to obtain a copy of the Bernard Shaw–Ellen Terry correspondence. It is not a very attractive edition but it is a good clean copy and I thought I had better send it as this is quite a popular book and it might be quite some time before another copy comes along. The price is approximately $2.65 and you have a credit with us of 50 cents.

I am afraid the complete Donne *Sermons* can be had only by buying Donne's *Complete Works*. This runs to more than 40 volumes and would be very expensive if in good condition.

We hope you had a good Christmas and New Year in spite of the Giant Modern Library.

Nora joins me in sending best wishes.

Sincerely,

Frank

Helene Hanff   *305 East 72nd Street, New York 21, N.Y.*

MAY 8, 1960

M. De Tocqueville's compliments and he begs to announce his safe arrival in America. He sits around looking smug because everything he said was true, especially about lawyers running the country. i belong to a Democratic club, there were fourteen men over there the other night, eleven of them lawyers, came home and read a couple of newspaper stories about the presidential hopefuls – stevenson, humphrey, kennedy, stassen, nixon – all lawyers but humphrey.

I enclose three bucks, it's a beautiful book and you can't even call it secondhand, the pages weren't cut. Did I tell you I finally found the perfect page-cutter? It's a pearl-handled fruit knife. My mother left me a dozen of them, I keep one in the pencil cup on my desk. Maybe I go with the wrong kind of people but i'm just not likely to have twelve guests all sitting around simultaneously eating fruit.

cheers

hh

Helene Hanff   *305 East 72nd Street, New York 21, N.Y.*

FEBRUARY 2, 1961

Frank?

You still there?

i swore i wouldn't write till i got work.

Sold a story to Harper's Magazine, slaved over it for three weeks and they paid me $200 for it. Now they've got me writing the story of my life in a book. they're 'advancing' me $1,500 to write it and they figure it shouldn't take me more than six months. I don't mind for myself but the landlord worries.

so I can't buy any books but back in October somebody introduced me to Louis the Duke de Saint-Simon in a miserable abridgement, and I tore around to the Society Library where they let you roam the stacks and lug everything home, and got the real thing. Have been wallowing in Louis ever since. The edition I'm reading is in six volumes and halfway through Vol. VI last night I realized I could not supPORT the notion that when I take it back I will have NO louis in the house.

The translation I'm reading is by Francis Arkwright and it's delightful but I'll settle for any edition you can find that you trust. DO NOT MAIL IT! just buy it and let me know what it costs and keep it there and I'll buy it from you one volume at a time.

Hope Nora and the girls are fine. And you. And anybody else who knows me.

Helene

MARKS & CO., Booksellers
84, Charing Cross Road
London, W.C. 2

15TH FEBRUARY, 1961

Miss Helene Hanff
305 East 72nd Street
New York 21, N.Y.

Dear Helene,

  You will be pleased to know that we have a copy of the *Memoirs of the Duke de Saint-Simon* in stock in the Arkwright translation, six volumes nicely bound and in very good condition. We are sending them off to you today and they should arrive within a week or two. The amount due on them is approximately $18.75 but please don't worry about paying it all at once. Your credit will always be good at Marks & Co.

  It was very good to hear from you again. We are all well, and still hoping to see you in England one of these days.

Love from us all,

Frank

Helene Hanff   *305 East 72nd Street, New York 21, N.Y.*

MARCH 10, 1961

Dear Frankie –

Enclosed-please-God-please-find a $10 bill, it better get there, not many of those float in here these days but louis wanted me to get him paid off, he got so tired of the deadbeats at court he didn't want to move in with one 270 years later.

Thought of you last night, my editor from Harper's was here for dinner, we were going over this story-of-my-life and we came to the story of how I dramatized Landor's 'Aesop and Rhodope' for the 'Hallmark Hall of Fame.' Did I ever tell you that one? Sarah Churchill starred as Landor's dewy-eyed Rhodope. The show was aired on a Sunday afternoon. Two hours before it went on the air, I opened the New York Times Sunday book review section and there on page 3 was a review of a book called *A House Is Not a Home* by Polly Adler, all about whorehouses, and under the title was the photo of a sculptured head of a Greek girl with a caption reading: 'Rhodope, the most famous prostitute in Greece.' Landor had neglected to mention this. Any scholar would have known Landor's Rhodope was the Rhodopis who took Sappho's brother for every dime he had but I'm not a scholar, I memorized Greek endings one stoic winter but they didn't stay with me.

So we were going over this anecdote and Gene (my editor) said 'Who is Landor?' and I plunged into an enthusiastic explanation – and Gene shook her head and cut in impatiently:

'You and your Olde English books!'

You see how it is, frankie, you're the only soul alive who understands me.

xx

hh

p.s. Gene's Chinese.

MARKS & CO., Booksellers
84, Charing Cross Road
London, W.C. 2

14TH OCTOBER, 1963

Miss Helene Hanff
305 East 72nd Street
New York 21, N.Y.
U.S.A.

Dear Helene,

You will no doubt be surprised to learn that the two volumes of Virgina Woolf's *Common Reader* are on their way to you. If you want anything else I can probably get it for you with the same efficiency and swiftness.

We are all well and jogging along as usual. My eldest daughter Sheila (24) suddenly decided she wanted to be a teacher so threw up her secretarial job two years ago to go to college. She has another year to go so it looks as though it will be a long time before our children will be able to keep us in luxury.

Love from all here,

Frank

MARKS & CO., Booksellers
84, Charing Cross Road
London, W.C. 2

9TH NOVEMBER, 1963

Miss Helene Hanff
305 East 72nd Street
New York 21, New York
U.S.A.

Dear Helene,

Some time ago you asked me for a modern version of Chaucer's *Canterbury Tales*. I came across a little volume the other day which I thought you would like. It is not complete by any means, but as it is quite a cheap book and seems to be a fairly scholarly job, I am sending it along by Book Post today, price $1.35. If this whets your appetite for Chaucer and you would like something more complete later on, let me know and I will see what I can find.

Sincerely,

Frank

All right, that's enough Chaucer-made-easy, it has the schoolroom smell of Lamb's Tales from Shakespeare.

I'm glad i read it. i liked reading about the nun who ate so dainty with her fingers she never dripped any grease on herself. I've never been able to make that claim and I use a fork. Wasn't anything else that intrigued me much, it's just stories, I don't like stories. Now if Geoffrey had kept a diary and told me what it was like to be a little clerk in the palace of richard III – THAT I'd learn Olde English for. I just threw out a book somebody gave me, it was some slob's version of what it was like to live in the time of Oliver Cromwell – only the slob didn't LIVE in the time of Oliver Cromwell so how the hell does he know what it was like? Anybody wants to know what it was like to live in the time of Oliver Cromwell can flop on the sofa with Milton on his pro side and Walton on his con, and they'll not only tell him what it was like, they'll take him there.

'The reader will not credit that such things could be,' Walton says somewhere or other, 'but I was there and I saw it.'

that's for me, I'm a great lover of i-was-there books.

i enclose two bucks for the chaucer, that leaves me a credit with you of 65¢ which is a larger credit than I have anywhere else.

xx

h

Helene Hanff   *305 East 72nd Street, New York 21, N.Y.*

MARCH 30, 1964

Dear Frank –

I take time out from a children's history book (my fourth, would you believe?) to ask if you can help a friend. He has an incomplete set of Shaw in what he insists is just called the Standard Edition. It's bound in rust-colored cloth, he says, if that helps. I enclose a list of what he *has*, he wants all the others in the set but if you have more than a few, don't send them all at once. He'll buy them piecemeal, like me he's a pauper. Send them to him direct, to the address on the list. That's 32nd *Avenue* in case you can't read it.

Do you ever hear anything of Cecily or Megan?

best

helene

MARKS & CO., Booksellers
84, Charing Cross Road
London, W.C. 2

14TH APRIL, 1964

Miss Helene Hanff
305 East 72nd Street
New York 21, New York
U.S.A.

Dear Helene,

About the Shaw for your friend, the Standard Edition is still available from the publishers, it is bound in the rust-coloured cloth as he describes and I think there are about 30 volumes in the complete set. Used copies seldom come along but if he would like us to send him new copies we shall be glad to do so and could send him three or four volumes a month.

We have not heard from Cecily Farr in some years now. Megan Wells had enough of South Africa in a very short time and did stop in to give us a chance to say I-told-you-so, before going out to try her luck in Australia. We had a Christmas card from her a few years ago but nothing recently.

Nora and the girls join me in sending love,

Frank

MARKS & CO., Booksellers
84, Charing Cross Road
London, W.C. 2

4TH OCTOBER, 1965

Miss Helene Hanff
305 East 72nd Street
New York 21, New York
U.S.A.

Dear Helene,

It was good to hear from you again. Yes, we're still here, getting older and busier but no richer.

We have just managed to obtain a copy of E.M. Delafields *Diary of a Provincial Lady*, in an edition published by Macmillan in 1942, a good clean copy, price $2.00. We are sending it off to you today by Book Post with invoice enclosed.

We had a very pleasant summer with more than the usual number of tourists, including hordes of young people making the pilgrimage to Carnaby Street. We watch it all from a safe distance, though I must say I rather like the Beatles. If the fans just wouldn't scream so.

Nora and the girls send their love,

Frank

HELENE HANFF   *305 East 72nd Street, New York, 21, N.Y.*

SEPTEMBER 30, 1968

Still alive, are we?

I've been writing American History books for children for four or five years. Got hung up on the stuff and have been buying American history books – in ugly, cardboardy American editions, but somehow I just didn't think the stately homes of England would yield nice English editions of James Madison's stenographic record of the Constitutional Convention or T. Jefferson's letters to J. Adams or like that.

Are you a grandfather yet? Tell Sheila and Mary their children are entitled to presentation copies of my *Collected Juvenile Works*, THAT should make them rush off and reproduce.

I introduced a young friend of mine to *Pride & Prejudice* one rainy Sunday and she has gone out of her mind for Jane Austen. She has a birthday round about Hallowe'en, can you find me some Austen for her? If you've got a complete set let me know the price, if it's expensive I'll make her husband give her half and I'll give her half.

Best to Nora and anybody else around.

Helene

MARKS & CO., Booksellers
84, Charing Cross Road
London, W.C. 2

16TH OCTOBER, 1968

Miss Helene Hanff
305 East 72nd Street
New York City, N.Y. 10021
U.S.A.

Dear Helene,

Yes, we are all very much alive and kicking, though rather exhausted from a hectic summer, with hordes of tourists from U.S.A., France, Scandinavia, etc., all buying our nice leather-bound books. Consequently our stock at the moment is a sorry sight, and with the shortage of books and high prices there is little hope of finding any Jane Austen for you in time for your friend's birthday. Perhaps we will be able to find them for her for Christmas.

Nora and the girls are fine. Sheila is teaching, Mary is engaged to a very nice boy but there is little hope of them getting married for some time as neither has any money! So Nora's hopes of being a glamorous grandmother are receding fast.

Love,

Frank

MARKS & CO., Booksellers
84, Charing Cross Road
London, W.C. 2

8TH JANUARY, 1969

Miss H. Hanff
305 E. 72nd Street
N.Y. 10021
U.S.A.

Dear Miss,

I have just come across the letter you wrote to Mr. Doel on the 30th of September last, and it is with great regret that I have to tell you that he passed away on Sunday the 22nd of December, the funeral took place last week on Wednesday the 1st of January.

He was rushed to hospital on the 15th of December and operated on at once for a ruptured appendix, unfortunately peritonitis set in and he died seven days later.

He had been with the firm for over forty years and naturally it has come as a very great shock to Mr. Cohen, particularly coming so soon after the death of Mr. Marks.

Do you still wish us to try and obtain the Austens for you?

Yours faithfully,
p.p. MARKS & CO.

Joan Todd (Mrs.)
Secretary

(UNDATED, POSTMARKED JANUARY 29, 1969. NO ADDRESS ON
LETTER.)

Dear Helene,

Thank you for your very kind letter, nothing about it at all offends
me. I only wish that you had met Frank and known him personally,
he was the most well-adjusted person with a marvellous sense of
humour, and now I realize such a modest person, as I have had letters
from all over to pay him tribute and so many people in the book trade
say he was so knowledgeable and imparted his knowledge with
kindness to all and sundry. If you wish it I could send them to you.

At times I don't mind telling you I was very jealous of you, as Frank
so enjoyed your letters and they or some were so like his sense of
humour. Also I envied your writing ability. Frank and I were so very
much opposites, he so kind and gentle and me with my Irish
background always fighting for my rights. I miss him so, life was so
interesting, he always explaining and trying to teach me something of
books. My girls are wonderful and in this I am lucky. I suppose so
many like me are all alone. Please excuse my scrawl.

With love,

Nora

I hope some day you will come and visit us, the girls would love to
meet you.

APRIL 11, 1969

Dear Katherine –

I take time out from housecleaning my bookshelves and sitting on the rug surrounded by books in every direction scrawl you a Bon Voyage. I hope you and Brian have a ball in London. He said to me on the phone: 'Would you go with us if you had the fare?' and I nearly wept.

But I don't know, maybe it's just as well I never got there. I dreamed about it for so many years. I used to go to English movies just to look at the streets. I remember years ago a guy I knew told me that people going to England find exactly what they go looking for. I said I'd go looking for the England of English literature, and he nodded and said: 'It's there.'

Maybe it is, and maybe it isn't. Looking around the rug one thing's for sure: it's here.

The blessed man who sold me all my books died a few months ago. And Mr Marks who owned the shop is dead. But Marks & Co. is still there. If you happen to pass by 84 Charing Cross Road, kiss it for me! I owe it so much.

Helene

EPILOGUE
OCTOBER, 1969

Winton Avenue
London, N. 11

OCTOBER, 1969

Dear Helene,

This is correspondent No. 3 of the Doel family speaking! First, may I apologize for the long silence. Believe me, you were often in our thoughts, we just never seemed to get around to committing those thoughts to paper. And then today we got your second letter, and were so ashamed of ourselves that we're writing immediately.

We're pleased to hear about your book and very willingly give permission to publish the letters.

We are now in our lovely new home. But although we love the house, and are very happy we moved, we often think of how much my father would have enjoyed it.

It's futile to have regrets. Although my father was never a wealthy or powerful man, he was a happy and contented one. And we're happy that this was so.

We all lead busy lives – perhaps it's better so. Mary works hard at the University library, and for relaxation goes on car rallies which last all night. I'm studying part time for a degree as well as teaching full time, and Mum – she never stops! So I'm afraid we're very bad correspondents – though delighted, of course, to receive letters. Nevertheless, we will try to write when we can if you would like this, and look forward to hearing from you.

Yours truly,

Sheila

The
Duchess of
Bloomsbury Street

Up, Up and Away

Theoretically, it was one of the happiest days of my life. The date was Thursday, June 17, 1971; the BOAC lifted from Kennedy airport promptly at 10 A.M.; the sky was blue and sunny, and after a lifetime of waiting I was finally on my way to London.

But I was also fresh out of the hospital after unexpected surgery I was terrified of going abroad by myself (I am terrified of going to Queens or Brooklyn by myself; I get lost) and I had no idea what I would do if something went wrong and nobody met the plane. I especially didn't know how I would manage the mammoth borrowed suitcase I couldn't budge, let alone carry.

Year after year I'd planned a pilgrimage to London, only to have it canceled at the last minute by some crisis, usually financial. This time it was different. From the beginning, heaven seemed to favor the trip.

I'd written a book called *84, Charing Cross Road*, and a few months after it came out in New York, a London publisher named André Deutsch bought it for publication in England. He wrote me that the London edition would be brought out in June and he wanted me there to help publicize the book. Since he owed me a small 'advance,' I wrote and told him to keep the money in his office for me. I figured it was enough to keep me in London for three weeks if I was frugal.

In March, the *Reader's Digest* bought an article I wrote about my fan mail and the *Digest* check bought the BOAC ticket, some expensive clothes and – as things turned out – an expensive surgeon.

With the surgery, contributions came in from all over. The Democratic Club I belong to didn't send flowers to the hospital, they sent a Harrods gift certificate. A friend just back from London stuck a wad of British pounds under my door labeled 'For theatre tickets.' And one of my brothers stopped by and gave me a hundred dollars 'to go to Paris with.' I had no intention of going to Paris (I never wanted to see any city but London) but the hundred meant an extra week in

London plus a few frills like cabs and hairdressers. So financially I was all set.

The night before I left, two friends gave me a farewell party. I'd spent the day packing, to the indignant fury of all my vital organs, and I left the party early and was in bed and asleep by midnight. At 3 A.M. I came staring awake, with my insides slamming around and a voice in my head demanding:

'What are you *doing*, going three thousand miles from home by yourself, you're not even HEALTHY!'

I got out of bed, had hysterics, a martini and two cigarettes, got back in bed, and whiled away the rest of the night composing cables saying I wasn't coming.

Paul, the doorman, drove me to the airport. I got on the passport line holding my coat, scarf, magazines and an extra sweater in one hand, while the other held up the pants of my new navy pantsuit which had refused to stay up by themselves since the operation.

Standing on line proved to be no more uncomfortable than hanging by my thumbs, and when I was finally allowed to board the plane I slid into my seat by the window blissful in the knowledge that for five hours I wouldn't have to move a muscle. Somebody brought me sandwiches and coffee I hadn't had to make; somebody brought me a martini; and somebody else was going to clean it all up afterwards. I began to relax.

When I was completely relaxed, the voice in my head inquired what I planned to do if something went wrong and nobody met the plane. To forestall panic, I got the letters out of my shoulder bag and read them over. Those letters were my lifeline.

The first was from Carmen, André Deutsch's publicity girl.

Dear Helene,

I've confirmed your reservation for June 17th at the Kenilworth Hotel. It's just up the way from Deutsch's so you won't feel too alone. The publication date of your book is June 10th, sorry you'll miss it but glad you're on the mend.

We're all looking forward to seeing you on the 18th.

Thanks to a mix-up I had two hotel rooms, one at the Kenilworth and one at the Cumberland. On the advice of well-traveled friends I'd hung onto both rooms in case one wasn't there for me when I arrived. But I was going to the Kenilworth first; it was cheaper.

The second letter was a hasty, last-minute scrawl from Nora Doel. *84, Charing Cross Road* is the story of my twenty-year correspondence with Marks & Co., a London bookshop, and particularly with its chief buyer, Frank Doel, whose sudden death had given rise to the book. Nora is his widow; Sheila is his daughter.

> Helene –
> Sheila and I will be at Heathrow Airport on Thursday night at ten. We're both very excited.
> Have a good trip.
>
> Nora

The third letter was from an Englishman who had written me a fan letter after he read *84, Charing Cross Road* and had asked when I was finally coming to London. I wrote and told him, and he wrote back:

> I am a retired publisher now working at London Airport. Please, if I can be of help. USE ME! I can meet you off your plane and see you through Customs and Immigration. Any friends meeting you would have to meet you AFTER you leave Customs. I would meet you off the plane before your dainty feet touched British soil.

I hadn't the slightest idea how he expected to manage it but I was counting heavily on his getting my dainty feet off the plane. What did I know about Customs and Immigration?

There was a fan letter from the wife of an American professor working at Oxford for a year, inviting me to visit them at Oxford. There was a fan letter from an American living in London who wanted to take me on a walking tour. And there was a letter from Jean Ely, a retired actress in New York whom I'd met as a result of the book:

> Dear Helene:
> I've written to a friend in London about you. He's an Old Etonian who knows London better than anyone I ever met. I've never imposed on him in this way before but I wrote him you were

one visitor he must take on a tour of London. His name if Pat Buckley. He'll get in touch with you at the Kenilworth.

I won't tell you to have a wonderful time, you couldn't possibly have anything else.

Jean

P.S. Keep a diary. So much will be happening to you, you won't remember it all without a diary.

I read all the letters over several times. I checked my passport and vaccination certificate several times; I studied an English Coins card somebody had given me, and I read a BOAC booklet I hadn't had time to read before, on What to Take With You on the Trip. It listed twenty-three items, fourteen of which I didn't have:

3 washable dresses
2 vests
2 pair gloves
small hat(s)
twin set
wool stole
evening dress
evening bag
evening shoes
girdle.

I'd brought three pantsuits, two skirts, several sweaters and blouses, a white blazer and one dress. The dress was silk, chic and expensive, it had a matching coat and was intended to cover large evenings.

I got out my Visitors' Map of London and pored over it. I can read maps only in terms of Up, Down, Left and Right, but I'd marked key places – St. Paul's, Westminster Abbey, the Tower of London – and I'd charted walking tours all over the map. The key places would have to wait till the end of my stay, when I hoped to be able to stand still for long periods, but meanwhile I could walk the city end to end. (I'd discovered I was all right as long as I kept moving.)

I was perfectly calm and happy until a voice announced over the intercom that it was 9:50 P.M. British time, we would be landing at Heathrow Airport in five minutes and it was raining in London.

'Don't panic,' I told myself. 'Just decide *now* what you'll do if Nora and Sheila aren't there and that nut at the airport forgot this is the day you're coming.'

I decided I would look up Nora and Sheila Doel in the phone book and call them. If they didn't answer I would look up Carmen and Deutsch's. If she didn't answer I would go up to an airport official and say:

'Excuse me, sir. I have just arrived from New York, I have a suitcase I can't budge, I don't know where the Kenilworth Hotel is and I am Not Well.'

The plane began its descent and the passengers moved about, collecting hand luggage. I had no hand luggage. I sat frozen and told myself that if nobody met me I would sit in the airport till the next plane left for New York and fly home. At which moment the voice spoke again into the intercom:

'Will Miss Hanff please identify herself to a member of the staff?'

I leaped to my feet and held up my free hand (one hand being permanently attached to the pants) only to find there wasn't a member of the staff in sight. The other passengers, lining up to leave the plane, stared at me curiously as, red-faced but awash with relief, I gathered up everything in my freehand and got on the end of the line. Now that I knew I was being met, I was giddy and half drunk with excitement. I had never really expected to make it to London – and I'd made it.

I reached the stewardess who was saying goodbye to disembarking passengers, and told her I was Miss Hanff. She pointed to the bottom of the ramp and said:

'The gentleman is waiting for you.'

And there he was, a big, towering Colonel Blimp with a beaming smile on his face and both arms outstretched, waiting to get my dainty feet onto British soil. As I went down the ramp to meet him, I thought:

'Jean was right. Keep a diary.'

THURSDAY, JUNE 17
MIDNIGHT

There's a radio in the headboard of this bed, the BBC just bid me goodnight. The entire radio system here goes to bed at midnight.

Arrival triumphant.

'Helene, my dear!' boomed the Colonel, stooping to kiss me on the cheek, nobody would have believed he'd never set eyes on me before. He's a beaming giant of a man with tufted gray eyebrows and tufted white sideburns, and a vast stomach that marches on ahead of him; and he strode off to see to my suitcase ramrod straight, a Sahib out of Kipling's Old Injah. He came back, followed by a porter with the suitcase on a trolley, put an arm around me and walked me past the Immigration and Customs tables, calling genially to the men behind them, 'Friend of mine!' and that was all I saw of Immigration and Customs.

'Now then,' he said. 'Are you being met?'

I told him Nora and Sheila Doel were there somewhere.

'What do they look like?' he asked, scanning the crowd jammed behind a rope that cordoned off the arrival area.

'I have no idea,' I said.

'Have they a snapshot of you?' he asked.

'No,' I said.

'Do they know what you're wearing?' he asked.

'No,' I said.

'But my dear girl!' he boomed. 'How did you expect to find them?! Wait here.'

He parked me in front of an Information Desk and strode off. A moment later, a voice over the public-address system asked Mrs. Doel to come to the Information Desk – and a pretty, black-haired woman ducked under the cordon directly in front of me, thrust a sheaf of roses in my arms and kissed me.

'Sheila said it was you!' said Nora in a rich Irish brogue. 'We saw every woman off the plane. I said, "That one's too blond," and, "That one's too common." Sheila just kept sayin', "It's the little one in the blue trouser suit, she looks so excited."'

The Colonel steamed up and got introduced, and we went out to Nora's car. She and Sheila got in front, I got in back and the Colonel announced he would follow in his car, unless Sheila would rather he led? Did she know the way to the Cumberland?

'The Kenilworth,' I corrected. I explained about the two hotel rooms and the Colonel stared at me in horror.

'Well, in that case,' he bellowed, 'some total stranger at the Cumberland has a roomful of beautiful roses!'

He drove off to the Cumberland to reclaim his roses and I drove off toward the Kenilworth with Nora's roses in my arms, thinking, '*It was roses, roses, all the way,*' and trying to remember who wrote it.

It was dark and rainy as we drove along a highway that might have been any highway leading to any city, instead of the road to the one city I'd waited a lifetime to see. Nora was lecturing me for not staying with her and Sheila in North London ('Frank always meant you to stay with us!'), and as we entered London both of them pointed out the sights:

'There's Piccadilly!'

'This is the West End.'

'This is Regent Street.' And finally, from Sheila:

'You're on Charing Cross Road, Helene!'

I peered out at the darkness, wanting to say something appropriate, but all I could see were narrow wet streets and a few lighted dress-shop windows, it could have been down-town Cleveland.

'I'm here,' I said. 'I'm in London. I made it.' But it wasn't real.

We drove on to Bloomsbury and found the Kenilworth on the corner of a dark street. It's an old brownstone with a shabby-genteel lobby, it's going to suit me.

I registered and the young desk clerk handed me some mail, and then Nora and Sheila and I rode up to inspect Room 352. It looked pleasant and cheerful with the drapes drawn against the rain. Nora surveyed it judiciously from the doorway and announced:

'It's gawjus, Helen.'

'My name's Helene,' I said.

She looked surprised but unimpressed.

'I've been calling you "Helen" for twenty years,' she said, peering into the bathroom. It has a shower stall but no tub. 'Look at this, Sheila, she's got her own loo!'

The loo is the toilet, Sheila thinks it comes from Waterloo.

We went back down and found the Colonel fuming in the sleepy lobby: he'd found his roses lying half dead on the Cumberland Package Room floor and had had a row with the management.

We went into the dining-room, empty but still open, and the Colonel located a young Spanish waiter who said his name was Alvaro and allowed we could have sandwiches and tea-or-coffee.

'You smoke too much, Helen,' Nora announced, after we ordered.

'I know it,' I said.

'You're too thin,' she went on. 'I dunno what kind of bloke that surgeon is, to let you come away so soon after your op. A hysterectomy is a very serious op.'

'Is it, Mum,' said Sheila mildly in her university accent. She and Nora exchanged a look, and Nora giggled. They're remarkable, they talk in code and finish each other's sentences, you'd never guess they were stepmother and daughter. Sheila's an attractive girl in her twenties, laconic and unruffled. ('Just like Frank,' Nora told me.)

Nora was much struck by the fact that she and the Colonel were both widowed two years ago. He has one child, a daughter who's being married in the country on Saturday.

'Now, why don't you three girls put on your prettiest dresses and come to the wedding?' he invited expansively. 'It's going to be a superb wedding'

I declined and Nora obviously didn't think she should go if I didn't, so she declined, too, wistfully. ('I don't know him, Helen,' she said when I got her alone. And I said: 'Who knows him?!')

They left at eleven. Nora said she would give me tomorrow to rest and would call me Saturday about the interview. ('We're being interviewed together by the BBC! You've made us all famous!')

The Colonel said he'd be in the country for a week and would call me when he got back and 'arrange a little trip into our glorious countryside.'

I came up and unpacked a few things and climbed into bed with the mail.

Postcard from Eddie and Isabel, old friends from back home. They'll be in town Monday and will pick me up to go sight-seeing.

A note from Carmen at Deutsch's:

Welcome!

I know you're going to be very tired but I'm afraid we have a journalist from the Evening Standard along to see you here at 10 A.M. tomorrow. Someone will be by to pick you up before 10.

On Saturday at 2:30, the BBC want to interview you and Mrs. Doel on 'The World This Weekend.'

On Monday at 3.30 an interview on 'The Woman's Hour,' also at Broadcasting House.

On Tuesday, visits to bookshops, including Marks & Co. (closed but still standing, and we want photos of you there), and at 2:30 an Autograph Party next door at 86 Charing Cross Road, Poole's Bookshop.

On Tuesday evening, André Deutsch will give a dinner for you to meet the Deutsch officers and a distinguished journalist.

I just got uneasy about remembering all those dates, and got out of bed and made a day-to-day calendar out of a pocket memo book. I'm also uneasy about how I'm going to break the news to Carmen that I don't have my picture taken. I'm neurotic, I don't like my face.

I lie here listening to the rain, and nothing is real. I'm in a pleasant hotel room that could be anywhere. After all the years of waiting, no sense at all of being in London. Just a feeling of letdown, and my insides offering the opinion that the entire trip was unnecessary.

The alarm clock went off at eight and I got out of bed and went to the window to see if it was still raining. I pulled back the drapes – and as long as I live I'll never forget the moment. From across the street a neat row of narrow brick houses with white front steps sat looking up at me. They're perfectly standard eighteenth- or nineteenth-century houses, but looking at them I knew I was in London. I got light-headed. I was wild to get out on that street. I grabbed my clothes and tore into the bathroom and fought a losing battle with the damnedest shower you ever saw.

The shower stall is a four-foot cubicle and it has only one spigot, nonadjustable, trained on the back corner. You turn the spigot on and the water's cold. You keep turning, and by the time the water's hot enough for a shower you've got the spigot turned to full blast. Then you climb in, crouch in the back corner and drown. Dropped the soap once and there went fifteen dollar's worth of hairdressing down the drain, my shower cap was lifted clear off of my head by the torrent. Turned the spigot off and stepped thankfully out – into four feet of water. It took me fifteen minutes to mop the floor using a bathmat and two bath towels, sop-it-up, wring-it-out, sop-wring, sop-wring. Glad I shut the bathroom door or the suitcase would have been washed away.

After breakfast, I went out in the rain to look at those houses. The hotel is on the corner of Great Russell and Bloomsbury Streets. It fronts on Great Russell, which is a commercial street; the houses I saw from my window are on Bloomsbury.

I walked slowly along the street, staring across it at the houses. I came to the corner, to a dark little park called Bedford Square. On three sides of it, more rows of neat, narrow brick houses, these much more beautiful and beautifully cared for. I sat on a park bench and stared at the houses. I was shaking. And I'd never in my life been so happy.

All my life I've wanted to see London. I used to go to English movies just to look at streets with houses like those. Staring at the screen in a dark theatre, I wanted to walk down those streets so badly it gnawed at me like hunger. Sometimes, at home in the evening, reading a casual description of London by Hazlit or Leigh Hunt, I'd put the book down suddenly, engulfed by a wave of longing that was like homesickness. I wanted to see London the way old people want to see home before they die. I used to tell myself this was natural in a writer and booklover born to the language of Shakespeare. But sitting on a bench in Bedford Square it wasn't Shakespeare I was thinking of; it was Mary Bailey.

I come of very mixed ancestry, which includes an English Quaker family named Bailey. A daughter of that family, Mary Bailey, born in Philadelphia in 1807, was the only ancestor I had any interest in when I was a little girl. She left a sampler behind, and I used to stare at that sampler, willing it to tell me what she was like. I don't know why I wanted to know.

Sitting in Bedford Square I reminded myself that Mary Bailey was born in Philadelphia, died in Virginia and never saw London. But the name persisted in my head. Maybe she was a namesake. Maybe it was her grandmother or great-grandmother who had wanted to go home again. All I knew, sitting there, was that some long-dead Mary Bailey or other had finally found a descendent to go home for her.

I came back here and fixed myself up so I'd make a good impression on Deutsch's. Brushed my navy suit jacket (which they will flatly refuse to believe back home) and spent half an hour tying my new red-white-and-blue scarf in an ascot so I'd look British. Then I went down to the lobby and sat bolt upright in a chair by the door, afraid to move for fear of mussing myself, till a young secretary blew in to escort me three doors up Great Russell Street to Deutsch's.

I met Carmen – very brisk and efficient and dramatic-looking – and got interviewed by a bouncy young reporter from the *Evening Standard* named Valerie Jenkins. After the interview the three of us and a photographer piled into a cab, and Carmen said to the driver:

'Eighty-four Charing Cross Road.'

I felt unreal, knowing I was on my way to that address. I'd bought books from 84 Charing Cross Road for twenty years. I'd made friends there whom I never met. Most of the books I bought from Marks & Co. were probably available in New York. For years, friends had advised me to 'try O'Malley's,' 'try Dauber & Pine.' I'd never done it. I'd wanted a link with London and I'd managed it.

Charing Cross Road is a narrow, honky-tonk street, choked with traffic, lined with secondhand bookshops. The open stalls in front were piled with old books and magazines, here and there a peaceful soul was browsing in the misty rain.

We got out at 84. Deutsch's had stuffed the empty window with copies of the book. Beyond the window the shop interior looked black and empty. Carmen went next door to Poole's and got the key and let us into what had once been Marks & Co.

The two large rooms had been stripped bare. Even the heavy oak shelves had been ripped off the walls and were lying on the floor, dusty and abandoned. I went upstairs to another floor of empty, haunted rooms. The window letters which had spelled Marks & Co. had been ripped off the window, a few of them were lying on the window sill, their white paint chipped and peeling.

I started back downstairs, my mind on the man, now dead, with whom I'd corresponded for so many years. Halfway down I put my hand on the oak railing and said to him silently:

'How about this, Frankie? I finally made it.'

We went outside – and I stood there and let them take my picture as meekly as if I did it all the time. That's how anxious I am to make a good impression and not give anybody any trouble.

When I came back to the hotel there was a letter at the desk. From Pat Buckley, the Old Etonian Jean Ely wrote to about me.

No salutation, just:

Jean Ely writes that you are here on your first visit. Can you have a bit of supper here on Sunday at 7:30? – and we will drive around and see a bit of old London.

Call me Saturday or Sunday before 9:30 A.M.

In haste –
P.B.

SATURDAY, JUNE 19

Totally demoralized.

Just came up from breakfast and phoned Pat Buckley.

'Oh yes,' he said in a very U accent, 'Hallo.'

I told him I'd love to come to supper tomorrow night and asked if there were other people coming.

'I'm not giving a supper party for you' he said impatiently. 'Jean wrote me you wanted to see London!'

I stammered that I was glad we'd be alone, I'd only asked so I'd know how to dress; if we were alone I could wear a pantsuit.

'Oh, Lord, must you?' he said. 'I loathe women in trousers. I suppose it's old-fashioned of me but I do think you all look appalling in them. Oh well, I suppose if you must, you must.'

It's fifty degrees here and raining, I'm not climbing into a summer skirt for him.

Nora just phoned, she'll pick me up at two this afternoon for the interview.

'You're right behind the British Museum, Helen,' she said. 'Go sit in the Reading Room, it's very restful.'

Told her I see enough museums in New York, and God knows I sit in enough Reading Rooms.

Will now slog out in the wet and tour Bloomsbury.

MIDNIGHT

Nora and I were interviewed at Broadcasting House, it's the only big modern building I've seen and I hope I don't see another one; it's a monstrosity – a huge semicircular block of granite, it looks obese. They don't understand skyscrapers here. In New York they don't understand anything else.

The interviewer was choice. First she told the radio audience that though Nora and I had corresponded over a twenty-year period we'd never met. Then she turned to us and asked us what we thought of each other: now that we'd met, were we disappointed? If we'd never corresponded and had just met, would we like each other?

'Now what kind of question was that to ask me?' Nora demanded when we came out. 'How-would-I-like-you-if-we'd-just-been-introduced. How do I know whether I'd have liked you or not? I've known you for twenty years, Helen!'

She drove me out Portland Place and through the Regent's Park section, which I loved passionately on sight. We passed Wimpole Street and Harley Street – and there I was in a *car*, I felt as if I were locked in a metal container and couldn't get out, but it was raining. I'm going back there on foot the first dry day.

There's a Crescent of Nash houses – I'm not too clear about when Nash lived but he built tall white opulent houses reeking of Beau Brummell and Lady Teazle – and when the rain stopped for a little we got out of the car and sat on a park bench so I could stare at the Crescent. We chose which houses we'll buy if we're born rich next time.

Nora told me she came to London as a poor servant girl from Ireland before the war. She worked in one of the houses of the gentry as a kitchen maid, cutting paper-thin bread for the cucumber sandwiches.

She drove me home to Highgate for dinner. She and Sheila bought a house out there after Frank died and the younger daughter married. We drove past Hampstead Heath on the way, and Nora stopped the car at the cemetery where Karl Marx is buried. The gates were locked but I peered over the wall at him.

Their house is high in the hills of North London on an attractive suburban street that blazes with roses, every house had a rose garden in full bloom. The roses here are as wildly colored as a New England autumn: not just red, pink and yellow, but lavender roses, blue roses, purple and orange roses. Every color has a separate fragrance, I went berserk smelling my way around Nora's garden.

We had strawberries and thick English cream for dessert, and when Nora came to her last berry she looked up at Sheila, stricken, and said:

'It came out "never" again, Sheila!'

She eats berries to the old children's rhyme to find out when she's going to marry again: 'This year, next year, sometime, never.' When it comes out 'never,' Sheila has to comfort her. Sheila's much more like Nora's mother than her stepdaughter.

Nora cut a fresh armload of roses for me, and Sheila drove me home. She teaches in a suburban school. There are two men who take her out; I think both of them bore her, she still hasn't met one she wants to marry.

Big excitement in the lobby when I came in because of the *Evening Standard* interview; one of the desk clerks had saved a copy for me.

Excerpt:

She steps into London, frightfully trim in a chic navy trouser-suit from Saks and a foulard tied French-style.

Kill yourself tying an ascot and it comes out French-style. Story of my life.

You can't imagine how funny it strikes me when somebody calls me chic. I'm wearing the same kind of clothes I've worn all my life and for years I was looked on as a Bohemian mess. My sister-in-law Alice, for instance, used to wear herself out every year trying to find a shoulder bag to give me for Christmas because I wouldn't carry a handbag and nobody else wore shoulder bags so no manufacturers made them. (Handbags make you choose between your wallet, your glasses and your cigarettes. Choose two of the three and maybe you can get your bag closed.) I also wouldn't wear high heels because I like to walk, and you can't walk if your feet hurt. And I lived in jeans and slacks because skirts are drafty in winter and hamper you when you walk, and besides, if you're wearing pants nobody knows there's a run in one stocking.

So for years I was this sartorial horror who ran around in low heels, pants and shoulder bags. I still run around that way – and after a lifetime of being totally out of it, I'm so With it my pantsuit gets a rave review in the *Evening Standard*.

SUNDAY, JUNE 20

Sallied forth with my map after breakfast and saw the sights of Bloomsbury. Got lost several times; it seems a street can be on the Left on your map without necessarily being Left of where you're standing. Various gents came out from under umbrellas to point me where I wanted to go.

It cleared after lunch and I'm now in a neighborhood park, lying in a deck chair soaking up the fog. There are three handkerchief-sized parks very close to the hotel. This one's just beyond the British Museum. Sign on the gate says:

RUSSELL SQUARE

PLEASE DON'T LEAVE LITTER

PERSONS WITH DOGS
ARE REQUIRED TO KEP THEM
UNDER PROPER CONTROL

There's a rose garden in the middle of the square encircling a very practical birdbath: a marble slab with a thin jet of water in the center. A bird can stand around and drink or wash his feathers without drowning. Wish whoever designed it would go to work on the English shower problem.

An elderly gentleman in uniform just came up, bowed and said:

'Fourpence, please.'

For the use of the deck chair.

He was apologetic about the weather, he and I are the only ones out here. I said the rain was good for the roses, and he told me the gardeners in London's squares compete every year for the honor of growing the best roses.

'I do think this year our chap has a chance,' he said. Told him I would definitely root for the Russell Square gardener.

Have to go put on the navy suit for Pat Buckley. Or I may just be mean and stay in my second-best coffee-brown on account of the weather.

I've been sitting on the edge of the bed for an hour in a complete daze. I told him if I die tonight I'll die happy, it's all here, everything's here.

Pat Buckley lives in Rutland Gate, it's down in Knightsbridge or Kensington below the left-hand edge of my Visitors' Map, I took a cab. Rutland Gate is a small compound of white stone houses round a green square. Everything in London is round a green square, they're like small oases everywhere.

He has a ground-floor flat. I rang the bell and he opened the door and said:

'Hallo, you found it all right.'

He's slight – thin build, thin face, indeterminate age – and he has one of those light, almost brittle, English voices, pleasant but neutral. He took my jacket and ushered me into an Oscar Wilde drawing room. There's full-length portrait of his mother in her court-presentation gown on one wall. On another wall, a glass cabinet houses his collection of gentlemen's calling-card cases – small square cases, gold, silver, onyx inlaid with pearl, ivory worked with gold filligree, no two alike. The collection is his hobby and it's dazzling.

He brought me sherry, and when I told him I found Eton very glamorous he brought me his Eton class book and showed me photos of his rooms there.

We had supper in the dining-room at a polished mahogany table set with heavy English silver. He has a 'daily' who leaves a cold supper for him and his guests and makes the coffee and sets the table before she leaves. The place setting was the same as at home – fork at the left, knife and spoon at the right – but lying horizontally above the dinner plate were an oyster fork and a soup spoon. I let him go first so I could see what you did with them.

We had chicken salad followed by strawberries and cream – and that's what you use them for: you spear a strawberry with the oyster fork, scoop cream up on the soup spoon, transfer the berry to the spoon and slurp.

After supper we climbed into his car. He didn't ask what I wanted to see, he just drove me to the corner where the Globe Theatre stood. Nothing is there now, the lot is empty. I made him stop the car and

I got out and stood on that empty lot and I thought the top of my head would come off.

He got out of the car then, and we prowled the dark alleys nearby – Shakespeare's alleys, still there. And Dickens' alleys: he pointed to an Artful Dodger peering furtively out the window of an ancient pile of stone.

He took me to a pub called The George, and as he opened the door for me he said in that light, neutral voice:

'Shakespeare used to come here.'

I mean I went through a door Shakespeare once went through, and into a pub he knew. We sat at a table against the back wall and I leaned my head back, against a wall Shakespeare's head once touched, and it was indescribable.

The pub was crowded. People were standing at the bar and all the tables were full. I was suddenly irritated at all those obtuse citizens eating and drinking without any apparent sense of where they were, and I said snappishly:

'I could imagine Shakespeare walking in now, if it weren't for the people.'

And the minute I said it I knew I was wrong. He said it before I could:

'Oh no. The people are just the same.'

And of course they were. Look again, and there was a blond, bearded Justice Shallow talking to the bartender. Further along the bar, Bottom the Weaver was telling his ponderous troubles to a sharp-faced Bardolph. And at a table right next to us, in a flowered dress and pot-bellied white hat, Mistress Quickly was laughing fit to kill.

He dragged me out of there and drove me to see St. Paul's by floodlight. I wanted at least to walk up the steps and touch the doors of John Donne's cathedral but it will be there tomorrow, there's time, there's time.

He drove me to the Tower of London, more huge and terrifying than I'd imagined, like a sprawling medieval Alcatraz. We got there just at ten, so I could watch the guards lock the Tower gates. For all their flashy black-and-scarlet uniforms, they are grim and frightening as they lock the gates to that dread prison with darkness closing in. You think of the young Elizabeth sitting somewhere behind the stone walls wanting to write and ask Bloody Mary to have her beheaded with a sword instead of an ax.

When the gates were locked, the guards marched back toward the huge iron Tower door. It rose to let them pass through, lowered and clanged shut behind them, and the light voice beside me said:

'They haven't missed a night in seven hundred years.'

The mind boggles. Even going back only three hundred years, you think of London during the Great Fire, the Great Plague, the Cromwell revolution, the Napoleonic wars, the First World War, the Second World War –

'They locked the Tower with all this ceremony,' I asked him, 'every night, even during the Blitz?'

'Oh yes,' he said.

Put THAT on Hitler's tombstone, tell THAT to that great American patriot, Wernher von Braun, whose buzz bombs destroyed every fourth house in London.

When he drove me home and I tried to thank him, he said:

'Oh, thank *you*! Most Americans won't take this tour. They'll drive around with me for a quarter of an hour and then they want to know where the Dorchester Bar is.'

He said most Americans he knows never see London.

'They take a taxi from the Hilton to Harrods, from Harrods to the theatre, from the theatre to the Dorchester Bar.'

He said he knows four American businessmen who've been in London for a week without ever leaving the Hilton.

'They stay shut up in their rooms all day with their telephone and a bottle of scotch, you wonder why they ever left the States.'

He gave me a list of sights to see but didn't suggest showing them to me himself.

MONDAY, JUNE 21

Eddie and Isabel picked me up this morning to go sightseeing; Isabel is an old school friend, they live in Texas. They are the most conventional, conservative people I know.

It was sunny this morning, and when they came for me the sight of them charmed me: Isabel wore cotton overalls and a print blouse, Eddie was in a sports shirt and slacks. It was the first time I'd ever seen them that they didn't look ultra proper-and-respectable. I had an interview at Broadcasting House at three and I thought I might not get back here first so I wore my marked-down beige linen pantsuit; next to them I was overdressed.

They'd been in London before and had seen the sights so we just wandered around the shopping district all morning. They like to window-shop and buy curios and good prints and we did that. At lunch time, we were wandering along a street when I stopped suddenly and gawked because there, directly ahead of us, was Claridge's.

Claridge's is where all the characters in Noel Coward lunch. For years I've had glamorous images of fashionable London sailing grandly into Claridge's.

Eddie asked what I was staring at and I explained.

'Fine,' he said promptly. 'We'll have lunch at Claridge's.'

It was a spontaneous, generous gesture very typical of him. I waited for Isabel to say, 'Now Eddie, not the way we're dressed!' but to my astonishment, she didn't.

'I think it's very fancy,' I said. 'Let's go home and change first.'

'They'll take our money,' said Eddie dryly – and took our arms and led us proudly into Claridge's.

I'm a slob by nature. On an ordinary day at home I couldn't care less how I look. But this was CLARIDGE'S. I sat through lunch in that room of grace and elegance surrounded by tables of perfectly groomed Londoners – sandwiched between two happy Texans dressed for a picnic and affectionately pleased at having taken me somewhere special.

After lunch they went with me to Broadcasting House, and then more window shopping, and at six we were in the theatre district. A few people were on line at the Aldwych hoping for last-minute return tickets to *A Midsummer Night's Dream*. Eddie spoke to a man on line and came back and said:

'There are always a few returns. If we get on line now, we can get tickets at seven, when the box office opens. It's a seven-thirty curtain, we'll eat afterwards.'

This was the Peter Brook production, you understand, the National Shakespeare Theatre Company production. I would have given a week of my life for a ticket. I'd tried to get them for Nora and Sheila and me through the hotel, it was the one show I couldn't get, it's sold out for the rest of the run. And much as I wanted to see it, I *couldn't* have walked into that theatre looking the way we looked – in clothes we'd worn since early morning and without so much as having washed our faces all day. And Eddie and Isabel, who wouldn't have dreamed of going to the theatre that way in Houston, were ready to do it in London.

The whole thing was academic for me: I couldn't have stood on that line for ten minutes, much less an hour. I'd stood peering in at shop windows most of the day with my teeth gritted and by six I'd had it. I told them I thought I'd call it a day and go sit somewhere before my insides fell out on the pavement. They're old friends, they immediately abandoned the project and we went to dinner at a little side-street pub instead.

Not till I got home did it dawn on me that they and I had completely reversed roles. Coming abroad, where nobody knows them, Eddie and Isabel have rid themselves of a lot of social inhibitions. Coming abroad, where nobody knows me, I've acquired a whole set of inhibitions I never had at home. Wild?

Carmen just phoned to remind me of the Autograph Party tomorrow and the Deutsch dinner tomorrow night. I told her I have a calendar propped against the traveling clock so it's the first thing I see when I turn the alarm off in the morning.

Asked her what I do if nobody shows up for my autograph; she said briskly Talk to the manager, he's a fan. After twenty minutes say you have a headache and he'll get you a cab.

We toured the bookshops in the rain. They all had *84* prominently displayed, and all the managers and sales people bowed and beamed and shook my hand, and after the third bookshop I got terribly poised and gracious about it all, like I was used to it. We got to Poole's at two-thirty for the Autograph Party – and would you believe a long line of people waiting for my important autograph? On a rainy Tuesday?

They'd set up a table for me at the head of the line and I sat down and asked the first man to tell me his name and a bit about himself so I could write something personal, I can*not* break myself of the habit of autographing books with chummy little messages that take up the whole front page.

A lady from California plunked down twelve copies and got out her list and said, This first one's for her brother Arnold in the hospital, could I write something cheerful? and this one's for Mrs Pratt next door who's watering her plants, and this one's for her daughter-in-law Pat, could I write 'To Pat from Mother Crawford Via –'? Twelve. Now and then I'd squint along the line (I wasn't wearing my glasses, I'm a celebrity) and apologize for keeping everybody waiting; they all just smiled and went on standing patiently, people are unbelievable.

I got nearly to the end of the line and said automatically without looking up, 'Will you tell me your name sir?' and he said, 'Pat Buckley,' meekly, and I looked up and there he was with two books under his arms. I told him I want to give him a copy. I autographed his two for him to give to friends.

He asked whether I'm free on Saturday if he's 'able to arrange a little outing'; I said I'm free for any outing he arranges any day at all, and he beamed and said he'd be in touch.

After the autographing, I had sherry with the manager, Mr Port. (Fact.) He gave me a letter someone had left there for me and I put it in my shoulder bag and brought it home and just now remembered it and got it out and opened it.

Dear Miss Hanff –

    Welcome to England. A benefactor from Philadelphia sent us your book and we love it, as do all our friends.

    I wonder if you could be free on Monday next, June 28, and would like to see Peter Brook's production of 'A Midsummer Night's Dream' with us? It is at the National Shakespeare Company's London theatre, the Aldwych. We are taking two Australian friends with us, both devotees of your book.

    My husband is English, so am I, but I had an American mother.

    We'd love it if you are free to come. Will you telephone me? – and we can plan where to meet and eat first.

Sincerely,
Joyce Grenfell

    I feel as if God had leaned down from heaven and pasted a gold star on my forehead.

    I'm sitting here all gussied up in the silk cocktail-dress-and-coat for the Deutsch dinner, ready half an hour early as usual. I'm afraid even to smoke, I'll get ashes on it.

1 A.M.

    The desk buzzed up when the car came, and when I went down to the lobby, Mr Otto, the Kenilworth manager, bowed ceremoniously and said:

'Madam's car awaits.'

    Told him this was my first and last chance to be a celebrity and I was gonna make the most of it. He nodded solemnly and said: 'Quite.' He and the two boys who work as desk clerks get a charge out of all my roses and phone calls and notes-left-at-the-desk. So do I, believe it.

    The dinner party was at a Hungarian restaurant called Victor's. Victor is a close friend of André Deutsch, they're both Hungarian but Victor is more so. He bowed and kissed my hand and told me I was 'beautiful' and 'Queen of London for a month' and my book was also 'beautiful.' I told Deutsch:

'He's straight out of Molnar.'

And Deutsch looked at me in mild surprise and said:

'Oh, did you know Ferenc?'

No, I didn't know Ferenc but Deutsch did. If any Molnar fan is still alive and reading this, you pronounce it Ference.

The dinner was in a private upstairs dining room; we paraded up the carpeted stairs, about eight of us, and into a dining room, where a large round table was just jumping with wine glasses and flowers and candles. I sat between Deutsch, very old-world and courtly, and the 'distinguished journalist' whose name I didn't get.

Everybody at dinner was bowled over to learn I was going to meet Joyce Grenfell. I know her as a comedienne in British films but she's much more famous over here for her one-man shows, which I never saw. She writes all her own material and the show always sells out. So now of course I'm nervous about meeting her.

Over coffee, somebody passed a copy of *84* around the table for all the guests to sign for me. Above the signatures somebody had written a flowery tribute to 'an author who combines talent with charm' and sociability with something else, and Deutsch read it and nodded vehemently and signed his name and handed the book to me with a flourish. And Victor read it and said Yes, Yes, it was So! and signed his name ('Your host!') and kissed my hand again, and dessert was a fancy decorated cake with WELCOME HELENE on it in pink icing.

Got home at midnight, swept into the lobby and informed Mr Otto and the boys at the desk I am hereafter to be known as the Duchess of Bloomsbury. Or Bloomsbury Street, at least.

The two desk clerks are students from South Africa. One of them has to go back in a few days, and the other advised him conversationally:

'If the police come after you, eat my address.'

WEDNESDAY, JUNE 23

Nora and I were taken to lunch by a rare-book dealer, and over lunch a bizarre story from Nora.

I gather book dealers are as clannish as actors, and the closest friends Frank and Nora had for ten years were a book dealer named Peter Kroger and his wife, Helen. The Doels and Krogers were inseparable despite the fact that the two men were competitors. One New Year's Eve, the Doels gave a party, and Helen Kroger arrived looking very exotic in a long black evening dress.

'Helen, you look like a Russian spy!' said Nora. And Helen laughed and Peter laughed and a few months later Nora picked up the morning paper and discovered that Helen and Peter Kroger *were* Russian spies.

'All the journalists came swarming round to the house,' Nora told me, 'offering me a couple of thousand quid to tell them about "the ring." I told them the only ring I knew anything about was my wedding ring.'

She visited the Krogers in prison and Peter asked if she remembered telling Helen she looked like a Russian spy.

'It must have given them a turn,' I said.

'I don't know,' said Nora. 'He just asked if I remembered it. Then we talked about something else.'

She and Frank went to the trial and discovered that everything the Krogers had told them about their past lives had been invented. I asked if this bothered her, Nora said No, she understood it.

'They were the best friends we ever had,' she said. 'They were fine people, lovely people. It was all political, I s'pose they had their reasons.'

A year later the Krogers were exchanged for a British spy held by the Russians. They live in Poland now. Helen and Nora still write to each other at Christmas.

Phoned Joyce Grenfell at dinner time, told her what movies I'd seen her in and she said:

'Then you'll know me, I'm the one with the bangs.' I'm to meet them for dinner Monday at the Waldorf, which is next door to the theatre.

THURSDAY, JUNE 24

I finally got a day to myself and did the Regent's Park area on foot. Walked around the Nash Crescent twenty or thirty times, saw the house on Wimpole Street where Robert Browning came to call on Elizabeth, walked Harley Street – and also Devonshire Street, Devonshire Place, Devonshire Mews, Devonshire Close and Devonshire Mews Close, this is a lovely city.

There was a note at the desk for me when I came back. No salutation.

> Can you be here at twelve noon *sharp* on Saturday? We are driving down to Windsor and Eton and have rather a lot to do.
>
> In haste –
> P.B.

We are driving down to Windsor and Eton. Me, this is.

I love the way he never uses a salutation. It always aggravates me, when I'm writing to some telephone-company supervisor or insurance man, to have to begin with 'Dear Sir' when he and I both know nobody on earth is less dear to me.

I'm writing this in the Kenilworth Lounge. Not to be confused with the Kenilworth TV Room, where everybody sits bolt upright on little straight chairs in total darkness staring at some situation comedy. The Lounge is just off the lobby. It's a pleasant room with easy chairs and a sofa, but if you want to write in your journal you have to slither an eye around the door before entering. If there's a woman alone in here she's looking for somebody to talk to. If there are two women already talking, they're gracious and friendly enough to include you in the conversation, and you can't decline to be included without seeming *un*gracious and *un*friendly.

Tonight when I came in there was only a man at the desk writing letters, he just left. He asked me for a light, and when he heard my American accent he told me he'd lived in New York for a year.

'And then one day I was walking down Fifth Avenue with an American friend and I said to him: "Why are you running?" And he said: "I'm not running!" And then I knew it was time to come home.'

People here ask you for 'a light' only if you're smoking and they can light their cigarette from yours. Nobody would dream of asking you for a match, it would be like asking you for money. Matches are not free over here. There are none in ashtrays in hotel lobbies and none on restaurant tables. You have to buy them in the store, I suppose they're imported and too expensive to fling around the way they're flung around at home.

A lady just came in, she asked Am I the writer? she heard about me at the desk. She lives in Kent, she doesn't care for London, she's here because her brother's in the hospital here but at least she's seeing a bit of Bloomsbury, he just won't hear of her staying in the room all day, so this afternoon she went out to the Dickens House in Doughty Street, have I been there?

She wants to talk so we'll talk.

FRIDAY, JUNE 25

I got the first week's hotel bill this morning, much steeper than I'd anticipated, what with assorted lunches and dinners and a 12 per cent surcharge added for tips. I just took it up the street to Deutsch's, to Mr Tammer, their accountant. He's a solemn, bespectacled gentleman who gives you a sudden warm smile when you say hello to him. He'll need it with me around, he's my personal banker. He's got all my 'advance' money in cash in the office safe and he's doling it out to me weekly. He gave me cash to pay the hotel bill and ten pounds, which is my Allowance for the week; when I run short I dip into my brother's hundred. I had ten of the hundred with me for him to change into pounds, and he got out all his charts and machines and figured the latest exchange rate very tensely and meticulously, God forbid he should cheat me out of fifteen cents.

There was a letter for me at Deutsch's which intrigues me, it's from a man I never knew existed. Nobody I corresponded with at Marks & Co. ever mentioned him.

Dear Miss Hanff,

I am the son of the late Ben Marks of Marks & Co. and want you to know how delighted I am that you are here, and how very much my wife and I would like you to dine with us.

I do not know where you are staying so could you please ring me at the above telephone numbers? The second one is an answering service and any message left there will reach me.

We're both looking forward to meeting you.

Sincerely,
Leo Marks

The secretary who gave me the letter told me he called and asked where he could reach me.

'But we never tell anyone where you're staying,' she said. 'We just ask them to get in touch with you through us.'

I took a very dim view of this and went into Carmen's office to straighten it out.

'Carmen, dear,' I said, 'I am not the kind of author who wants to be protected from her public. Any fan who phones might want to feed me, and I am totally available as a dinner guest. Just give out my address all over.'

She said there are at least two interviews to come and she'll make them both over lunch. Some interviewer asked me if I planned 'to buy silver and cashmere here – or just books?' I said I planned to buy *nothing* over here, everything I see in a shop window has a price tag reading 'One Day Less in London.'

Off to Parliament.

MIDNIGHT

I'VE BEEN TO THE OLD VIC, shades of my stagestruck youth, walking into that theatre was a thrill. Nora and Sheila and I saw *Mrs. Warren's Profession*. The theatre has the atmosphere of the old Met in New York and the Academy of Music in Philadelphia; the audience files in with a kind of festive reverence, like people going to church on Christmas Eve.

Sheila had trouble parking the car, she got to the theatre three minutes after the curtain was up and was promptly shunted off downstairs to the lounge to watch the first act on closed-circuit TV, you do not trail down the aisle after Mass has started.

I'll never understand why they did *Mrs. Warren's Profession* in turn-of-the-century costumes. Politicians and businessmen don't own whorehouses any more? Poor girls are not expected to starve virtuously rather than eat unvirtuously any more? Moral pillars of society don't keep mistresses in country cottages any more? Who does such a play as a costume piece belonging to some other era? Bernie Shaw would have a fit.

I asked Nora about Leo Marks, she said she only met him and his wife a few times but 'they seemed a nice young couple.' She said he's a writer.

I'm sitting here eating vitamin C, think I'm getting a cold. Tried reading Mary Baker Eddy once, should've stuck with it.

It finally turned sunny and warm, thank God, so I could wear a skirt for PB. (Headline in the newspaper read ENGLAND SWEL-TERS IN 75-DEGREE HEAT.) Wore my brown linen skirt and the new white blazer, and he beamed and said, 'You look charming,' and asked if the brown-and-white scarf came from Harrods. (I borrowed it off the cocktail dress.)

He said as we drove that we wouldn't be able to go through Windsor Castle after all, 'the Queen's in residence,' but we would stop at Windsor for sherry with two elderly sisters, he thought I'd find them and their house delightful.

On the way to Windsor there's a Home for Tired Horses. Their owners visit them on Sundays and bring them cream buns.

Windsor is full of casual anachronisms. The sisters live on a seventeenth-century street in one of a row of Queen Anne houses, each with a car parked at the curb and a TV antenna sticking out of the roof. PB parked at the back of the house by the rose garden and we were met there by the dominant sister, who cut a pink rose for me to wear and took us into the house and along a narrow old-fashioned hall to the living-room, where the shy sister met us. The shy sister poured sherry and both of them regretfully informed PB that their ghost had gone.

The ghost was living in the house when they bought it twenty years ago and stayed on. He was very quiet and no trouble most of the time. But he liked the house to be lived in, he liked people about; and every time the sisters packed for a trip and made arrangements to close the house, the ghost went berserk with fury. Pictures were knocked off the walls, wine glasses went hurtling off the sideboard and broke, lamps crashed to the floor, pots and pans were clattering and banging round the kitchen all night long. The rampage lasted till the sisters left for their holiday. For twenty years, this happened every time they went up to London during the season or into the country or abroad. This year, for the first time, the sisters made plans to go away, they packed for the trip – and the house remained silent. The pictures and wine glasses and lamps were undisturbed, the kitchen was quiet, the ghost had gone. The sisters were rather sad about it, they'd got fond of him.

One of the sisters took me up to the top-floor bathroom to look out the window. They run up there to see whether the Queen has arrived. From the bathroom window you can see the Windsor Castle flagpole. If the Queen's in residence the flag is flying.

They apologized for not giving us lunch, they were going to watch Philip play polo.

PB and I picnicked on the Windsor lawn. He (or the daily) had packed a basket with three kinds of sandwiches, a thermos of iced tea, peaches and cookies – and after-dinner mints, I love him to death, there's an Edwardian finishing touch to everything he does. Like the china ashtray he keeps on the front ledge of his car, he obviously doesn't care for the tin one that comes built in.

There's a footbridge connecting Windsor and Eton. PB wore his Eton tie, and the gate keeper saw it and said, 'You're an Eton man, sir!' and let us into rooms not open to tourists.

If you're born in the U.S. with a yearning love of classical scholarship and no college education, you are awed by a school in which for centuries boys have learned to read and write Greek and Latin fluently buy the time they're in their teens. PB took me into the original classroom, five hundred years old, and made me sit at one of the desks. They're dark, heavy oak, thickly covered with boys' initials scratched into the wood with pocket knives. Five hundred years' worth of boys' initials is something to see.

We went into the chapel where the senior boys worship, there's a roll book hanging from the aisle pew of each row so that every boy's presence can be checked off by a monitor. We read the names in one – 'Harris Major. Harris Minor. Harris Tertius' – Eton never does in English what it can do in Latin.

Along the hall outside the classrooms the high oak walls have names cut into them as thickly as the initials in the desks. PB told me when a boy graduates he pays a few shillings to the college to have his name carved in the wall. We saw Pitt's name and Shelley's (and PB showed me his own). You could spend a month crawling up and down the walls looking for names.

Heart-rending plaques to Eton's war dead. One family lost eight men in World War I, seven of them in their twenties. The Grenfells (Joyce Grenfell's husband's family) lost grandfather, father and one son – and six men in the Boer War a dozen years earlier.

We went outside and saw the playing fields where all those wars were supposedly won. Boys were playing cricket, a few strolled by swinging tennis rackets. On Saturdays the boys are allowed to wear ordinary sports clothes but we saw several in the Eton uniform: black tail coat, white shirt, striped trousers. PB says they don't wear the top hat any more except on state occasions. (Those top hats kept the boys out of trouble. If an Eton boy tried to sneak into an off-limits pub or movie, the manager could spot that top hat from anywhere in the house and throw him out.)

The faces of the boys are unbelievably clean and chiseled and beautiful. And the tail coats – which must have looked outlandish in the 1940's and 50's – look marvelously appropriate with the long hair the boys wear now. What with the cameo faces, the long hair brushed to a gleam and the perfectly cut tails, they looked like improbable Edwardian princes.

We drove back to London at four; PB wanted to take me through Marlborough House and it closes at five and we had to stop off at his flat first to get his letter. The letter opens extra doors at Marlborough House the way the Eton tie did at Eton. It's on Marlborough House stationery, it's dated 1948, it begins 'Dear Cousin Buckley' and it's signed 'George R.' (If you're an ignorant citizen of the classless American republic, the R is for Rex. For George R read George VI.) I didn't read the letter, I think it invites him to show visitors through the house whenever he likes.

We drove to Marlborough House but couldn't go through it, the guard explained the house is closed for cleaning. The Royal Chapel is open, and PB told me to go to services there one Sunday. He said it's never crowded or touristy since few people know it's open to the public. Queen Mary was married there, so I'm going, out of affection for her and Pope-Hennessy.

LATER

Laura Davidson just phoned from Oxford. She wrote me a fan letter telling me her husband, a Swarthmore professor, was working at Balliol for a year and that they and their fifteen-year-old son were fans of the book and wanted me to come to Oxford. I wrote back and told her when I was coming to London and she actually rescheduled a Paris vacation just so she'd be in Oxford when I came. When I picked up the phone just now and said hello, she said:

'Hi, it's Laura Davidson, how are you, when are you coming to Oxford? My son is dying of suspense.'

We settled on next Friday. She said there are trains almost every hour, call and let her know which one I'm on and she'll meet it. She'll carry the book so I'll know her.

I'm paranoid enough about traveling when I'm home and healthy, and the prospect of strange railroad stations and train trips over here kind of wears me out. But Oxford I have to see. There's one suite of freshman's rooms at Trinity College which John Donne, John Henry Newman and Arthur Quiller-Couch all lived in, in various long-gone eras. Whatever I know about writing English those three men taught me, and before I die I want to stand in their freshman's rooms and call their names blessed.

Q (Quiller-Couch) was all by himself my college education. I went down to the public library one day when I was seventeen looking for books on the art of writing, and found five books of lectures which Q had delivered to his students of writing at Cambridge.

'Just what I need!' I congratulated myself. I hurried home with the first volume and started reading and got to page 3 and hit a snag:

Q was lecturing to young men educated at Eton and Harrow. He therefore assumed that his students – including me – had read *Paradise Lost* as a matter of course and would understand his analysis of the 'Invocation to Light' in Book 9. So I said, 'Wait here,' and went down to the library and got *Paradise Lost* and took it home and started reading it and got to page 3, when I hit a snag:

Milton assumed I'd read the Christian version of Isaiah and the New Testament and had learned all about Lucifer and the War in Heaven, and since I'd been reared in Judaism I hadn't. So I said, 'Wait here,' and borrowed a Christian Bible and read about Lucifer and so forth, and then went back to Milton and read *Paradise Lost*, and then finally got back to Q, page 3. On page 4 or 5, I discovered that the point of the sentence at the top of the page was in Latin and the long quotation at the bottom of the page was in Greek. So I advertised in the *Saturday Review* for somebody to teach me Latin and Greek, and went back to Q meanwhile, and discovered he assumed I not only knew all the plays of Shakespeare, and Boswell's *Johnson*, but also the Second Book of Esdras, which is not in the Old Testament and not in the New Testament, it's in the Apocrypha, which is a set of books nobody had ever thought to tell me existed.

So what with one thing and another and an average of three 'Wait here's' a week, it took me eleven years to get through Q's five books of lectures.

Q also introduced me to John Henry Newman, who taught at Oriel, Oxford, and when I finish with Trinity I'm going over to Oriel and sit in John Henry's chapel and tell him I still don't know what he was talking about most of the time but I've got whole pages of the *Apologia* by heart, and I own a first edition of *The Idea of a University*.

SUNDAY, JUNE 27

PB is right, the Royal Chapel at Marlborough is not at all touristy and few people know it's open to the public. If it is.

I dressed very carefully and went down there this morning. Only a handful of people attended the service. All of them obviously worship there every Sunday, all of them obviously know each other and all of them spent most of the service trying to figure out who I was. From the whispers and sidelong glances you could reconstruct the dialogue:

'My dear, don't look now . . .'

'. . . back there on the end pew, a few rows behind . . .'

Bzz-bzz-bzz.

One angular, elderly lady got out her spectacles just to have a good long squint at me. Then she turned to the wispy friend sitting next to her and shook her head 'No!' firmly. The wispy lady refused to be daunted. She kept staring at me and with the tentative half-smile you use when you know the face but just can't place it. I made the mistake of smiling back, and from then on neither of them took their eyes off me.

I was also the only shoulder bag in the house, if I have to add that.

At the end of the service I was the first one up the aisle and out of there.

Had to come back up here for lunch, NOTHING is open here on Sunday, you could starve.

AFTERNOON

I'm lying under a tree in St. James's Park. There are three downtown parks adjoining each other – St. James's and Green, both small, and the big one, Hyde Park.

All the parks here are very serene, very gentle. Young couples go by, arm in arm, quietly, no transistor radios or guitars in hand. Families picnic on the lawn sedately. Dogs go by on leashes, equally sedate, looking neither to the right nor to the left. There was one exception: a woman came by with a small gray poodle on a leash, I said hello to the poodle and he veered toward me, always-glad-to-meet-a-friend, but the woman yanked him back.

'Please don't do that!' she said to me sharply. 'I'm trying to teach him good manners.'

I thought, 'A pity he can't do the same for you,' and had a sudden vision of Dog Hill on a Sunday afternoon and wondered how everybody was.

We had a picnic there one night – Dick, who lives in my building and owns an English sheep dog, and my friend Nikki and I. I had some cold turkey for sandwiches and I deviled some eggs, and Dick made a thermos of bloody Marys and we went over to the hill with Chester-the-Sheep-Dog. Nikki came up from her office and met us there. You have to be crazy to picnic on Dog Hill, but Dick and I thought we'd try it. We didn't get there till six-thirty, most of the dogs had gone home.

Dog Hill, is a broad, sloping hill in Central Park, and the largest canine Social Hall in the world. On a weekend afternoon you'll see forty or fifty dogs up there, charging around off leash meeting friends. (You don't take a dog to Dog Hill unless he's a friend to the world but I never met a New York dog who wasn't.) On a good day you'll see everything from Afghans and Norwegian elkhounds to Shih-tzus and Lhasa Apsos, not to mention all the standard brands. The dog owners sit on the grass or stand around like parents at a children's party, keeping an eye out for sudden spats over whose stick it is or whose ball it is.

'George, if you can't play nicely we're going home!'

'Mabel, get off him! I don't wanna hear about it, just get off him!'

You do not stretch out on the grass to sunbathe because if a couple of great Danes and a collie are having a race and you're lying in their path they're not going to detour for you.

Dick and Nikki and I settled at the top of the hill and Dick poured out the bloody Marys in paper cups. A few dogs were playing halfway down the hill, and normally Chester-the-Sheep-Dog would have joined them. But he'd smelled the picnic basket all the way to the park so he just loped down the hill and sniffed everybody and then came back up, figuring he'd hang around us till dinner time.

I understood this, so when I got out the sandwiches I gave Chester a sliver of turkey out of mine. That was all it took. In five seconds, there was a semicircle of dogs in front of me: every dog left on the hill had come to the picnic.

There were two basset-hound brothers named Sam and Sid, Romulus, who is a great Dane, a beagle I didn't know and a very timid German shepherd pup named Helga – all standing stock still, eyes glued to me and my turkey sandwich. The beagle was drooling.

I had an extra sandwich in reserve so I sacrificed the one I'd started on and gave each dog in turn a sliver of turkey. (Helga was very nervous, she was anxious to step up for her piece of turkey but how did she know I wouldn't bite her?)

Chester-the-Sheep-Dog figured there was too much competition, so he left and trotted back to visit Nikki's sandwich. And just as I was feeding the rest of the dogs the last of the turkey, Nikki set up a great to-do because Chester had taken a sip of her bloody mary. Dick called, 'Chester! Sit!' And Chester, wanting to show how well-trained he was, sat on Nikki's deviled egg. Whereupon Nikki took a fit. (She's young and pretty and she went to the London School of Economics for a year, but she's a cat lover.) I turned and called Chester, hoping to lure him away from her – and the instant my back was turned, the beagle (Morton, I think his name was) seized the untouched reserve sandwich and made off down the hill with it.

His mother came up to apologize and thank me; she said he only eats chicken and now she wouldn't have to cook for him when they got home.

We walked back down through the park to the Seventy-second Street entrance, past a baseball game and an impromptu marimba band fighting a rock concert that penetrated clear up from Fifty-ninth Street.

Lying in peaceful St. James's, I realize how much a city's parks reflect the character of its people. The parks here are tranquil, quiet, a bit reserved, and I love them. But on a long-term basis I would sorely miss the noisy exuberance of Central Park.

9 P.M.

The Colonel phoned up, he's back. He said, What part of our glorious countryside did I want to see most? I told him I was going to Oxford next Friday and I'd be very grateful if he wanted to drive me there.

'Well, now!' he boomed. 'We can do much better than that, my dear! If you're free on Thursday, we can drive through the Cotswolds and be in Stratford-on-Avon in time for dinner and the theatre, and drive on to meet your friends in Oxford on Friday.'

I was wildly excited, which surprised me. I'm not terribly attracted to birthplaces, to me Shakespeare was born in the Globe Theatre. But when he said he was taking me to Stratford-on-Avon I shouted in my excitement, you can't help it.

Asked if he knew a shop where I could buy a cheap overnight bag and he said:

'Nonsense, I'll send a nice BOAC bag round to you.'

I tell you it's insidious being an ersatz Duchess, people rushing to give you what you want before you've had time to want it. If I kept this up for more than a month it would ruin my moral fiber.

I'd left my number with Leo Mark's answering service and he called back this morning. He was a beautiful Oxford baritone. (Or Cambridge, I don't know the difference.) He and his wife will pick me up for dinner tomorrow night at seven.

Dinner and *Midsummer Night* with the Grenfells tonight, so this morning I took my cocktail dress downstairs and said to the young desk clerk:

'Can I have this pressed before five this evening?'

'D'you want it cleaned or laundered?' he asked.

'No, just pressed,' I said.

He stared at me blankly.

'Do you want it sent to the Cleaner's?' he repeated, emphasizing each word as carefully as if I were Russian or deaf, 'or do you want it sent to the Laundry?'

'I don't want it cleaned *or* washed,' I said, enunciating as carefully as if *he* were Russian or deaf, 'I just want it *pressed*. It's *wrinkled*.'

This seemed to stun him. He stared at me a moment. Then he pulled himself together, mumbled, ''Scuse me,' and went off to consult the Office. In a minute he was back.

'If you'll go up to Room 315 and speak to the housekeeper,' he said, 'p'raps she can help you.'

I went up and knocked on the door of Room 315 and explained my problem to the motherly-looking housekeeper. She nodded understandingly and said, 'Come this way, dear,' and led me down to the end of the hall and opened the door to a little dungeon with an ironing board and an ancient monster iron in one corner.

'You can press it right here, dear,' she said. 'Mind the iron, the cord's a bit frayed.'

I was a bit frayed myself by this time. The dress is silk, the iron was unfamiliar and didn't look friendly. I took the dress down to the desk and told the clerk to send it to the Cleaner's, he was very relieved. This is what comes of being allergic to chemical fabrics in a drip-dry world.

I got lost trying to find the Waldorf on foot, overshot it by two blocks, ran back and tore into the lobby ten minutes late – and Joyce Grenfell must have been watching the door, she came out to meet me looking exactly as she looks on the screen.

She led the way into the dining room and introduced me to her husband – 'RegGEE!' she mostly calls him – and their Australian friends, Sir Charles and Lady Fitts, he's a famous doctor. I sat down, suddenly shaken by the fact that these four distinguished people had wanted to meet *me*. I tell you, life is extraordinary. A few years ago I couldn't write anything or sell anything, I'd passed the age where you know all the returns are in, I'd had my chance and done my best and failed. And how was I to know the miracle waiting to happen round the corner in late middle age? *84, Charing Cross Road* was no best seller, you understand; it didn't make me rich or famous. It just got me hundreds of letters and phone calls from people I never knew existed; it got me wonderful reviews; it restored a self-confidence and self-esteem I'd lost somewhere along the way, God knows how many years ago. It brought me to England. It changed my life.

The Grenfells had got house seats for themselves and the Australians, and when Joyce read I was in town she invited me along – even though it meant Reggie had to give up his house seat to me and go sit in the balcony, I was horrified.

It's an experience walking down a theatre aisle with a famous theatre personality. Every eye in the audience was on her, and when we took our seats you could feel necks craning all over the house.

Peter Brook's production initially a shock, half play, half noisy circus. Mrs G. was immediately entranced; I kept worrying about whether Puck was going to fall off his stilts or drop the plates he was juggling. Halfway through the second act I was suddenly moved, and I thought, 'I resent it but I love it.' Stimulates you to death, seeing Shakespeare explode all over a stage like that.

They drove me home after saying goodbye to the Australians. Joyce drove because it's a new car and Reggie wanted her to get the feel of it.

She had a hell of a time in Bloomsbury. The one-way streets here set drivers crazy, you have to go five blocks out of your way to find a street going in the right direction. And she was NOT going to drop me across Shaftesbury Avenue on the wrong corner of Great Russell Street, she would NOT drop me round the corner on Bloomsbury Street, the hotel entrance was on Great Russell and she was By God going to drop me in front of the door. And after zigzagging north and south for half an hour she triumphantly did it and accepted my congratulations graciously.

She said they're 'going on holiday' but will be back on July 13 for her church dialogue. She has a monthly church dialogue with a minister – on The Nature of Love and The Nature of Beauty and so forth – at a noon service at St. Mary LeBeau's Church in Cheapside. She said Why don't I come to the July 13 dialogue and then come to dinner that night and they'll drive me around to see the sights. I told her I wasn't certain I'd still be here on the thirteenth, though I'm hoping to last till the fifteenth.

During the second act, that cold caught up with me. I started to cough and nearly strangled trying to muffle it. I leaned over and whispered to Joyce apologetically:

'I've been fighting a cold all weekend.'

She thought about this a moment and then leaned over and whispered back:

'Oh, have it.'

So I'm having it. Sitting up in bed hacking and snuffling and even that doesn't depress me. I seem to be living in a state of deep hypnosis, every time I mail a postcard home I could use Euphoria for a return address.

TUESDAY, JUNE 29

I'm in the dining-room having my fourth or fifth cup of coffee, feeling the way you feel the first morning of a full-blown cold. I was going to call Leo Marks and cancel dinner but if I stay in the hotel all day I'll want to get out of it tonight so I'll keep the date and try not to cough in their faces.

The dining-room's emptying out now; between eight and nine every morning it's jammed and the waiters are frantic. The room rate here includes 'Full English Breakfast' and we all eat everything: fruit juice or cereal, bacon and eggs, toast and marmalade, tea or coffee (and the girl who brings the coffee pot asks: 'Black or white?').

The breakfast regulars always include British Willie Lomans up from the country on business and a sprinkling of middle-aged women for all over 'the U.K.' traveling alone. They never say 'Great Britain,' it's 'the U.K.' – United Kingdom.) Several pale, pointy-nosed professors are stowing away enough fuel to see them through the day at the British Museum, they all look as if they lunch on yogurt.

This morning, a long table of Scots matrons here for a conference accompanied by a scrubbed young vicar. Ladies all complained they didn't sleep a *wink* for the noise, the motorcars go by in the street just-all-NIGHT. Quietest place I ever slept in. They should try tucking up over Second Avenue, where the trucks start rolling at 3 A.M.

Lots of Russian and Czech tourist families here, with blond, well-behaved children. Several parties of German tourists, middle-aged to make it worse. (The young ones you don't mind; they-didn't-do-it.) The tourist parties all eat with one eye on the clock, they've all signed up for some bus tour and the buses leave the hotel at nine sharp. At two minutes to nine there's a heavy Russian-Czech-German bustle and a ponderous exodus to the lobby – where the Czechs gesticulate wildly at signs they can't read and the German tour leader bawls, '*Achtung!*' and '*Halte!*' to get everybody lined up. The Russians just stolidly find the bus and get on it.

The only Americans here besides me turned up at breakfast this morning for the first time: three California college girls, blond, tanned, radiantly healthy, conferring anxiously on whether Full English Breakfast meant you could order everything, it's all free with the room? I asked the waitress for more coffee and when they heard my American accent one of them came over to my table to ask about what you can order and Are you supposed to tip. I said No, the management adds 12 per cent to your bill for tips. Alvaro was scandalized when I tried to tip him the first day. No, No! he said, It is all cared for!

Will now retire to my room with last weekend's newspapers and their fiendish crossword puzzles and spend the morning 'enjoying poor health,' as my mother used to say.

Crime Note

From Saturday's evening paper:

£50 FINE FOR TEACHER
WHO ASSAULTED GIRL
AT WIMBLEDON

A 54-year-old teacher of statistics at London University ... appeared in court today charged with insulting behavior at Wimbledon tennis championships.

He was fined £50 after admitting indecent assault in the standing area of No. 1 Court.

Temporary Det. Con. Patrick Doyle told Wimbledon magistrates that [the defanant] put an arm around an 18-year-old girl and held her breasts.

[The defendant], who is married, said:

'I suffered a temporary lapse of commonsense.

'It is ridiculous that a man in my position should do such a thing.'

A Wimbledon umpire ... aged 66, was also accused of insulting behavior at Wimbledon. Altogether 10 men appeared, charged with insulting behavior.

The sixty-six-year-old umpire was extra lucky, they put his picture in the paper.

Here's a help-wanted ad for you:

BUCKINGHAM PALACE. Vacancy in the central wash-up of the main kitchen, for female applicants only. Non-residential. . . . Apply in writing to Master of the Household, Buckingham Palace, London SW 1

Wouldn't you like to take that job for one day, just to listen to the gossip?

11 P.M.

Leo Marks phoned up from the lobby at seven, I went down to meet them in my silk-dress-and-coat, red nose and watery eyes, and Leo, who is dark-haired and good-looking, said:

'How d'you do, we're very glad you could come, go back upstairs and get a coat, it's chilly and it's raining.'

I came up and got my old blue coat, went down and told him:

'You've made me ruin the effect of my whole costume.'

And Ena – his wife, very small and blond – said earnestly:

'You can take the coat off when we get to the restaurant, we're dining at a hotel, you can take it off in the lobby!' and peered at me anxiously to see if that was all right.

She ought to look delicate but doesn't, you get a sense of wiry strength. She might be a small blonde athlete but she's a portrait painter. She paints under her own name, Ena Gaussen. Leo told me she's done portraits for Hayley Mills and Pamela Brown and won all sorts of citations; she doesn't look old enough.

They took me to the Stafford, a very old, gracious hotel rather like the Plaza. I had a couple of martinis to clear the sinuses and discovered Leo is a gin drinker. He's also a TV and film writer and we found we'd worked for the same TV producer – in different seasons and on different continents – and we talked shop. Ena didn't mind, she thinks we're both terribly witty.

He calls her 'little thing.'

'Little thing, you want the lobster again?'

He asked me if I knew of the pianist Eileen Joyce and told me: 'She's just been made a Dame of the British Empire and she wants the little thing to paint her in her Dame's robes.'

When it was too late to go see it, Ena told me one of Leo's films was playing around the corner; I was very impressed. I've always believed film writing is the most difficult form a writer can work in.

'Tell me,' said Leo. 'You've written a beautiful book. Why haven't we heard of you before? What was wrong with your earlier work? Too good or not good enough?'

'Not good enough,' I said. And he nodded and went on to something else, and I think that's when we became soul mates.

It was a marvelous evening. I'd love to see them again but I haven't the nerve to call and suggest it. Being a visiting fireman has its own courtesy rules.

cough-cough–cough–cough–cough.

WEDNESDAY, JUNE 30

Being a celebrity means you're paged to the phone three times during breakfast, and the first time you come back to the table your eggs are cold, the second time you come back your eggs are GONE and the third time you carry a fresh plate of eggs out to the lobby phone booth with you.

Joyce Grenfell phoned to ask how my cough was and to say Do-be-here-on-the-thirteenth. I told her I mean to. The hotel switchboard operator recognized her voice and didn't put the call through to the booth, I took it at the desk, and the switchboard operator and cashier both like to collapse when I held the receiver out so they could hear her call, 'RegGEEE!' when she wanted to ask him something.

Nora phoned and heard my croak and said Why didn't I come out to North London and let her nurse me? That's all she needs; she's working at a full-time job since Frank died.

The Colonel phoned to say the BOAC bag 'will be sent round this A.M.' and he'll pick me up at ten tomorrow morning for the trip to Stratford-and-Oxford.

After breakfast I went across the street for Kleenex and cough drops. There's a string of small stores opposite the hotel on Great Russell Street: a stationary store, A Unisex Beauty Shop, a Cinema Bookshop and an Indian food store that carries health-food items. There's also a large YWCA Women's Residence and a curb-side fruit stand. I stopped at the fruit stand for some peaches, and while I was waiting for change I noticed a bulletin board in a glass case outside the stationary store. Got my change and went over to read the bulletin board. At first glance the notices seem to be Items-for-Sale and Situations-Wanted ads, but you don't have to read very far to discover your mistake. To the pure in heart, however, all bulletin boards are pure, viz.: (This is the entire bulletin-board list.)

Hot Pants for sale. Phone . . . .

Ex-actress will give lessons. French or anything. Phone
. . . .

Male model. All services. TV, photog, rubber, leather.
Corrective training. Phone . . . .

Model seeks unusual positions. Miss Coucher. Phone
. . . .

New lovely blonde doll for sale. Walks, talks. Phone . .

Tom Tamer gives lessons in the most strict deportment.
Phone . . . .

French girl. Ex-governess, many positions. Seeks new
pupils. Both sexes. Phone . . . .

Three rucksacks wanted. Good condition. Reasonable.
Contact YWCA, Great Russell St.

---

7 P.M.

Ena blew in at five-thirty with a brown paper bag full of lemons, honey and lime juice for my cough. She said she had an urge all morning to call me and hang on the phone but felt shy about it; I said we're both too inhibited. She wanted me to have dinner with them tomorrow night. I told her I'd be in Stratford but would be back Friday, and her face fell.

'We go down to the country on Friday and we won't be back until the tenth!' she said.

'Never mind,' I said. 'I have every intention of lasting till the fifteenth.'

She looked distressed.

'You can't go home that soon! We've only just met you!' she said, 'Look, when you run out of money why don't you go down and stay at our place in the country? We shan't be using it at all after the tenth, you could stay there all summer – if you don't mind our coming down weekends?' peering at me anxiously. People unhinge me.

She just left to meet Leo at his mother's.

The BOAC bag arrived, and I phoned the Colonel and thanked him. He advised me to eat a lot:

'You must always feed a cold. If you don't give the germs food to eat they'll feed on you.'

Will now go down to the dining room and feed the germs.

LATER

I ordered 'Chicken Maryland,' which turned out to be a slice of chicken, breaded and fried flat like a veal cutlet, accompanied by a strip of bacon and a fat sausage. Dessert was 'Coupe Jamaica,' I didn't order it but the couple at the next table did: a long, narrow cookie sticking out of a ball of vanilla ice cream that rested on a slice of canned pineapple. It would probably confuse Jamaica as much as the chicken would confuse Maryland. But somebody once told me there's a restaurant in Paris that lists on the menu 'Pommes à la French Fries.'

THURSDAY, JULY 1
STRATFORD
MIDNIGHT

I'm writing this in bed, in a luxurious motel room: wall-to-wall carpet, easy chair, TV set, dressing table and a beautiful adjoining bath in mauve tile, life at the Kenilworth was never like this.

I tell you my Colonel has got to be the world's kindest, most considerate man. We left London in the usual gray weather, it gets to you after a while; I told him I was beginning to crave sunshine the way a thirsty man craves water. We drove into the Cotswolds and about mid-morning the weather cleared and the sun came out briefly. The minute it did, he pulled over to the side of the road, got a deck chair out of the trunk and set it up on a stretch of grass for me so I could lie in the sun the little while it lasted. He told me his wife died of cancer 'after two years of hell'; he must have been marvelous through it.

We passed Stoke Poges and he told me that's where Gray's country churchyard is. Gray's 'Elegy' was my mother's favorite poem, I'd like to have seen the churchyard but we didn't have time for the detour.

As we drove, he told me a long-winded story about a widow he knows who fell in love with a man and was invited to his villa in Italy, and when she got there she found she had no room of her own, the man actually meant her to share his BEDroom, d'ye see, and Well-I-mean-to-say, said the Colonel, she wasn't aTALL that sort, and it was a shock to find the Bounder wanted only One Thing. I wondered why he told me the story since he didn't figure in it – and then it dawned on me that this was his tactful way of assuring me that he didn't expect me to share his bedroom at Stratford. It had never occurred to me; he's much too straitlaced and old-school, it would have been out of character.

He told me he retired from publishing to nurse his wife, and after she died he took the job at Heathrow for the fun of it.

If I see a man and his wife and grown daughters standing together looking a bit out of sorts, I walk up to the man and say: "Sir, which of these ladies is your wife?" And he beams! And she beams!' And the Colonel roars with laughter.

'If I see a middle-aged couple looking a bit down, you know, I walk up to them and ask: "Are you folks on your honeymoon?" and you ought to see their faces! They know I'm joshing – some of 'em do – but still, y'know, they can't help being pleased.

'If I see a child crying – some of them get very tired and upset at a big airport, they're hungry, they want to be at home – and when I see one crying I walk up and ask the parents if they know where I can find a nice little girl because mine is grown up. And then I discover the little girl who's crying and I say she's exactly the sort of little girl I've been looking for, and I ask if she'd consider being my little girl.' And he ends each story with that booming laugh of pure pleasure.

The Cotswolds are just what I always thought they'd be: stretches of green countryside pocketed with English villages that seem not to have changed since the time of Elizabeth I. We had lunch at a pub near a country church where, said the Colonel, 'Hampden started the Revolution.' Didn't have the nerve to tell him I don't know who Hampden was.

Stratford is beyond Oxford, we backtrack tomorrow. We passed Oxford road signs and I told him about Great Tew. Years ago, somebody sent me a postcard – a photograph of five thatched cottages falling down a hillside – and wrote on the back:

This is Great Tew. You can't find it on the map, you have to get lost on the way to Oxford.

The photo was so idealized a view of rural England I didn't believe the village really existed. I used to stare at that postcard by the hour. Kept it for years, stuck in my Oxford English Verse.

'Well!' said the Colonel, inspired by the challenge. 'We shall just have to find Great Tew and see if it's still the same.'

He wove in and out through the Cotswolds and finally we came to signs pointing to Tew and Little Tew and rounded a curve and there was Great Tew, looking exactly as it had looked on my postcard: five ancient stone houses with thatched roofs, still falling down the hillside. The Colonel said they date back to Henry VIII. Five hundred years later they're still lived in: there were white curtains and flower boxes at the windows, and every front lawn had a rose garden.

He parked the car – the only car in sight – and we got out. Down the road from the cottages was the village's only other building, a one-room

General Store and Post Office. We went in. There was no one in there but the woman who runs it, and we hadn't seen a soul outside.

The Colonel bought ice cream, I asked for a glass of milk and was handed a quart bottle and a straw. The Colonel told the proprietress that I had come 'all the way from New York' and had 'particularly asked to see Great Tew.' While they talked I was clutching the quart bottle, entirely preoccupied with trying to get at least half a pint of it inside me so as not hurt her feelings. When I'd drunk that much I looked around for an inobtrusive place to park the bottle, and discovered that the store had suddenly filled up with people – men in country caps and women in print dresses. I moved out of their way and they all stepped up to the counter and bought cigarettes and newspapers. A few children came in and were promptly shooed out by the proprietress.

The Colonel finished his ice cream, took my milk bottle off my hands and disposed of a pint and a half of milk as if it were a glass of water, and we left.

'Well!' he said as we walked back to the car. 'We've given them something to talk about for a month! Did you notice how the entire village came in to see the people from Outer Space? As soon as they saw my car with the London plates they came running. Did you see how she shooed the kids out? That was to make room for all the grownups. They won't see travelers here from one year's end to the next. And from New York? Not in a lifetime!'

And we were a few hours from London by car.

Everybody I knew who went to Stratford had warned me that it was a commerical tourist trap, so I was prepared for it. The first thing we saw as we drove in was a huge billboard advertising the JUDITH SHAKESPEARE WIMPY HAMBURGER BAR, the Colonel was purple with fury. It doesn't matter in the least. You find Shakespeare's house and pay your fee to enter – and just to walk up the stairs gripping the huge railing, just to walk into the bedroom and touch the walls, and then come back down and stand in the kitchen that saw him in and out every day of his growing up has to melt the bones of anyone born speaking English.

We saw *Much Ado* at the shiny modern theatre, very conventional, but very well acted. The Colonel slept through most of it and I didn't blame him.

Will now go climb into the mauve bathtub, we leave for Oxford early in the morning and I mean to get the most out of this posh palace first.

I saw Trinity College and walked the Yard John Donne walked; I saw Oriel and sat in John Henry's chapel. And what I went through to see them, you purely will not credit. I think I finally had a temper tantrum. I hope I did.

We reached Oxford a little before noon and found the Davidson's house on a typical tree-shaded, college-town street. Laura was there waiting for us. She said the Professor was working and son David was in school counting the hours till he could join us for tea.

She has a throaty voice and a lovely, odd accent; she was born in Vienna and grew up in England. She and her husband were both refugee children from Hitler's Germany.

She was vastly amused by the Colonel, she called him 'the Commahnder' and said he reminded her of Winnie the Pooh. My problem was that by this time the Colonel and I had already had thirty straight hours of Togetherness and I'm not equipped for it, not even with the best friend I have on earth, which he isn't. Over lunch in a campus pub, he announced (à propos of nothing, I think he was just carried away by Oxford):

'The British Empire will be brought back by popular demand! An Egyptian said to me recently: "Why do you English sit modestly at home when you're needed all over the world?"'

For some reason this aggravated me and I said something rude, and we had at it for a couple of minutes till Laura tactfully inserted herself between us like a housemother, and restored harmony.

After lunch, my troubles started. I said Could we please go see Trinity and Oriel Colleges? and Laura said First we must visit the Bodleian Reading Room, it was a magnificent Wren building and her husband was working there and wanted to meet me. We went there and I met the Professor and saw the Reading Room, vaulted ceiling, towering shelves and staircases, all spectacular.

We came out, and I said Now could we go see Trinity and Oriel? and Laura said Did I know the Bodleian library stacks ran for a mile under the pavements? and showed me which pavements. And the Colonel said he had studied one summer at Wadham College and I must see Wadham Yard. And he and Laura agreed they must take me down the main street to Blackwell's Bookshop, very famous bookshop and they both knew how interested I was in bookshops. (I despair of ever getting it through anybody's head I am not interested in bookshops, I am interested in what's written in the books. I don't browse in bookshops, I browse in libraries, where you can take a book home and read it, and if you like it you go to a bookshop and buy it.)

So, on the one shining day of my life when I was actually in Oxford, I'm dragged down the main street, I'm having every monument and every church pointed out to me, they're all by Wren (everything's by Wren), I'm hauled through Blackwell's Bookshop table by table and shelf by shelf, and the next thing I know I'm walking around the Yard of some place called Wadham, for God's sake. And it's getting later and later, any minute we'll be off to Laura's house to meet her son for tea and after tea the Colonel and I will be leaving for London.

So I had a tantrum.

I stood in the middle of Wadham Yard and hollered: 'WHEN ARE WE GONNA SEE SOMETHING *I* WANNA SEE?'

Laura hurried over to me and got very kindly and understanding (she used to be a Social Worker) and said:

'The Commahnder's loving it. Wadham is his only link with Oxford.'

And I replied reasonably: 'HE LIVES OVER HERE, HE CAN SEE IT ANY DAMN DAY HE WANTS TO!'

And she said Sh-sh, and the Colonel strode over and said What is it? What's the matter? And they both thought it over and decided I was right, Now what was it I specially wanted to see? And Laura said Was I sure there was an Oriel College, she couldn't find it on her map, and the Colonel said Was I perhaps thinking of Trinity-Cambridge, Prince Charles had gone to Trinity-Cambridge.

And I said carefully No, I was thinking of John Henry Newman, who taught Anglican theology at Oriel College and died a Catholic cardinal and was a little cracked in many ways but who wrote English like few men on God's green earth ever wrote English, one of the few being John Donne, and they both went to Trinity-Oxford, so could I please see Trinity and Oriel.

We came out of Wadham Yard and stood on a corner and Laura studied her map again and sure enough, there was an Oriel College. We went there and I sat in the chapel by myself and communed with

John Henry. (Outside, I learned later, the Colonel was telling Laura I was 'a crazy, mixed-up kid.')

We went to Trinity and I walked around the Yard. And that was all. Tourists are not allowed inside the college buildings.

Unless you're interested chiefly in the architecture, visiting Oxford is very frustrating. All that is open to tourists at any college is the Yard outside it and the chapel just inside the front door. Everything else is off limits. So I'll never see those freshman's rooms and I'll never know whether there is still 'much snap-dragon' growing outside the window, as there was in Newman's day. And I'll never see the rooms Milton wrote in or the rooms Q taught in at Cambridge because Cambridge has the same restrictions.

We got back to Laura's house – five minutes before fifteen-year-old David came home panting and breathless, he'd run all the way just to meet me, I've never been so flattered.

The Colonel had a cup of tea and then marched off to a bedroom and took a nap and Laura and David and I sat in the kitchen and swapped stories about Philadelphia, where their home is and where I grew up. They go back in September.

Over tea, Laura got very guilt-ridden about my day and begged me to sneak back up on a train one day and do Oxford by myself. ('Don't even let us know you're here if you don't want to,' she said, and David said, 'Why can't she let us know she's here?') I told her I'd seen what I most wanted to see – and within the limits of what was possible, it was true.

Driving back to London we passed a village called Thame – pronounced as spelled, like 'same' with a lisp – and the Colonel told me why the Thames is pronounced Temmes. Seems the first Hanover king had a thick German accent and couldn't pronounce *th*. He called the river 'te Temmes' and since the-king-is-always-right everybody else had to call it the Temmes and it's been the Temmes ever since.

He told me about all the widows who depend on him for advice, they all seem to have 'lashings of money' and children who adore him.

We got home at nine. I'll be grateful to him all my life for the trip, but it was a lot of togetherness. I holed up in the bar to write this; the Lounge is more comfortable and also free but anybody who talked to me tonight would've got bit.

Flock of messages for me at the desk. Marc Connelly phoned, the

London *Reader's Digest* phoned, Nikki's Barbara phoned and a woman I never heard of phoned. The desk clerk was very impressed by all the messages. So was I.

SATURDAY, JULY 3

I just called Marc Connelly. He was a reigning playwright when I was a child and my parents were rabid theatregoers. They should have lived to see the fan letter he wrote me. It came just before Christmas and I almost threw it away without opening it. His name is on some way-out charity I don't care for, and I thought the letter was another appeal. Not till my hand was hovering over the wastebasket did it occur to me that the envelope was very thin for a charity appeal. So I opened it.

> Dear Miss Hanff:
> What with all those other letters closing in on you (How many grateful people have written up to now — one million? two million?) I don't expect you'll get around to reading this for a year or more.
> Anyway, sooner or later you'll find it's just like all the others: telling you that '84 Charing Cross Road' is tender and funny and incandescent and beautiful and makes the reader rejoice to be living in the same century with you.
>
> Genuflections,
> Marc Connelly

And I almost threw it away without opening it.

I met him a few months later, and he told me he'd be in London in July, at his club, and he'd take me to see what a gentleman's club looks like.

He'll pick me up tomorrow at one for lunch.

Can't call Nikki's Barbara or the *Reader's Digest* till Monday, both offices are closed Saturdays. Nikki — the friend whose deviled egg Chester-the-Sheep-Dog sat on at our Central Park picnic — works for a news magazine in New York. Barbara works for the same news magazine in London. The two girls have never met but they talk to each other every day over the teletype so they're good friends. Nikki made us promise to meet while I'm here.

I can definitely make it till the fifteenth, dinner invitations coming in nicely. I just phoned that woman I never heard of who called while I was away. She said she and her husband are fans of the book and want me to come to dinner to see their part of London. I'm going there Tuesday.

Every breathing tourist who has breakfast in this hotel has seen a piece of royalty but me. (How I know is, whoever is breakfasting alone at the next table strikes up a conversation with you, usually beginning with, '*Might* I trouble you for the marmalade?') Either they saw the Family leave for Windsor, or they were getting on the elevator at Harrods just as the Queen Mother was getting off it, or they saw Princess Anne wave as she entered the hospital, or they just-by-good-chance happened to be passing by this boys' school as seven-year-old Prince Edward was coming out with the other boys. So this morning I'm going down to Buckingham Palace and try my luck.

10 P.M.

Went down to Buckingham Place, walked up and down along the spiked iron fence for a while but all I saw was one more anachronism: a seventeenth-century carriage drawn by white horses, driven through the gates by a fancy-dress coachman, and inside the carriage a pair of cold-eyed diplomats in top hats with cigarettes hanging out of their twentieth-century faces.

I find the treatment of royalty distinctly peculiar. The royal family lives in palaces heavily screened from prying eyes by fences, grounds, gates, guards, all designed to ensure the family absolute privacy. And every newspaper in London carried headlines announcing PRINCESS ANNE HAS OVARIAN CYST REMOVED. I mean you're a young girl reared in heavily guarded seclusion and every beer drinker in every pub knows the precise state of your ovaries.

Walked home by way of Lincoln's Inn Fields, a park this side of the Inns of Court facing a lovely row of houses on a street called King's Bench Walk. Sat on a bench and looked at the houses and listened to the conversations going by:

'. . . well, not uncouth, he looks like a Highland rabbi.'

'. . . but she wasn't getting anywhere out there so she packed it in and now she's home, looking . . .'

'They're all out to save their own neckties, you can bloody well bet on that!'

I'm in the bar again. I don't normally drink after dinner but in this hotel they think you're strange if you drink *before* dinner. So at 10 P.M. I'm having a martini. More or less.

The first night I came in here I said to the young bartender:

'A martini, please.'

He reached for a bottle of Martini & Rossi vermouth and poured a glass full of it before I could scream WAIT A MINUTE!

'Would you put the gin in first, please?' I asked.

'Oh!' he said. 'You want a *gin* martini.'

He got the gin bottle and a shaker, and I said:

'Would you put some ice in the shaker, please? I like it cold.'

'Right-o!' he said. He put an ice cube in the shaker, poured a jigger of gin on it, added half a cup of vermouth, stirred once, poured it out and handed it to me with a flouish. I paid him and shuffled over to a table telling myself sternly:

'Don't be like all those American tourists who can't adapt to another country's customs, just drink it.'

Nobody could drink it.

The next time I came in it was dinner time, the bar was empty and the bartender and I got chummy; he said Wasn't I the writer?? and told me his name was Bob. I said Did he mind if this time we used my recipe instead of his and he said Right-o, just tell him exactly what I wanted.

I said First could we start with four ice cubes in the shaker. He thought I was crazy but he put three cubes in (he was short on ice). He poured a jigger of gin in the shaker, and I said:

'Okay, now another jigger of gin.'

He stared at me, shook his head in disbelief and added a second jigger of gin.

'Okay, now one more,' I said.

'MORE gin?' he said, and I said:

'Yes, and lower your voice.'

He poured the third jigger, still shaking his head. He reached for the vermouth bottle, and I said:

'I'll pour that.'

I added a few drops of vermouth, stirred vigorously, let him pour it out for me and told him it was perfect.

Now he makes it by himself but he never can bring himself to add that third jigger of gin, he thinks he'll look up later and see me sprawled face down on a bar table sodden drunk.

SUNDAY, JULY 4

Got very gloomy remembering the days before the Vietnam War when I gloried in my country's history and July 4 meant something.

Marc Connelly picked me up at one. I wore the brown skirt and white blazer, and he said, 'Don't you look fine in your little yachting outfit,' and saluted. He said we'd have lunch at the Hilton because nothing else is open.

The Hilton has several dining rooms, he took me into the largest. It was crowded with sleek, well-groomed men and beautifully dressed women; nobody looked dowdy the way they do at the Kenilworth. And the strawberries were huge and the cream was thick and the rolls were hot and the butter was cold and the chicken livers were done to perfection.

But at the Kenilworth, nobody sends the eggs back. Nobody talks to the waiters with the casual rudeness that says, 'I am better than you are because I am richer.' And the waiters don't answer with that studied blend of contempt and servility, and none are obsequious – my God, Alvaro couldn't even pronounce it. And nobody at the Kenilworth breakfast table looks bitter or discontented, no men at the Kenilworth moodily drink their lunch, no women with hard-painted faces keep a sharp eye on their handbags.

You look at the faces in the Hilton dining room and first you want to smack them and then you just feel sorry for them, not a soul in the room looked happy.

After lunch Marc took me to his club on St. James's Street. The building looks narrow from the street; but you step through the doorway into an enormous drawing room with other large rooms beyond it, you climb a great curved staircase, the wall alongside lined with portraits of club presidents all looking like Peter Ustinov, and upstairs you find more spacious rooms – breakfast room, game rooms, reading rooms. We watched cricket for a while on color TV in one of the game rooms. At least, I watched it. Marc went to sleep. He's eighty, he's allowed.

I woke him at three to say I was leaving and he said cheerfully, 'Now you know what I think of cricket!' and saw me to the door and told me to walk down Jermyn Street and look in the shop windows.

I did that, and then went over to Regent and was walking down

Waterloo on my way to St. James's Park when who should I run into, standing on a corner on a little pedestal looking small and spruce, but Gentlemanly Johnny Burgoyne who lost the Battle of Saratoga to us rebels. I think he was supposed to link up with some other general's forces but there was a snafu and Burgoyne's entire army was captured. He'd be pleased to know he's the most appealing character in *The Devil's Disciple*, he was a playwright himself. He wrote a play and produced it in Boston, with his officers in the cast, when his troops occupied the city. Can't imagine what possessed the British to put up a statue to him, I suppose he won some battle somewhere but he lost the American Revolution almost singlehanded.

Wished him a happy Fourth.

When I got down to the Mall there was a band concert going on. In honor of the Fourth of July the band played 'Dixie' and 'The Battle Hymn of the Republic.' Well, why not? I don't know who Hampden was, why should they know July Fourth doesn't commemorate the Civil War?

Sunned myself in St. James's Park for a while but the band concert went on and on and I wasn't in the mood so I thought I'd walk up to Lincoln's Inn Fields instead. I couldn't get back up the broad marble steps, they were jammed with concert listeners, so I walked along the Mall looking for another exit. I came to a small flight of steps, maneuvered my way around the people sitting on them and came up into Carlton Gardens, a beautiful street of very plush apartment houses. It reminded me a little of Sutton Place: the buildings, the expensive cars at the curb, the starched nanny going by pushing a pram, all reeked of money. I walked around it and maybe I walked along an adjoining street, I'm not sure. Then I turned a corner and found myself on a street I had not been on before and the likes of which I never expect to be on again.

I don't know where I was. I could find no name to the street, I'm not even sure it was a street. It was a kind of enclosed courtyard, a cul-de-sac behind Clarence House and St. James's Palace. The anonymous white buildings on it might be the backs of the palaces. The white stone glows sumptuous and the street is absolutely still. A footstep is loud and you stand without moving, almost without breathing. There is no reek of money here, only the hallowed hush of privilege. Your mind fills with stories of the fairy-tale splendor of monarchy, the regal pomp of England's kings and queens. And then suddenly you remember Karl Marx in an untroubled grave in Highgate, and Queen Mary welcoming Gandhi as she had welcomed the rajahs before him, as George III had been forced to welcome as Ambassador to the Court of St. James old upstart John Adams. You are awed by the contrasts – by the *fact* of St. James's and Clarence House resting so serenely in Socialist England.

You decide to stop using the word 'anachronism' when a seventeenth-century carriage drives through the gates of Buckingham Palace carrying twentieth-century Russian or African diplomats to be welcomed by a queen. 'Anachronism' implies something long dead, and nothing is dead here. History, as they say, is alive and well and living in London.

MONDAY, JULY 5

Nikki's Barbara phoned this morning; we made a lunch date for Friday. I gave her a couple of questions to ask Nikki over the teletype, she'll bring the answers to lunch with her.

I called the *Readers Digest* office and the girl there said they're using the fan-mail article in the English edition but it deals only with American fan mail, didn't I have any English fans? Shades of the Colonel, didn't I just. I explained that the article was written and sold before the English fan mail arrived, and she said Would I dreadfully mind writing a page or two about the English fan mail? They go to press in a few days, they would have to have the new pages tomorrow, could I possibly?

I felt like saying, 'Lady, this is the first real vacation I've ever had in my life and I've only got ten days of it left!' But unfortunately it crossed my mind that I wouldn't be having the first real vacation of my life if it weren't for the *Reader's Digest*, so I said it would be a pleasure.

Will now shlep up the street to Deutsch's and borrow a typewriter.

LATER

Wrote three new pages and took them down to the *Digest* office in Berkeley Square and walked home by a lovely new route, straight up the Visitors' Map to the Regent's Park area and then over. Somewhere along the way I came upon a mews with a small sign on the entrance gate addressed to the passing world. The sign orders flatly:

COMMIT NO NUISANCE

The more you stare at that, the more territory it covers. From dirtying the streets to housebreaking to invading Vietnam, that covers all the territory there is.

There was a letter at the desk for me when I came back:

Can you be here Wednesday at noon *sharp*, for a visit to two stately homes of England?

In haste —
P.B.

Mary Scott just phoned. She wrote me last spring that she and her husband are Californians who spend every spring and summer in London, and she offered to take me on a walking tour. She told me she's had house guests for a month, they've just left and she's finally free for that walking tour, she'll pick me up for the tour Thursday morning and take me home to dinner afterwards.

Tomorrow night I'm having dinner with the English couple who phoned while I was in Stratford, and the Scotts are feeding me Thursday, so I may just spring for a hairdresser on the dinner money I'm saving.

TUESDAY, JULY 6

Had my hair done at a little shop out Regent's Park way on Paddington Street, and the pretty hairdresser asked Was I from the States, and I said Yes.

'How do you find London?' she asked. 'Do the noise and the crowds bother you?'

The what?

For a big city, London is incredibly quiet. The traffic is worse than at home because the streets here are so narrow; but the cars are very quiet going by in the street and there are no trucks at all, a city ordinance bans them. Even the sirens are quiet. The ambulance sirens go *BlooOOP, blooOOP,* like a walrus weeping under water.

And I haven't seen anything here, not even on a bus, that a New Yorker would describe as a crowd.

MIDNIGHT

Those English fans who invited me to dinner are a charming couple, they live in Kensington in a mews. A mews is an alley built originally for stables and carriage barns, and the fad is to convert the barns and stables into modern homes, everybody wants to live in a converted stable, it's chic.

But stables and carriage barns were built of stone and they don't have windows. And the horses weren't interested in indoor plumbing or electricity. You buy one of these stables and kill yourself turning a horse's stall into a very peculiar kitchen (cramped between two high stone partitions); you wire all the stalls for electricity, you pipe them for water, you get all your kitchen and bathroom equipment and furniture moved into the proper horses' stalls – and when you're all through you still can't chop a hole through a foot-thick stone wall for windows, so you have everything you need but air. The couple I had dinner with live in a charming little stable which, they explained to me cheerfully, is so hot all summer they get out of it as soon after supper as possible. In winter they freeze without heat and suffocate with it.

Across the street from them is Agatha Christie, just as comfortably situated and a lot older.

Demented.

They fed me an elegant salmon steak and drove me through Chiswick – pronounced Chizzick – and we walked along the Strand on the Green. The Strand on the Green is a lovely avenue overlooking the Thames, you can run down the front steps of the houses and jump in the river. The houses were built by Charles II for his mistresses. They are very beautiful and charming, very expensive and soughtafter, and the elite who live in them are envied just as much as if the Thames didn't overflow every now and then and flood all their living rooms.

I don't remember what we were talking about, but I described something-or-other in Central Park and my hostess looked at me in horror.

'You mean you actually go into Central Park?' she asked. 'I thought people got killed in there.'

I said I was in it almost every day, and offered to take her and her husband on a guided tour of it if they ever came to New York. And then they told me that last year they spent three days at the Plaza Hotel and never left their hotel room for fear of being killed. They didn't walk down Fifth Avenue. They didn't see the park, even from a hansom cab. They didn't set foot in a single skyscraper. They didn't get on a sight-seeing bus.

They never left their room.

'We were too terrified,' the wife said.

Since I arrived in London, three college boys have been found shot to death as they slept at a camp site; a girl was found stabbed to death in her flat; and there are signs all over town reading LOCK UP LONDON. I asked PB about them, he said they're part of a campaign to get Londoners to lock doors and windows when they go out because of the wave of robberies; three of his friends' flats were robbed in one weekend.

Crime is a hundred times worse in New York. We probably have more murders and muggings there in a week than London will see in a year. Still, for what it's worth, no umpire or fan in Shea Stadium will ever take his eyes off the baseball diamond long enough to make a pass at a girl. And no New York dog will attack three children on the street, killing one of them, which happened here last week.

I mean things are tough all over. Tougher in New York. But not so tough as to justify two Londoners huddling together in a hotel room for a weekend, *declining* the only chance they'll ever have to see the one fabulous city the twentieth century has created.

One of these days I'm going to write a book about living in New York – in a sixteenth-story apartment house complete with families, bachelors, career girls, a ninety-year-old Village Idiot and a doorman who can tell you the name and apartment number of everyone of the twenty-seven resident dogs. I am so tired of being told what a terrible place New York is to live in by people who don't live there.

WEDNESDAY, JULY 7

PB took me to Syon house, the ancestral home of those miserable Northumberlands who tried to make Jane Grey queen and sided with Mary of Scotland against Elizabeth. The rose gardens there are beyond anything I've seen: acres of roses in a spectacular rainbow of colours. PB told me he spent the weekend with friends in the country who have a double rose garden and didn't offer him so much as a bud to take home. Londoners miss their gardens, he and the other tenants in his building do a little gardening in pots on the roof.

We went from Syon House to Osterly Park, another ancestral home, I forget whose. I'm learning a little about Nash houses and Wren churches; today at Osterly Park it was Adam walls: polished wood panels covered with intricate marquetry. You can examine a single wall for hours and not see all the details in the carving. In a century dominated by watches, cars, planes, schedules, it's hard to imagine an age in which men had the endless time and patience needed for such work.

Driving home, PB told me he worked in Hollywood off and on for years as a consultant on films with English locales. The notion of PB in Holywood in its heyday, when it was a synonym for everything tasteless and overdone, was grotesque at first, but then I realized he's one of those originals who would be at home in almost any setting; nothing rubs off on him. He's been everywhere and knows everybody, he's very social – there are always a dozen invitations propped up on the mantel – but he seems always a little apart from those around him.

He told me he once spent months hauling an American architect all over England for the Essex House in New York. The Essex House was doing over its cocktail lounge and wanted to re-create an English pub.

'They sent a chap over here to see me and I drove him round the country to see all the best of the old pubs. He went back to New York and drew up the plans and sent then to me. I'll show them to you when we get home.'

We got back to Rutland Gate and he showed me the drawings and they were marvelous: a pub with wood-paneled walls, antiqued wooden tables and benches and a high, old-fashioned wooden bar with kegs above it. The pub looked warm and mellow and the woods burnished in the glow of old-fashioned lamps that swung from the ceiling.

'Is the pub still there?' I asked.

'I think so,' he said.

'I'll go see it when I get home,' I said. 'Did he write and tell you how it looks?'

'Oh, yes' – in that light, noncommital voice – 'the Essex House did the pub in lucite, chrome and black leather.'

He goes to Wales for a week on Saturday. I'll be gone when he gets back.

THURSDAY, JULY 8

Mary Scott took me on a walking tour of Knightsbridge and Kensington, we went to Harrods first because I'd never seen it. It's an incredible store, you can buy anything from a diamond necklace to a live tiger, they have a zoo. I thought of Chester, the sheep dog who lives in my building, he came from Harrods.

On the ground floor there's a florist's shop, and if you want to buy a dozen roses you can choose twelve roses individually. You can pick all buds or all open blooms or half and half, and you can buy one of every color in stock. I ran amok rounding up twelve to send to PB to brighten his flat before he leaves for Wales. Didn't know any other way to thank him.

We wandered the mewses and closes and poked into hidden gardens and alleys. Chelsea, Kensington and Knightsbridge all seem to me self-consciously charming, compared with Regent's Park. The Scotts live out that way and I told Mrs Scott if I were able to take a flat in London it's out Regent's Park way I'd want to live. She said it's not called Regent's Park, it's called Marylebone.

They have a spacious flat on Gloucester Place and she'd made a beautiful salmon mousse for dinner, loaded with cream. Salmon is a great delicacy here; people serve it as a compliment to their guests the way they serve filet mignon or lobster at home.

Got back here about ten and have had the Lounge to myself for an hour but my luck just ran out. A woman just came in looking for somebody to talk to. She says Be sure and see the Temple, locate Middle Temple Lane and you'll see two large white doors leading into the Temple, the Inner Temple and Middle Temple Hall, and the porter will show you the room where Dickens wrote *Great Expectations*. Doesn't seem the time to tell her I found *Great Expectations* very boring, it's the sort of conversation-stopping sequitur you learn is really *non* sequitur.

She says the Knights Templar were buried under the floor of the church and that's why it's called the Temple. She says the church was destroyed during the war and after the war all the Knights' bones were dug up and they're now in a common grave under the floor of the rebuilt church. It's a good thing I want to see all this, because if I didn't plan to I'd have to keep out of the Lounge, I gather she spends all her evenings in here.

Two women just came in — early thirties, very neat, they may be schoolteachers; they're from Toronto — and it seems the Temple woman sent them somewhere on a day's outing and they are now telling her How Right She Was. Greenwich-by-boat. Maritime Museum.

Temple woman says This will interest me because I'm an American, she says there are Pilgrim artifacts at Greenwich, the Pilgrims tool ship from there. Always thought it was Plymouth. Didn't say so. I'm controlling an insane impulse to turn to the three of them and say chattily:

'Did you know that when the Pilgrim Fathers caught a Pilgrim having a love affair with a cow, they not only hanged the Pilgrim, they also hanged the cow?'

One of the teachers wants to know Am I the writer? They've heard such a lot about me at the desk. If they should be able to get a copy of my book tomorrow would I be kind enough to autograph it for them? Soitinly. Told a woman the other night she was passing up a chance to own the only unautographed copy in existence, she just looked at me baffled, nobody understands me.

FRIDAY, JULY 9
RUSSELL SQUARE

A man came by at 10 A.M. to interview me for Radio London and I dragged him and his tape recorder over here. I'm not sitting in a dark hotel lobby on a sunny summer morning.

He told me a play was done here last season about Lord Nelson and Lady Hamilton and a script was sent to Buckingham Palace. It came back to the producer's office with a note:

> The Duke of Edinburgh thinks you've treated Lady Hamilton very shabbily. The Queen reserves judgment.

Everybody over here has a Philip anecdote for you, they're proud of the fact that he's so unstuffy. It's appealing how people regard the Royal Family as relatives, it's a kind of Cousin-Elizabeth-and-her-husband-and-the-children attitude. So everybody feels free to criticize them, what else are relatives for? Elizabeth, Philip and Prince Charles all very popular. Feelings mixed about Princess Anne; most people I've met are defensive about her. You ask an Englishman:

'What's Princess Anne like?' and the Englishman says:

'Well, you must remember she's still very young, she's new to all this, after all she's only twenty, you can't expect –'

And all you said was: 'What's she like?'

But they're very impressed by her horsemanship, they tell you with great pride: 'She's good enough to ride for England!'

Feelings also mixed (this surprised me) about the Queen Mother. One woman told me:

'Her public image is a masterpiece of press agentry. I once stood next to her at Harrods and caught her eye, and she has the coldest eyes I ever looked into.'

Have to go back to the hotel to meet Nikki's Barbara for lunch. She doesn't like curry but she's being magnanimous and taking me to a curry place near me on Charlotte Street.

LATER

There was a thank-you note at the desk when I got back from Russell Square.

The super roses arrived – they are on my desk as I write this and perfume the whole room. How very thoughtful – thank you. I just spoke to Jean Ely, she and Ted arrived at the Connaught last night. I thanked her for introducing us.
Will be back on the 18th. Do be in London still.

In haste –

P.B.

I leave Thursday, the fifteenth.

VIA TELETYPE

JULY 6, 1971
TO NIKKI FROM HELENE VIA BARBARA   TWO
REQUESTS FIRST ANDY CAPP COMIC BOOKS OUT OF
PRINT   COULD YOU THINK OF SOMETHING MORE
CULTURED FOR HER TO BRING YOU   SECOND SHE
WOULD LIKE NAMES OF TWO BEST INDIAN CURRIES
SOHO IN THE NATIVE TONGUE ALIVE AND WELL

TO BARBARA FROM NIKKI MANY THANKS FOR THE
MESSAGE FROM HELENE HER POSTCARD SOUNDS LIKE
SHE IS HAVING A BALL HAVE YOU MET HER YET

NOT YET BUT AM HAVING LUNCH WITH HER THIS
FRIDAY DO YOU HAVE CURRIES FOR HER

NOT YET WILL CHECK IT OUT WITH MY INDIAN
FRIEND AM JUST BACK FROM VACATION   TELL HER I
AM IN LOVE

GOOD FOR YOU BI

JULY 8, 1971
1510 GMT LONDON
TO BARBARA
FROM NIKKI
TWO CURRY NAMES ARE MURGI KARI AND MURG
MASALAM ALSO COULD YOU GIVE HER THE FOLLOW-
ING MESSAGE FROM KEN MILLS ALL IS LOST ROOT FOR
DODGERS IN WESTERN DIVISION OR BETTER STILL
TAKE UP CRICKET HAVE FUN AND THANKS NIKKI END

OKAY NIKKI WILL DO BI

JULY 9, 1971
TO NIKKI NEW YORK
JUST HAD LUNCH WITH HELENE AND SCRIBBLED OUT
THE FOLLOWING MESSAGE FOR YOU DUCHESS OF

BLOOMSBURY STREET SAYS HOW THE HELL CAN ALL
BE LOST ITS ONLY JULY METS WILL START WINNING
WHEN SHE IS HOME TO ROOT THEM THROUGH
DUCHESS SAYS YOU ARE FORBIDDEN TO ENTER INTO
BETROTHAL WITHOUT HER CONSENT SHE WILL HAVE
TO LOOK HIM OVER FIRST END

———————————————

I think everybody who works should have Saturday afternoons off, but they have got goofy ways of managing it over here.

Went down to Fortnum & Mason to buy small tokens of esteem for friends back home and by the time I finished it was lunch time. The store has an attractive coffee shop so I went there. There was a long line of people waiting for tables but a few counter seats were empty and I climbed up on a stool and picked up a menu. People were being served on both sides of me and the waitress was rushed. I waited till she'd brought everybody else's tea-and-tart and when she finally turned to me, I said:

'I'll have a –' and she said:

'We're closed, Madam,' and I said:

'You're what?' and she said:

'We're closed.'

And she pointed to a waiter who was carrying a standard to the door. He set the standard down in front of the long line of people waiting for tables and sure enough, the sign on the standard said CLOSED.

At high noon on a Saturday with the store open and jammed with shoppers, the coffee shop closed. Which is what I call having a good strong Union.

Did the Temple this afternoon. It was raining when I came out, I took a bus home. You have to watch it with these buses. A sign on the bus says DO NOT ALIGHT FROM THE COACH UNTIL REQUESTED TO DO SO. Believe me, it's there for your health.

The driver is at one end of the bus with his back to the passengers. Theoretically, the conductor is at the other end, where you get off. But he also has to go through the bus asking new passengers how far they're going and giving them tickets and taking money and making change, and the buses are double decker so half the time he's upstairs.

If he's upstairs when the bus comes to your stop, DO NOT GET OFF THE BUS, just ride past your stop and wait till he comes down. Because if the conductor isn't there to signal the driver when you're safely off, the driver doesn't really stop at your corner, he just slows down there and pauses, and then drives on, on the *assumption* that you're safely off. I'm small and limber, I hopped nimbly off the bus and even so I nearly fell on my face, the bus took off with my left foot on the bottom step.

I just phoned Jean Ely at the Connaught to thank her for asking PB to show me London. She said come to dinner Thursday night, she wants to hear all about it.

I saved my three high spots – the Abbey, the Tower and St. Paul's – for my last week and I'm glad I did. Knowing I'm going to see them has kept me from getting depressed about going home when I'm not ready to go home. Woke in high excitement this morning because Sheila and Nora and I were doing the Abbey this afternoon.

It's full of odd things nobody ever told me about – like a plaque to the memory of Major John André, 'Mourned Even by his Enemies,' it says. 'His Enemies' were us rebels. André was the British spy Benedict Arnold betrayed us to. The Americans caught him and hanged him just as the British had caught and hanged Nathan Hale a little earlier. But you wouldn't believe how many American historians make a much bigger fuss over André's death than they do over Nathan Hale's. Nathan Hale was a poor farm boy. John André was a dashing British aristocrat – see. In class-conscious Philadelphia, where André was stationed, you'd better believe he was 'Mourned by His Enemies.'

It positively outraged me to find Henry Irving buried in Westminster Abbey when Ellen Terry isn't. Henry Irving was one of those legendary actors like Garrick, he was the idol of London in the 1890's. Ellen Terry was his leading lady. I got very fond of her through her correspondence with Shaw and I consider it pure male chauvinism to bury Irving in the Abbey while Ellen's ashes, according to Sheila, are in the little Actors' Church near Convent Garden Market, I'm going there.

Sign of the times: there's a long bench now placed over one grave so all you can see of the inscription is 'Rudyard Ki —.'

We passed the War Office when we came out. It was hot today – eighty-four degrees, very hot for London. Outside the War Office, sitting on a horse in the hot sun, was a guard. He wore a solid brass helmet-and-noseplate, which must have been blazing hot. He was dressed in a heavy wool uniform, long leather gloves and leather knee boots, he had a Persian lamb saddle rug tucked around him and he was clutching a spear which was bending slightly from the heat. Bundled up for the Russian Front, all by himself on a hot Sunday, he was guarding the atomic secrets of the War Office with a bent spear. Him and his fur-covered horse.

Sheila says he's there to please tourists like me, he's the fancy-dress

London we come looking for. Maybe so. But far away in Wales I could hear a light voice remarking:

'They haven't missed a night in seven hundred years.'

On the way back to Highgate for dinner we stopped off at Waterlow Park; it's so high above the city the legend on the park sundial informs you:

THIS SUNDIAL IS LEVEL WITH THE
DOME OF ST. PAUL'S CATHEDRAL

and when you look across the hills the dome is level with your eyes.

In the center of the park there's a two-story house with a high balcony, Sheila told me Charles II built it for Nelly Gwyn. Nell bore him a son there and she kept asking Charles to give the baby a title and Charles kept putting it off. So one day, when she saw the King riding toward the house to visit her, Nell walked out onto the balcony with the baby in her arms and called down to him:

'If you don't give your son a proper title this instant I shall drop him to his death!'

'And Charles II cried:

'Madam, don't drop the Duke of –!' and that's how the baby got his title.

LATER

Ena just phoned, they're back. They want me to have dinner with them tomorrow night and then see their flat in Ealing. She and Leo will pick me up here at hoppusseven. Nobody over here says 'six-thirty' or 'seven-thirty,' they say 'hoppussix' and 'hoppusseven.' And 'in' at home is 'trendy' here and 'give it up' 'pack it in' and 'never mind!' is 'not to worry!'

And when they pronounce it the same they spell it differently. A curb's a kerb, a check's a cheque, a racket's a racquet – and just to confuse you further, jail is spelled 'gaol' and pronounced 'jail.'

And a newsstand's a kiosk, a subway's the tube, a cigar store's a tobacconist's, a drug store's a chemist's, a bus is a coach, a truck is a lorry, buying on time is hire purchase, cash and carry is cash and wrap and as Shaw once observed, we are two countries divided by a common language. I am now going to bed because it's quataposstwelve.

O Frabjous Day!

From now on I remember the *Reader's Digest* in all my prayers. I picked up mail at the desk, there was a letter from the London *Digest* office, I assumed it was page proof on the three new pages. I opened it and inside was a check for FIFTY POUNDS, I thought I would die where I stood.

I hunted up Mr Otto and asked if I could keep the room an extra ten days, he was shocked at the question, he said, 'Did you think we'd put you out?!' and clucked.

I tore up the street to Deutsch's to tell everybody the news and Carmen said Ann Edwards of the *Sunday Express* wants to interview me Wednesday over lunch.

'And guess where? The River Room of the Savoy! It's the most divine place in London. I'm so happy for you.'

Mr Tammer couldn't cash the check for me, he said it's made out in such a way only a bank can cash it. Will take it to the bank tomorrow.

I phoned Nora and told her the news and she wants to give a buffet supper for me on Friday to meet all the rare-book dealers, she wanted to do it before but they were all 'on holiday.'

Joyce Grenfell phoned about dinner tomorrow night, she's putting a note in the mail with complete instructions for finding their flat by bus. It impresses me that in London you can mail an in-city letter on Monday and know for certain it will arrive on Tuesday. In New York you can mail a letter on Monday to an address a block away – and maybe it'll get there on Wednesday and very possibly it won't get there till Thursday.

My social life being what it is, I just faced the fact that I can't get along for two more weeks on one dress. God bless my Democratic Club and my brother, am off to Harrods with the gift certificate and the last of the cash reserve, Ena says they're having a close-out sale of summer dresses.

LATER

Harrods sale overpriced and mostly midi-skirts they got stuck with. I went up the street to Harvey Nicols and bought a toast-and-white linen on sale and then went back to Harrods and swapped the gift certificate for a sand-colored shoulder bag on sale. Transferred everything to it and threw my old white straw in a Harrods' wastebasket, it's been unravelling for a week.

Took a cab to Johnson's house and lunched at the Cheshire Cheese (money means nothing to me) and stopped at the *Evening Standard* to see Valerie – the girl who interviewed me the day I landed – to tell her the *Standard*'s interviewing me over again. (Now-that-I've-been-here-how-do-I-like-it.) While I was there, the catch on my new shoulder bag broke. Valerie was very shocked; I said, 'That's why it was on sale.' She said, 'Yes, but not *Harrods*!' Nobody ever says 'Bonwit's' in that tone.

She sent me to a little shop off Fleet Street to have it fixed, and while the man repaired it for me I asked if he could point me toward Bloomsbury, I wanted to walk home. He said:

'Go on up to O-burn Street and follow the bus.'

Looked for O-burn Street, looked for Auburn Street and finally stumbled on the street he meant: High Holburn. And that's what they mean by a cockney accent.

Time to go crouch under that sadistic shower and then climb into the new dress for Leo And Ena.

MIDNIGHT

Leo took us to dinner at a plush seafood restaurant. The shellfish looks the same here as at home but tastes very different; the crabmeat and lobster are much richer here but very bland, almost tasteless to an American palate till you get used to it.

They drove me to their flat and I saw Ena's portraits of Hayley Mills and Pamela Brown. Pamela Brown I have a special love for, dating back to an old, old English film called *I Know Where I'm Going* and to a stage performance I saw her give in *The Importance of Being Earnest*.

I know nothing about painting, not even the right thing to say when you like it; but those faces spoke to you. I was bowled over, I told Ena it's indecent to be that talented when you're pretty and blond and look fresh out of school.

Leo announced he was going to make me his special summer drink, for which he is famous, and he trotted off to the kitchen and banged around and came back with three long, tall drinks. I don't drink after dinner and I don't like carbonated drinks so I don't know one long-tall-drink from another. I sipped this one and said:

'It's ginger ale, isn't it? It's very nice.'

'It's gin and tonic,' said Leo, wounded.

'The gin kind of gets lost, doesn't it?' I said, and he loped back to the kitchen for the gin bottle. Ena was doubled up with unkind wifely laughter.

'That's his special drink, he's so proud of it!' she gasped and went off into convulsions. I felt terrible. I told Leo I go through life saying the wrong thing. He put some more gin in my drink and then sat and watched me as I sipped it. When he thought I had enough of it inside me, he said:

'The little thing wants to ask you a favor.'

I looked at Ena and said, 'What's the favor?' but she just smiled nervously. And Leo said:

'She wants to paint you.'

And I said:

'You're crazy.'

I know that painters see planes and angles in faces that look commonplace to the rest of us – and I still cannot understand why anyone should want to paint a plain, ordinary middle-aged face. Which I told Ena. To her, I have an interesting face, 'it changes all the time.' I said I wished it would.

I never felt so trapped. All my life I've avoided being photographed – and here was Ena asking earnestly Would I sit for her? She'd only need a few sittings, 'p'raps three or four?' Anxious little face peering at me wistfully.

I told her I'd do it on two conditions: one, she has to paint me in Russell Square, I'm not sitting indoors in some studio; and two, she has to promise not to make me look at the portrait either in progress or when it's finished.

She agreed to both conditions. She's finishing something this week, we start next week.

TUESDAY, JULY 13

Paranoid morning.

Joyce Grenfell's note arrived with instructions for finding her flat tonight but nothing on how to find St. Mary LeBeau's Church in Cheapside for her dialogue with the minister at noon. I located Cheapside on my map and then decided to get the *Digest* check cashed before I went down there.

I went to the nearest bank and then to another one across the street from it. Both banks were shocked to be asked to cash a *Reader's Digest* check for a total stranger whose identification they declined to look at. Neither would phone the *Digest* or Deutsch's for me, it wasn't bank policy.

I went to a third bank, where a teller passed me on to an officer who conferred with another officer and then came back and said Wouldn't it be better if I just mailed the check to my bank in New York? I explained that I needed the cash here, which shocked him deeply. You do not say 'I need cash' to a banker.

I told him my New York bank was Chemical and asked whether there was a branch in London. He said Yes, reluctantly, but he doubted whether the London branch would cash the check. (He said 'could.') I went down to Chemical – and after asking to see everything but my teeth, they cashed it. Nothing infuriates me like those friendly, folksy bank ads in magazines and on TV. Every bank I ever walked into was about as folksy as a cobra.

By this time I had barely half an hour to get down to Cheapside. I got on a bus and discovered I'd forgotten my map. I told the conductor I wanted to go to St. Mary LeBeau's, Cheapside, and he let me off down near St. Paul's, pointed to a yonder street and said:

'Walk that way a bit and turn left.'

I walked that way a bit and turned left and walked this way a bit and turned left and turned right and asked six people, all of whom turned out to be tourists. A bus slowed down at a corner, I called to the conductor Could he tell me how to get to St. Mary LeBeau's Church and he called back:

'Sorry, luv, it's m'first day on the job!'

I wished him luck, you might as well, and kept on walking. Found three wrong churches, a Goldsmith's Hall and a lot of interesting alleys but no St. Mary LeBeau's. By this time the dialogue was over anyway and I holed up in a smoky little pub and ate myself pleasant.

MIDNIGHT

Joyce met me at the door and took me on a guided tour of the living-room walls, hung with Grenfell and Langhorne family portraits and photographs. Her mother was one of the Langhorne sisters of Virginia. One sister married Charles Dana Gibson and was the original Gibson Girl, another married Lord Astor and was the famous Lady Astor, M.P., and the third married Joyce's father.

Very few theatrical photos on the wall. The one she's proudest of is the Haymarket marquee with her name in lights. The Haymarket has a rule against putting a star's name in lights, it only lights the name of the show. But when Joyce did her one-man show there, she wasn't just the star, she was the show.

She gave me a biography of Florence Nightingale she thinks I'll like. She sets her alarm for six every morning and reads in bed till seven; she said if she hadn't formed that habit, she'd never find time to read anything. As it is, it seems to me she's read everything.

I'm always so ashamed when I discover how well-read other people are and how ignorant I am in comparison. If you saw the long list of famous books and authors I've never read you wouldn't believe it. My problem is that while other people are reading fifty books I'm reading one book fifty times. I only stop when at the bottom of page 20, say, I realize I can recite pages 21 and 22 from memory. Then I put the book away for a few years.

After dinner they drove me around Chelsea and showed me the house where they were married. Joyce told me they were almost childhood sweethearts.

'I was seventeen and Reggie was just down from Oxford. The first time I played tennis with him I still wore my hair in a braid, I only put it up in the evening.'

They drove down into the old City of London and showed me St. Mary LeBOW's Church, it now turns out you spell it. Only the English could tack 'bow' onto 'le.' Too dark for me to see where I went wrong.

They kept up an amiable running argument about what to show me.

'Oh, not St. Paul's, dear, she'll have seen that.'

'She might like to see it illuminated, RegGEE!'

'She's probably seen it illuminated half a dozen times, why don't you show her Fleet Street?'

I piped up from the back seat that I'd like to see London's slums.

'I'm afraid,' said Joyce gently, 'there aren't any.'

Add that fact to Britain's free medical care and you know all you need to know about the difference between Capitalism and Socialism.

Ann Edwards of the *Sunday Express* took me to lunch at the Savoy and refused to believe I wasn't disappointed in London.

'When I heard you were coming,' she said, 'I wanted to write you and say, "My dear, don't come. You're fifteen years too late."'

For what, Westminster Abbey?

I tried to tell her that if you've dreamed of seeing the Abbey and St. Paul's and the Tower all your life, and one day you find yourself actually there, they can't disappoint you. I told her I was finally going to St. Paul's when I left her and I could guarantee her it wouldn't disappoint me. But she's lived in London all her life, she harks back wistfully to the days when her family owned an upright Rolls Royce, 'which, every time it started, coughed gently, like a discreet footman.'

The Savoy River Room is beautiful and the food marvelous. (I liked Claridge's better but I romanticize Claridge's.) Had crabmeat and lobster thermidor both, couldn't eat my way through either, the portions were enormous, I finished up with strawberries and cream all the same. English cream is addictive – and every time I eat strawberries here I think of the English clergyman who remarked:

'Doubtless God could have made a better berry than the strawberry and doubtless God never did.'

She walked down along the Embankment with me after lunch and pointed me the straightest route to St. Paul's.

It was lovely to walk along the river with John Donne's cathedral looming ahead. Thought about him as I walked, he's the only man I heard of who actually *was* a rake reformed by the love of a good woman. He eloped with the daughter of the Lord Lieutenant of the Tower and her outraged papa had them thrown into the Tower for it. John was in one wing, his bride was in another, and he sent her a note, which is how I know he pronounced his name Dunn, not Donn. The note read:

> John Donne
> Anne Donne
> Undone

He was also a little batty. When Anne died, he had a stone shroud made for himself, and he slept with that shroud in bed with him for twenty years. If you write like an angel you're allowed to be a bit cracked.

I walked up the steps of St. Paul's – finally, finally, after how many years? – and in through the doorway, and stood there looking up at the domed ceiling and down the broad aisles to the altar, and tried to imagine how Donne felt the night King James sent for him. And for at least that moment, I wouldn't have traded the hundreds of books I've read for the handful I know almost by heart. I haven't opened Walton's *Lives* in ten years, at least; and standing there in John Donne's cathedral the whole lovely passage was right there in my head:

> When his Majesty was sat down he said after his pleasant manner, 'Dr. Donne, I have invited you to dinner and though you sit not down with me, yet will I carve you a dish I know you love well. For knowing you love London I do hereby make you Dean of St. Paul's and when I have dined, then do you take your beloved dish home with you to your study, say grace there to yourself and much good may it do you.'

And as Eliza Dolittle would say, I bet I got it right.

There were guides with large tourist parties in tow, each guide giving the standard lecture, some in English, one in French, one in German, the monotone voices jarring against each other. I got as far from them as I could and wandered around by myself. I went down a side aisle looking at all the plaques and busts, walked around the altar and started back up the other side looking at more plaques and busts. Even so, I almost missed it. It was an odd shape, it wasn't a bust and it wasn't a full-length statue, so I stopped and read the inscription. There in front of me, hanging on the wall of St. Paul's Cathedral, was John Donne's shroud.

I touched it.

There's a small chapel just inside the door, with a sign that says: 'St. Dunstan's Chapel. Reserved for Private Meditation.' I went in and gave thanks.

Fifteen years too late indeed.

THURSDAY, JULY 15

Ken Ellis of the London *Reader's Digest* came around this morning with his pretty assistant and a photographer, to take my picture. I put up the usual squawk but my heart wasn't in it (I'd be flying over the Atlantic this minute if it weren't for the *Digest*) and I trotted meekly back to 84 Charing Cross Road with them and had my picture taken sitting on the window sill of the bleak, empty upstairs room. Ken scooped up all the peeled and rusting white letters that once spelled Marks & Co. for me. I want to take them home.

(And one September day when I'm doing my fall cleaning I'll come on them and ask myself, 'What do you want these for – so you can weep over them when you're an old lady?' and throw them out.)

They took me to Wheeler's for lunch (the famous seafood restaurant everybody takes you to) and Ken explained to me why everybody over here hates the new money. It has to do with the Englishman's need to be different. The decimal system is much simpler than the old ha'penny-tuppenny-guinea-tenner-tanner system, but the old money was *theirs*; no other country had it and nobody else could understand it. He said they hate entering the Common Market for the same reason. They don't want to be part-of-Europe, they want to be separate, different, set apart. He illustrated this by quoting an old headline which has become a cliché joke over here. During a spell of bad weather when the whole island was enveloped in fog, one English newspaper headline read: FOG ISOLATES CONTINENT.

I'm having dinner with the Elys and Jean just called to warn me that the Connaught is very old-world and still doesn't admit women in pants to the dining room, told her with dignity I have two dresses.

11 P.M.

The Connaught is near Grosvenor Square so I went there first to see the Roosevelt Memorial. Somebody told me that after Roosevelt's death the British government decided to raise money for the Memorial by public subscription and to limit individual contributions to one shilling so that everyone could subscribe. They announced that the subscription would be kept open as long as necessary to raise all the money in one shilling contributions.

The subscription closed in seventy-two-hours.

The story moved me a lot more than the Memorial did. It's a statue of FDR standing tall, holding a cane, cape flying. The features are there; the character and personality are entirely absent. And I resent a statue of FDR standing, on legs that were shriveled and useless throughout his White House life. You can't take the measure of Roosevelt if you ignore the fact that his immense achievements were those of a man paralyzed from the waist down. I'd carve him sitting, with the blanket he always spread over his knees to hide the withered legs. Anything else belittles the gallantry and humor in that indomitable face. Since the gallantry and humor are missing from the statue's face I don't suppose it matters. It's nice to know so many Englishmen loved him anyway.

Jean and Ted Ely still astonish me. They invited me to dinner in New York after they read the book. They live in a very gracious Fifth Avenue apartment, all polished mahogany and old carpets and warm colors, and I thought they were the most beautiful couple I'd ever seen. Both of them are slim and straight, both have thick gray hair, regular features and serenely smooth faces – and when Jean told me casually they were in their mid-seventies I was stupefied. They are as improbably handsome and untouched by time as the parents of the debutante in a 1930's movie.

We talked about PB through dinner. I sent him a note to tell him I'll be here another two weeks, Jean said maybe he'll take the three of us somewhere.

A chauffeured limousine drove me back here; I do not know how anybody expects me to adjust to life on Second Avenue when I get home.

Ena phoned, How's Sunday morning, am I free to Sit? The things I agree to with a little gin in me.

FRIDAY, JULY 16

Just got back from Nora's buffet supper – where I arrived an hour and a half late and I was the guest of honor, I mean this evening got off to a horrendous start.

Nora had phoned this morning to say a car would pick me up here at seven-fifteen, so as usual I was dressed and waiting in the lobby at seven. No car came at seven-fifteen, no car came at seven-thirty, and by seven-forty-five I decided Nora's friends must have forgotten to pick me up and I called her. She said she'd ordered a cab for me 'to bring you out in style.' It never came. She told me to go out in the street and hail a cab and come on out.

I went out in the street and hailed a cab and got in. But North London is apparently equivalent to the far end of Brooklyn, and London cab drivers are grimly equivalent to New York cab drivers. I gave the driver Nora's address, and he stared at me mask-like.

'I don't know where that is, Madam,' he said in a flat voice. I innocently explained it was in Highgate. He stared straight in front of him this time and repeated in the same expressionless voice:

'I don't know where that is, Madam.'

I got the message and got out of the cab and waited ten minutes for the next cab to come along and got in. I gave the driver Nora's address, and we went through the same charade. But this driver was so anxious to get rid of me that when I got out of the cab he shot off before I'd gotten both feet on the ground, and I fell and split my leg open. So there I was, blood all over my leg at eight-fifteen of a seven-thirty supper in my honor. I couldn't go back up to the room and clean the wound and put on fresh stockings because that would have made me fifteen minutes later still.

I went back into the lobby and consulted the desk clerk and he said what I needed was a minicab, they take you anywhere. Minicabs are the London equivalent to New York's limousine services (and cost as much). The clerk phoned the minicab service for me and a cab arrived ten minutes later. The driver told me his name was Barry, he's a hospital intern, he drives a minicab nights to earn a little money. He took the hills of North London like he had a death wish for both of us, but never mind, he got us there and gave me a high old time on the way.

He told me he studied at McGill in Canada and spent summers working in Manhattan. The first day he landed in New York he found himself on the traffic island at Broadway and Forty-second Street, he didn't know where he was, he just knew he wanted to go to Times Square. There was a cop directing traffic, and Barry, wanted to ask directions, stepped up behind the cop and tapped him on the shoulder. Whereupon the cop, true to the tradition of courtesy and helpfulness of New York's Finest, turned around and stuck the muzzle of a gun in Barry's stomach.

'I only want to ask directions to Times Square, Officer.' said Barry.

'Izzat right,' said the cop.

'I'm a tourist, I don't know my way about,' Barry explained. 'I'm British.'

'No kiddin',' said the cop without taking his gun out of Barry's stomach. So Barry gave up and said:

'Officer, if you're going to shoot me, please step back so you don't kill the four hundred people behind me.'

The cop let him go then, and Barry crossed the street and asked a passer-by how to get to Times Square. The passer-by studied the problem thoughtfully and then said:

'Walk one block, turn left, walk one block, turn left, walk one block, turn left and you'll be there.'

So Barry walked around the block and that's how he discovered he'd been standing on Times Square all the time. He'd been looking for an English Square – with a park in it. What the passer-by didn't know was that in London you can walk one block, turn left, walk one block, turn left, walk one block, turn left – and be nowhere near where you started from.

He sold Britannicas and fountain pens door-to-door. Most of the housewives slammed the door in his face. ('I used to have to call, "Madam, will you please open the door so I can get my tie back?"') so he switched to demonstrating fountain pens at Woolworth's. He discovered the way to beat that system was to get very good at it and be promoted to teacher. 'Teaching other guys how to demonstrate,' he explained, 'you at least got to sit down.'

He dropped me at Nora's and said he'd pick me up at midnight for the return trip.

I could have brained Nora, she hadn't told the guests I'd been ready and waiting since seven-fifteen. One woman turned to me and said politely:

'Do you mind my asking what held you up?' and I was so stunned I couldn't answer her, I just fled upstairs with Sheila and hid out in her room till I got calmed down. I have no poise.

All the rare-book dealers regaled me with stories of the trade. They told me that after the war there were too many books and not enough bookshop space, so all the dealers in London BURIED hundreds of old books in the open bomb craters of London streets. Today the buried books would be worth a fortune if they could be recovered, if the new buildings could be torn down and the rebuilt streets torn up. I had a sudden vision of an atomic war destroying everything in the world, except here and there an old book lying where it fell when it was blasted up out of the depths of London.

Everybody brought me small gifts and I think I made a faux pas with one of them. A very charming woman who deals in autographs gave me a beautifully bound pocket notebook. I needed one, since I'd converted my old one into a calendar, and when the rare-book man from Quaritch's gave me his name and the address of the shop, I wrote them down in the new notebook. From the quality of the silence that followed, I think writing in that notebook was a kind of desecration. I had a horrible feeling the notebook was one of those antique items you're not supposed to use, you're just supposed to look at it. What the hell do I want with a notebook you can't use? I get in trouble this way all the time.

Barry arrived on the dot of twelve and drove me home. He told me to visit his hospital if I get down that way, it's St. Bartholomew's, he said Go in by the Henry VIII gate and see the chapel, it's beautiful. I wrote his name — Barry Goldhill — in the desecrated notebook and asked him what he's specializing in. He said, 'Gynecology,' I said, 'Too late, honey, I can't do a thing for you.'

SATURDAY, JULY 17

Note in the mail from Rutland Gate, he's back.

See you here, Monday, 19th, at 11 *promptly* for sherry with
Charles II and lunch with Charles Dickens.

In haste —
P.B.

I thought I'd better bone up on Dickens first, so after breakfast I
walked out to the Dickens House in Doughty Street. It's only a few
blocks beyond Russell Square, I just never had enough interest in
Dickens to go there before – which you don't tell to ANYbody over
here, it is flat heresy not to like Dickens. I mean Dickens is the
national household god.

Except for PB, not one single Londoner has ever mentioned
Shakespeare's pub to me. Nobody mentions the Pepys landmarks,
nobody mentions Wimpole Street – and nobody knows what you're
talking about when you ask about the house where Shaw courted his
'green-eyed millionairess.' But every living soul tells you where Mr
Pickwick dined and where the Old Curiosity Shop is and Do see the
house on Doughty Street where *Oliver Twist* was written and This is
Camden Town, where Bob Cratchit lived and The-porter-will-
show-you-where-Dickens-wrote-*Great Expectations*.

Doughty Street is another of those streets lined with the gentle,
narrow brick houses that still shake me. The Dickens House is
furnished much as it was when he lived in it, and the room at the
back of the house where he worked has a complete set of Dickens
first editions. Walls of every room are crammed with cases of
Dickens memorabilia – letters, drawings, cartoons, theatre programs
with his name in the cast list. (Never knew he was such a rabid
amateur actor.) All the tourists going through the house, mostly
from 'the U.K.,' knew every character and every incident depicted
in every drawing and cartoon. Just incredible.

I had lunch at Tanjar's, the curry place on Charlotte Street, and
then walked down to Covent Garden to see Ellen Terry's ashes. The
church is called St. Paul's Covent Garden but when you get to the

Market there's no church in sight. Wandered around, peering at my map and then at Covent Garden Market. A young man with a brown beard came breezing along, went past me, wheeled, came back and inquired:

'Lost, luv?'

I told him I was looking for the Actors' Church and he said: 'Are you an actress?'

I said No, but I'd been a frustrated playwright in my youth and I loved the Shaw-Terry correspondence and wanted to see Ellen's ashes.

'Isn't that dear of you,' he said. 'Nobody ever comes looking for our church but people in the profession.'

He's an actor. Out of work. He said Just keep going round the Market till you come to an alleyway, cross it and turn the corner and you'll see the church.

I thanked him and wished him luck and he said, 'Luck to you, too, luv!' and went breezing on his way – and looking after him I purely hated myself because I hadn't bothered to ask his name. People oughtn't to breeze into your life and out again in ten seconds, without leaving even a name behind. As Mr Dickens once pointed out, we're all on our way to the grave together.

I picked my way through the rotting fruits and vegetables lying on the pavement in front of the Market, walked to the corner and came to the alley, a kind of open square used for parking produce trucks and littered with garbage. I crossed the alley and turned the corner and there it was – a small church in a green churchyard, with a garden beyond.

The church was empty. For which I was grateful. I am emotional, and if you're emotional you never know what may suddenly move you to tears. I thought Ellen's ashes might.

There was a pile of mimeographed sheets on a table, and a sign invites the visitor to take one and sit down and read it so you'll know 'something about where you are.' The church was built by Inigo Jones back in the 1630's. William S. Gilbert was babtized there, Wycherley is buried there, Davy Garrick worshiped there – and Professor Enry Iggins first saw Eliza Dolittle selling her flaaars under the church portico in the rain.

I went along the right-hand wall reading plaques to the memory of long-dead actors and composers. Almost at the end of the wall, near the altar, in a niche behind iron grillwork in a silver urn polished to a pristine gleam, Ellen Terry's ashes. Surprised to find myself smiling at the urn; it's a luminous, cheerful sight.

I crossed the nave and came back up along the left-hand wall and read more plaques clear to the door. Just inside the door as I was leaving I came upon the most recent plaque:

VIVIEN LEIGH   D. 1967

and was suddenly moved to tears.

SUNDAY, JULY 18

Sat.

Ena picked me up in a clattery station wagon and drove me to Russell Square and parked at the entrance. The station wagon has sliding doors which I natually tried to open outward, nearly broke the door and my arm both. Ena was convulsed, she said: 'You're exactly like Leo!' It seems he never gets the hang of anything mechanical either.

I got out and she climbed out after me, all five feet of her, lugging a six-foot easel, a four-foot box of paints, a palette, some magazines and a radio the size of a portable TV set. I wasn't allowed to help: the Subject is not permitted to fetch-and-carry.

We set up deck chairs – lounge chair for me, straight-backed one for her – and I was surprised and relieved to learn that when you Sit you don't have to sit still and hold a pose. Ena told me I could lie back, sit up, stretch, move, smoke, anything as long as I kept facing her. She then went into great detail about how to operate the radio; it turned out she'd brought the radio and magazines for me, to keep me from getting bored. It struck me funny.

'I don't get bored in Russell Square and I don't get bored with you,' I told her. 'Can't we talk while you work?'

'Oh, I'd love that,' she said. 'None of my subjects ever talks to me. They sit in silence hour after hour.'

'With me,' I said, 'that is not likely to be your problem.'

My friend the ticket taker came over to stand behind her and watch her paint. So did two English ladies, an Indian student and a middle-aged Jamaican with a walking stick.

'How's she doing?' I asked them, only wanting to be sociable. But being spoken to directly seemed to embarrass them and they mumbled, 'Very good,' and, 'Very nice,' and melted away. Ena thanked me, she said the gallery made her nervous. So from now on my function is to shoo away what New Yorkers call the Sidewalk Superintendents. In London you shoo them away by talking to them. In New York talking to them would just get you their life stories.

It's fascinating to watch a portrait painter work. There Ena sat, her red-and-white gingham dress flouncing around her, looking completely relaxed, talking, laughing, asking questions as she painted – and all the time, her eyes were darting with incredible speed up to my face, down to the easel, up to the face, down to the easel, up-down up-down up-down, in a motion as quick and sharp and rhythmic as a metronome at high speed. Hour after hour she talked and laughed and painted, and the quick up-and-down darting of the eyes never stopped for an instant. I tried it myself for about twenty seconds and my eye muscles were sore.

She painted till one and then drove me down to Kensington for lunch. We didn't try to talk on the way; the station-wagon clatter was as deafening as a New York subway. English cars are blissfully quiet going by you in the street but very noisy to ride in. American cars exactly the opposite.

She took me to a little Italian place for lunch, down near where she and Leo live, called Panzer's Pasta amd Pizza, it's their favorite neighborhood hangout. I had the best martini I've had in London and a chicken-with-garlic-butter they can serve me in heaven.

Ena was shocked that I hadn't been to a single gallery and firmly dragged me to the National Portrait Gallery after lunch – where I amazed myself by going clean out of my mind meeting old friends face-to-face. Charles II looks exactly the dirty-old-man he was, Mary of Scotland looks exactly the witch-on-a-broomstick she was, Elizabeth looks marvelous, the painter caught everything – the bright, sharp eyes and strong nose, the translucent skin and delicate hands, the glittering, cold isolation. Wish I knew why portraits of Mary and Elizabeth always look real and alive, and portraits of Shakespeare, painted in the same era and the same fashion, always look stylized and remote.

I stared at every face so long we never got out of the sixteenth and seventeenth centuries. We're going back next week for the eighteenth and nineteenth, I am now passionately determined to see everybody.

The Colonel phoned, he's driving me into the country for dinner on Wednesday.

Got to Rutland Gate at eleven. That's a lie. I'm always so afraid I won't get there '*promptly*' I always take a cab, I always get there twenty minutes early and walk around the neighborhood till it's late enough to ring his bell. I enjoy it, it's an interesting neighborhood.

He took me to the Old Wine Shades in Martin Lane, Cannon Street, for sherry-at-eleven. It's the only pub in London that survived the Great Fire of 1666. It was built before 1663 and doesn't seem to have changed since. There are ancient wine kegs over the bar, the wooden tables and benches are age-stained, even the menu sounded archaic, I could imagine Sam Pepys ordering the Veal and Sweetmeat Pie.

He took me to the Bank of England, where the doormen and floorwalkers are dressed in red waistcoats and breeches, and bow as they bid you good morning. (Aside from them, it's just one more folksy cobra.)

We had lunch at the George & Vulture where, it quotes on the menu, 'Mr. Pickwick invited about five-and-forty people to dine with him the very first time they came to London.' The restaurant is the headquarters of the Pickwick Club. Dickens cartoons on the walls; steaks and chops done over an open fire in a great stone fireplace.

Around the corner from the George & Vulture is 'the Church of St. Michael Cornhill with St. Peter Le Poer and St. Benet Fink.' I'm putting St. Benet Fink on my favorite Saints list right under the two New Orleans saints.

Back around 1801, when the U.S. bought Louisiana, American firms moved in on the Catholic icon business and began sending crates of church statuary down to New Orleans. The crates were labeled FRAGILE and EXPEDITE. New Orleaners were French, they couldn't read English and they didn't know what the two words meant. They decided the words must be the names of two new saints whose icons were inside the crates. Next thing anybody knew, the most popular saints in New Orleans were St. Fragile and St. Expedite.

St. Fragile lost ground after a while but the last I heard you could

still pick up a New Orleans newspaper any day and read in the
Personals Column:

> Thanks to St. Expedite for
> special favor granted.

According to the icons, he's an ancient Roman, he wears a toga.
Wish I knew as much about St. Benet Fink, PB didn't know who he
was.

We walked Lombard Street, PB said the London banking business
was founded by Jews from Lombardy in the 1400's. Each money
lender hung out an emblem to identify his establishment, and from
then on Lombard Street banks all hung out emblems on brass plates.
The emblems still swing in the breeze: the Bank of Scotland's
emblem is a Cat-and-a-Fiddle, another bank has a Grasshopper, a
third has a Rampant Horse. PB didn't know where the symbols came
from or what they originally meant, they're hundreds of years old.
(So along comes the U.S. and opens a bank on Lombard Street and
sees all these cats-and-fiddles and grasshoppers and rampant horses
and says, 'Lissen, *we* oughta hang out something!' and promptly hangs
out an American Eagle, we have no national imagination.)

PB is driving Jean, Ted and me into the country to a stately home
on Saturday. He upset me by taking me into a jeweler's to approve
a lapel pin he's having made for me. It's gold with the red-and-white
crest of the City of London.

Will see him Saturday for the last time, they'll have the pin ready
then.

TUESDAY, JULY 20

I got to Russell Square before Ena, and my friend the ticket taker, after setting up a chair for me, folded his arms behind him leaned down and inquired conspiratorially:

'Are we anybody we should know?'

Assured him we weren't anybody, and he shook his head reproachfully.

'Painters,' he said, 'do not paint protraits of Just Anyone.'

I told him I was a writer but not famous or important, and he took out a little black book and carefully wrote down my name and Ena's, just as Ena came wobbling round the bird-bath with easel, paint box, palette and the mammouth radio she still lugs in case I get bored – though all I ever do with it is make rude remarks about the BBC's taste in music. There's only one classical-music station and whoever runs it is a chamber-music nut, that's all they ever play.

Ena told me I've changed her entire attitude toward portrait painting.

'I never painted anyone out-of-doors before,' she said. 'The atmosphere and feeling are quite different. From now on I shall have to decide with each subject whether he or she's an outdoors or an indoors subject. You were quite right: you're an outdoors subject.'

'We're not out here because I'm an outdoor subject,' I said. 'We're out here because I'm a selfish subject.'

I think she'd love to paint all day long, but no matter what I say, she insists on quitting at one because I have so little time left to see anything.

As we packed up and headed for the station wagon, she looked around Russell Square and said pensively:

'You were right about this place. There's a special quality to it.'

It startled me. I'd never said that. Till she said it, I'm not sure I even knew it.

We had lunch at Panzer's and then went back to the National Portrait Gallery, I saw Jane Austen and Leigh Hunt and Willie Hazlitt and the eerie Brontë portrait – the faces of the three sisters and in the middle a gray wash where Bramwell's face once was.

The story is that Bramwell painted himself and his sisters, and then wiped out his own image in a fit of self-hate. And of course you can't concentrate on the sisters' faces, the portrait is dominated by that gray wash in the middle. You can't help wondering whether Bramwell knew it would be.

The Colonel outdid himself again. I'd forgotten that when we passed Stoke Poges on the way to Stratford I'd wanted to detour to see Gray's churchyard just because the 'Elegy' was my mother's favorite poem. The Colonel didn't forget; he drove me out to Stoke Poges for dinner, though it's a two-hour drive.

We got there just at twilight. Not a soul around and when we entered the churchyard the bells were tolling the knell of parting day.

Gray's mother is buried there. He wrote the inscription on her monument:

> She had many children of whom only one
> had the misfortune to outlive her.

The church is seven hundred years old, very simple and plain. There were fresh wild flowers in the altar urns. Going down the center aisle you walk on ancient graves of parishioners buried centuries ago beneath the stone floor, their names on the stones obliterated now.

The Colonel strolled the graveyard and let me sit in the church by myself. I wished my mother could know where I was. I felt like the child who calls from a new perch: 'Hey, Ma! Look!'

The Colonel's widowed sister-in-law lives near Stoke Poges. She teaches in London and commutes four hours a day, they're as crazy that way here as they are at home. We drove to her house to pick her up for dinner. She lives in a beautiful country suburb that could be anywhere in Connecticut – as Nora's house and suburb might be anywhere in Queens. It's amazing how alike and anonymous all suburbs are, as undistinguishable from one another as highways. Maybe that's why I love cities. There's not a row of houses in London that could possibly be mistaken for New York. There isn't a square block in Manhattan that will ever for a moment remind you of London.

We had dinner at a beautiful pub called The Jolly Farmer. 'Pub' is a very elastic term; it can mean a corner bar, a bar-and-grill, a cocktail lounge or an expensive restaurant. The Jolly Farmer is a typical Connecticut country restaurant: excellent, expensive and relentlessly charming. I had shrimp curry, and when I told the manager it was better than the curry I make, he brought me a jar of his own curry paste to take home to New York.

'Tell me,' the Colonel's sister-in-law said to me over coffee, 'why are all Americans so fond of Gray's "Elegy"?'

Never knew they were, frankly. Except for my mother I never heard any American mention it. But the Colonel's sister-in-law meets a much larger cross section of American tourists at Stoke Poges than I'll ever meet in Manhattan, and they've all come there because of Gray's 'Elegy,' so I took her word for it. And because I didn't have the moral backbone to say, 'I don't know,' I explained the whole thing to her – off the top of my head.

'We are a nation of immigrants,' I said. 'All our forebears were the poor and despised masses of Europe and Africa. We went to school and studied English poetry, and the poets we read all celebrated the aristocracy: kings and queens and Sidney's-sister-Pembroke's-mother and the spires of Oxford and the playing fields of Eton. Except Gray. Gray celebrated the mute inglorious nobodies. And since all Americans are descended from mute inglorious nobodies, I suppose he strikes a chord with us.'

I hope I was right because she and the Colonel believed it. I even believed it myself. Got so carried away by my own eloquence that when we were driving home I began to wonder whether in explaining the American affection for Gray, I'd stumbled on a clue to the English passion for Dickens. They may admire Shakespeare more but it's Dickens they love. Maybe the average Englishman, being neither king nor peasant, identifies less with the kings and peasants of Shakespeare than with the lower and middle-class upward-mobility types in Dickens. Even PB shares the national mania for Dickens – but he told me that one of his great-grandfathers was a fishmonger, and that when he was at Eton he was taunted by the other boys because his mother was 'a Colonial,' born in Australia.

The Colonel is giving a farewell party for me on Sunday night. He'll be at the airport Monday when I leave.

I'm getting so guilty about forcing Ena to paint me out-of-doors in London's well-publicized climate. We were rained out this morning for the second time. Yesterday when we were rained out she drove me to the Tower but there were long lines waiting to get in and I still can't stand on line very long. Today we started for the Tower again, but halfway there the weather cleared suddenly and I made her drive back to Russell Square. We'll do the Tower Sunday, I like having it the last London sight I'll see.

My friend the ticket taker is now entirely carried away by the project. He told Ena solemnly:

'That portrait will be worth hoff-a-million one day.' I told her if it is I get half.

Leo drove up and found us there at six. I could see Ena grinding her teeth, she'd wanted to paint as long as the light lasted. She'd told him we'd be in Russell Square and he should pick us up for dinner, but she counted on his not finding it till seven; like me, he has no sense of direction. He found Russell Square with no trouble at all and it infuriated her. And dear, obtuse Leo, who worships her and didn't know he'd committed a faux pas, went and committed a worse one: he stood behind her with his hands locked behind his back and gazed profoundly down at the portrait (Ena hates a gallery even if the gallery's Leo) and announced to me that it was 'going to be beautiful.' That ended the sitting and we drove down to Panzer's, Ena and I in the station wagon, Leo following in the car. He'd wanted to take me somewhere very grand for our farewell dinner but I told him I'd rather have it at Panzer's.

We were finishing our drinks and were trying to find a day for me to drive down to Chartwell, Churchill's old home, which friends of theirs have bought, when I heard someone say:

'Hello, Helene.'

I looked up and saw coming toward us a woman I've known casually for years. She runs a successful shop in New York and she's very high-fashion. She'd always perfectly friendly and pleasant when we meet but she's never considered me worth more than a passing hello.

I said Well-for-Heaven's-sake-Dorothy, and introduced her to Leo and Ena. Leo invited her to join us for dinner, which she did. She explained she's here on a quick buying trip and she'd just landed. Leo, who has the world's most beautiful manners, ordered dinner for her and then engaged her in conversation so Ena and I could work on the Chartwell problem.

The problem was that since I'm leaving on Monday morning I haven't a free day to go down there with them.

'Tomorrow,' I told Ena, 'Sheila Doel is driving me to Hatfield, it's the only palace I've ever wanted to see; and then we drive back to Highgate for my last dinner with Nora. Saturday is my last day with Pat Buckley, he's taking me somewhere in the country.'

'I want the Manns to meet you,' said Leo. 'If they can have us on Sunday, can you drive down with us then?' And he explained to Dorothy that Christopher Mann and his wife, Eileen Joyce, had bought Chartwell.

'Sunday's the only day we have left for a sitting,' I said. 'I think Ena's counting on it.'

'You need another sitting?' Leo asked, and Ena nodded, and he explained to Dorothy about the portrait painting.

'I don't see why you have to go home on Monday,' said Ena, and sighed. And I sighed. And Leo sighed. And then he turned to Dorothy and asked how long she'd known me. She said vaguely: 'I don't know. Eight or ten years.'

'Tell me,' said Leo in his vibrant English baritone, 'we've only known her a few weeks. Why is it so difficult for us to part with her?'

I turned to Dorothy, ready to say something joking, but I never said it. She was literally open-mouthed, gawking at Leo. She mumbled something and then turned her gaze on me, still open-mouthed, still with that incredulous look on her face. Looking at her, I saw my own inward reaction to being a five-week Duchess mirrored in Dorothy's face.

We left Panzer's and Dorothy thanked Leo for dinner and declined a lift to her hotel, she said it was just up the street. Then she turned to me and, struggling to make it sound light and teasing instead of plainly baffled, said:

'I don't suppose there's any use asking you to fit *me* into your busy schedule?'

I wanted to say:

'Never mind, Dorothy. Next week the ball will be over and Cinderella will be back at the pots and pans and typewriter in an old pair of jeans and a hand-me-down T-shirt, same as always.'

I just grinned and said I'd see her in New York.

FRIDAY, JULY 23

God bless Sheila, Hatfield House was the crowning touch. It's not the oldest palace or the most beautiful, it's just Elizabeth's. She grew up there. One wing of her palace is still standing, we saw her dining rooms – and more of her kitchens than she ever saw of them.

We sat on a stone bench in the garden. It was quiet and deserted and four hundred years dropped away, you could imagine yourself there in the garden with her when the gentlemen of the Council rode up and dismounted and knelt to tell her she was Queen of England.

We drove back to Highgate for dinner and Nora gave me some photographs of Marks & Co. to take home, and one of Frank. She told me how furious she used to be when he brought one of my letters home to read to the family.

'I'd say to him, "What kind of husband are you, to bring another woman's letters home!"'

'If he hadn't brought them home,' I said, 'you'd have had cause to worry.'

She looked at me and nodded.

'That's just what Frank used to say,' she said.

Her garden almost done; she gave me the last of the roses to bring home.

SATURDAY, JULY 24

With PB and the Elys to Losely House, An Elizabethan mansion. Elizabeth herself was once a house guest there. And wrote her host a long list of complaints and criticisms when she got home.

The three of them are having dinner tomorrow night at a pub Sam Pepys dined at, they wanted me to come along. I said I'd try to make it before the Colonel's party, I knew perfectly well I couldn't but I'm a coward, I didn't know how to say goodbye-and-thank-you to PB. Will call him tomorrow and say goodbye on the phone.

After we dropped the Elys at the Connaught, he took me to the jeweler's to get my label pin. It's a gold crossbar with the red-and-white London seal and the city's motto in gold:

DOMINE DIRICE NOS

Trust He will go on directing them.

SUNDAY, JULY 25

Did most of my packing last night so Ena could get an early start in Russell Square this morning, and she painted till noon, when we were rained out again.

She drove me through Regent's Park for a last look at the Nash Crescent and all the lovely streets, and then on down to Panzer's for a farewell lunch before we headed for the Tower.

We drove to the Tower and found people standing on line four abreast, waiting to get in. The line stretched for a city block along the Tower gates, and it wasn't moving. I knew then I would never see the inside of the Tower of London. I could have gone so many times. I let it go too long.

'Next summer,' said Ena brightly, 'We'll make a list of all the places you didn't see and we'll do the Tower first off!'

She's going to drive me to the airport in the morning.

LATER

The Colonel has a comfortable flat in Chelsea and his friends are all pleasant and easy to be with: two men, several attractive widows and a shy young couple from Switzerland. I don't remember any of their names or what we talked about, I couldn't concentrate. The party broke up early since I leave for the airport at 10 A.M. Nora was there. She drove me home and we said goodbye and promised to write.

I'm writing this in bed. With the packed suitcase standing open on the floor, the dresser top bare and the drapes drawn against the rain, the room looks exactly as it did the night I came.

Had the suitcase brought down after breakfast and paid the bill. Phoned PB to say goodbye but no answer.

Went up the street to Deutsch's and autographed twenty copies of the book for Australian booksellers due here tomorrow for a convention. Don't know their names and *still* couldn't bring myself just to write my name and let it go at that, it seems unfriendly. Wrote 'To an unknown booklover' in every copy, sometimes I think I'm crazy.

Said goodbye to Carmen and Mr Tammer and all the other people at Deutsch, except André who hadn't come in yet. Then went over and said goodbye to Russell Square. My friend the ticket taker hadn't come on duty yet; I was there by myself.

Came back to the hotel and tried PB again but still no answer. Decided to write him the minute I get home but would have done that anyway. When I came out of the phone booth Mr Otto bowed and said solemnly:

'Madam's Jag-U-Ar awaits.'

And there was Ena in a borrowed Jag, she said Leo had the car and she wasn't going to drive me to the airport in a station wagon too noisy to talk in.

She gave me a ring set with two small pearls because she once heard me say I like pearls.

The Colonel met us at Heathrow. He had my suitcase taken care of and then led us grandly into the VIP Lounge for sherry. Over sherry, he announced that after my plane left he was going to take Ena on a VIP tour of the airport buildings.

He and Ena walked me to the plane. The Colonel handed me over to a stewardess and told her to take good care of me, and he and Ena kissed me goodbye. I had a seat by the window and I slid into it and peered out, looking for them. Just as I saw them and lifted my hand to wave, they turned away and vanished in the crowd.

The plane lifted – and suddenly it was as if everything had vanished: Bloomsbury and Regent's Park and Russell Square and Rutland Gate. None of it had happened, none of it was real. Even the people weren't real. It was all imagined, they were all phantoms.

I sit here on the plane trying to see faces, trying to hold onto

London, but the mind intrudes with thoughts of home: the mail piled
up waiting for me, the people waiting, the work waiting.

Bits of Prospero run in my head:

> Our revels now are ended. These our actors
> . . . were all spirits and –
> Are melted into air, into thin air . . .
> The cloud-capped towers, the gorgeous palaces,
> The solemn temples . . . dissolve
> And, like this insubstantial pageant faded,
> Leave not a rack behind. We are such stuff
> As dreams are made on. . . .

Rest in peace, Mary Bailey.

Apple of
My Eye

Dedication

When New York City went bankrupt (became poor?), its Department of Civic Affairs and Public events was closed down, and all the duties formerly shared by several executives devolved upon one small Assistant to the Mayor, still in her thirties, named Arlene Wolff.

Arlene creates mammoth street fairs and city-wide holiday celebrations at almost no cost to the city. She does it by commandeering the services of New York's business community, hotels, airlines and public relations firms, and the Police, Fire, Sanitation and Parks Departments, and galvanizing all of them into a work force to brighten the lives of New Yorkers all year round.

She does this in addition to her routine duties of planning and managing all official entertainments and receptions for distinguished visitors, given by the Mayor at Gracie Mansion, and arranging all citations and awards given by the city to individuals and organizations.

Her awesome talents in the performance of these duties and her selfless devotion to the City of New York, are equalled only by her talent for selfless and devoted friendship.

This book is for her.

To Arlene from Helene. With love.

Christmas 1976.

Prologue

On April Fool's Day, I came home from a meeting with a publisher, hurried through my apartment-house lobby and told all the tenants waiting at the elevator:

'I've got the dream assignment of all time! I'm going to write copy for a book of photographs of New York City!'

Everybody congratulated me. Riding up in the elevator everybody assured me that a book of photographs with copy by a knowledgeable New Yorker like me would help to counteract the city's unfortunate image.

As soon as I had my coat off, I phoned all my friends and told them the news.

'If I'm an expert on nothing else,' I said, 'I'm an expert on New York, New York!'

Everybody agreed.

Confining the book to 'New York, New York' ('So nice they named it twice,' it says on T-shirts all over town this season) meant I wouldn't have to do research on Brooklyn or Queens, both of which are out on Long Island, or on the Bronx, which is up on the New York state mainland, or on Staten Island which is off the coast of New Jersey. All I was going to have to worry about was the original City of New York on Manhattan island, where I've lived all my adult life and which, as I told my best friend on the phone, I know like the back of my hand.

That was on Thursday. On Friday, I hurried round to my local branch of the New York Public Library and brought home three books about New York. They were old books; the library can't afford to buy new ones due to the city's financial crisis. But I thought they'd give me the facts and figures I ought to have. I got paper and pencil, carried all three books to the desk, opened all three to page one and began dipping into all three at once.

Each book had a list of Must See sights and I began copying out those that had made all three lists:

The Statue of Liberty
Wall Street and the Stock Exchange
Times Square
Empire State Building
Rockefeller Center
United Nations
The Cloisters
Grant's Tomb

Grant's Tomb?

I put the pencil down, closed the books and stared at the list. I'd never been to the Statue of Liberty. I'd never been to Wall Street or the Stock Exchange. I'd been to Times Square, and while it's admittedly a sight these days, it's not the kind you put on anybody's Must See list.

I'd been to the top of the Empire State building, but the Empire State building was no longer the world's or the city's tallest building and it no longer had the best view of the New York skyline. It had been superseded by the 110-story World Trade Center, and I'd never been to the World Trade Center.

I'd been in and out of certain Rockefeller Plaza buildings several hundred times, but I'd never taken a tour of the entire Center. And while I had been to the Cloisters once, years ago, I had only a hazy memory of it.

If I have to add this, I'd never been to Grant's Tomb.

I stewed over this for a few hours. Then I remembered that Patsy Gibbs was coming to lunch on Monday, and with great relief I put the whole problem out of my mind till then. Patsy Gibbs was not only a native New Yorker, she was a Radcliffe graduate married to a Harvard graduate and their son and daughter were both currently Harvard students. Nobody else I knew combined a native's knowledge of New York with access to two generations of Harvard brains.

Patsy and I had met and become friends back in the early sixties as members of the same neighborhood Democratic club. Then she had moved to the West Side and in recent years we'd seen each other very rarely. I considered it providential that we'd run into each other on Fifth Avenue the week before and had made a lunch date for Monday.

Patsy arrived promptly at one. (She's generally called 'Pat' but to me, the name 'Pat' suggests somebody tall, cool and unruffled. Patsy Gibbs is small, excitable and enthusiastic, with a face that registers emotions like a silent movie heroine and I've always called her Patsy.)

'Listen, I need your help,' I said as I took her coat. 'I'm writing copy for a book of photos of New York and I've just discovered I've never been to any of the tourist attractions! Would you believe I'm going to have to take a boat to the Statue of Liberty next week?'

I was about to ask her what I ought to know about the Statue when the look on her face stopped me. Patsy was staring at me with intense, imploring eagerness.

'Can I come with you?' she pleaded. 'I've never been there!'

'You've never been to the Statue of Liberty?' I demanded. 'But you were born here!'

'My parents took me when I was five but I don't really remember it,' said Patsy. 'And when my kids were old enough, they went with their grandparents so I never got to go!' And again with that beseeching look: 'Can I come with you? Would you mind?'

I did not ask her whether she had an equal craving to tour the New York Stock Exchange or stand on the 110th Floor Outdoor Observation Platform of the World Trade Center, and I did not ask how she felt about Grant's Tomb.

'Of course you can come with me, Patsy,' I said kindly.

'I keep telling you it's Pat!' she said impatiently. 'Patsy doesn't suit me!'

Believe me, it was about to.

Pride goeth.

During the rest of that week, I copied information industriously out of the library books. At the end of the week I knew how long the Statue of Liberty's right arm was, how many tons the George Washington Bridge's cables weighed and how many acres of floor space were occupied by the American Museum of Natural History.

I also had a page of earnest *Instructions for Tourists*. (1. Stop at the nearest bank or subway station and buy bus-and-subway tokens. 2. Stop at the Convention & Visitors' Bureau for sightseeing brochures and maps.) And I had made a tentative list of sights to see and trips to take. On the night before our scheduled trip to the Statue of Liberty, I was feeling in complete command of the entire project, and studying the Yellow Pages, when Patsy phoned.

'We have to take different subways down there!' she said in a panicky voice. 'We've never been around Battery Park! How are we going to find each other?'

'We're not going by subway,' I said. 'I've drawn up a list of *Instructions for Tourists* and Item 3 on the list is: "Don't take subways, take buses." You can't see New York from a subway window. So I thought we'd take a regular Sightseeing Bus down to Lower Manhattan, to see what it's like, and then get off the bus at Battery Park and go out to the Statue.'

'Oh, great!' said Patsy enthusiastically. 'I've always wanted to take a Sightseeing Bus. Where do we get it?'

'Well, I'm looking at the ads in the Yellow Pages,' I said. And Patsy said: 'Wait, I'll get the phone book.' When she came back, I said: 'Page 1671,' and we studied the bus company ads.

'The Port Authority has the biggest ad,' said Patsy. 'You want to take that one?'

'The Port Authority Bus Terminal,' I said, 'runs from Eighth Avenue to Ninth, they don't have signs to tell you which way is Eighth and which is Ninth, and there are always thousands of people streaming in and out of both entrances and up and down the escalators. You and I are both small, I'm nearsighted, we both panic easily and we'd never find each other.'

We settled on a smaller bus company in the west Forties and arranged to meet on the sidewalk in front of the bus office at nine-thirty A.M. for the ten o'clock tour of Lower Manhattan.

We met on time. (I got off the Fifth Avenue bus and ran half a block to the bus office and was just in time to see Patsy running half a block from Sixth Avenue; it turned out we're both fanatically prompt.) We bought our tickets and then went up the block to a drug store, climbed on counter stools and ordered coffee. I took out of my shoulder bag the large Composition book I'd bought for note-taking and showed Patsy my collection of Facts-and-Figures.

Patsy looked impressed as she read them.

'This is going to be a very heavy tourist guide,' she said a little nervously.

'Well, I want to do it right,' I said complacently. At which moment a fat woman in a fur coat sitting on the counter stool next to me turned to us and demanded:

'Where's Cartier's?'

I stared at her blankly. I don't live a Cartier life.

'It's on Fifth Avenue,' Patsy told her.

'Yes, I know that, dear,' said the fat woman. 'Where on Fifth?' No answer. Patsy doesn't live a Cartier life either.

'Have you ever been to Tiffany's?' I said. 'It's a beautiful store, it's –'

'Tiffany's is on the south-east corner of Fifty-Seventh and Fifth,' said Patsy. 'It's a very famous –'

'No dear. Cartier's,' said the fat lady firmly. 'Never mind, I'll find it.'

We walked back to the bus depot in subdued silence. Ten or twelve tourists were boarding the bus and we filed in after them. The bus had a heavy roof, narrow windows and poor visibility. We took seats in the back and the bus moved out of the dingy side street and rolled down a West Side avenue past more dingy West Forties streets. I stared out of the dirty window, very tense.

'Why does he have to drive through the dreariest streets in New York?' I said to Patsy. 'Why can't he go down Fifth?'

'This is a two-hour bus trip and you're not allowed to smoke and there's no john,' said Patsy morosely. 'Write that down, it's the kind of information people need.'

The bus rolled down into the garment district and the guide called everybody's attention to the fur trolleys and heavy racks of dresses being pushed along the sidewalk. I went on fuming. The garment district wasn't pretty. Anything that wasn't pretty I didn't want visitors to see.

At Thirty-fourth Street the bus turned east, and as we came to Fifth Avenue the guide announced dramatically:

'Straight ahead, on your right, folks, is the Empire State building!'

And everybody looked out the right-hand windows and saw the restaurant on the ground floor of the Empire State building. What else can you see out of a narrow window on a solidly roofed bus?'

Patsy slid way down in her seat and twisted sideways and peered up through the dirty window.

'Lie down,' she advised the other passengers. 'If you lie down and look up sideways you can almost see the top.'

They ought to open these windows so people can lean out and look up,' I said loudly. 'In New York, you have to remember to look Up.'

Thus bus proceeded down the only dull stretch of Fifth Avenue and then turned east again and the guide announced joyfully:

'We're coming to the Bowery, folks! New York's Skid Row! Watch out your windows for the Bowery bums. Sometimes you can see 'em layin' right in the gutter sleepin' it off!'

This galvanised the passengers. They half rose out of their seats and pressed their noses to the windows. As the bus moved slowly along the Bowery, a wide avenue lined with missions, some of the passengers ran across the aisle to peer out the opposite windows in the hope of seeing bums in the gutter.

'Bowery bums are a big draw!' Patsy murmured in surprise. As luck would have it, there were only two or three bums out that morning and they were standing up.

The bus made its first stop in Chinatown and we all got out and filed into a Buddhist temple and then into an adjoining curio shop, full of the usual cheap souvenirs-of-New-York and some fine jade jewelry. Then we came out and stood on the sidewalk for a few minutes, looking up and down Pell Street at the huge Chinese signs that hung from upper-story tenement windows and dwarfed the Chinese vegetable markets and restaurants huddled below them. After this we were herded back in the bus, which rolled on down toward Lower Manhattan.

On the way, we passed a huge construction site with a giant sign above reading CONFUCIUS PLAZA; and Patsy and I were so absorbed in speculating about this that we didn't notice much else along the way. As the bus careened down along the eastern edge of Lower Manhattan to the bottom of the island, Patsy said uncertainly:

'Do you get the feeling we're missing something?'

'I get the feeling we're missing everything,' I said. 'This is no way to see New York.'

At Battery Park, the passengers were invited to leave the bus again and walk along the river's edge for a few minutes. As I stepped down from the bus, Patsy, ahead of me, spotted a ticket booth with a sign reading: Liberty Island Ferry. Statue of Liberty.

'Come on!' she called, and we raced for the ticket booth and bought the last two tickets for a boat which was just about to pull away from shore. Clambering aboard it, we felt as if we'd been let out of school.

We made our way to the far rail of the ferry and hung over the edge, staring out at the statue. Liberty stood with her back to us.

'I should have known that,' I said. 'She's facing the immigrant ships that sailed in from Europe, she's holding the torch up for them, not for us. She can afford to turn her back on us; we have it made.'

'Look back!' said Patsy sharply. And I turned and looked back at the Lower Manhattan skyline. DO NOT DO THIS. You'll have plenty of time to stare at the skyline on your return trip. On your way out to the statue you have to keep your eyes on her; you'll have only one chance, as the ferry rounds Liberty island, to see her face, the torch in her hand, the Declaration of Independence in the crook of her left arm and the broken shackles at her right foot. And just once, you have to see her, face to face. Not because she's a work of art; for all I know, she isn't. You have to see her face because if you're an American, she's the symbol of what you're supposed to be. Looking at her, I had a sudden memory of Franklin Roosevelt beginning a formal address to a convention of the D.A.R. with: 'My fellow immigrants.'

Across the water from Liberty island we could see the abandoned, ruined buildings of Ellis Island which the Federal government closed down years ago. Looking from those buildings to the statue, I felt a fierce pride that my city was still making room for the 'huddled masses' nobody else wanted, even while it went bankrupt caring for them.

The ferry guide told us the boat would be back to pick us up in an hour and a quarter, and Patsy said: 'What are we going to do with that much time?'

Neither of us knew, till we saw it, that inside the pedestal of the statue there's a remarkable Immigration Museum.

The exhibits include photographs of the tense, hopeful faces of immigrants peering out at us from under their Old Country shawls, and photographs of the involuntary, hopeless immigrants chained together in the holds of slave ships, staring at us with bewildered eyes.

There's a room containing twelve talking statues, mostly of Revolutionary War heroes, each of whom describes his contribution to his adopted country in English heavily accented by his native France, Poland, Germany, Scotland or Ireland.

Patsy charged up to every statue, listened to its recital and then charged back to me like a gnat:

'Did you hear that? Write that down! Did you hear the ones on this side? Are you writing down what each one did?'

I used to write American history books for children, so I said with annoyance:

'I don't need to write everything down! I know who James Wilson and L'Enfant were!'

'You do?' said Patsy, round-eyed. 'I never heard of most of these people!'

So much for Harvard, I thought smugly.

I pointed to the statue of one Tadeusz Koscuisko and said graciously:

'I will tell you about him, because every New Yorker knows his name. More or less.'

'I don't,' said Patsy meekly. 'How do you pronounce it?'

'Ko*shoos*ko,' I said. 'He was a Polish engineer, he came over here to fight for the American cause and General Washington put him in charge of building West Point. Now: have you ever listened to a New York City traffic report in the morning? Have you ever heard the new York City Police Department give you the traffic conditions on the Kosky-Osko bridge?'

'Sure,' said Patsy.

'Well,' I said, 'the Kosky-Osko bridge was named for Koscuiszko, the Polish engineer who built West Point. Kosky-Osko is the closest a New York cop can get to Koshoosko.'

'How do you know all that?' Patsy marveled. I could have answered honestly: 'We had a Polish super in our building who told me how to pronounce it,' but I didn't, I just glanced around to see whether any other tourists were impressed by my story – and that's how I discovered we were the only two tourists left in the museum. We bolted out of there and had to run the length of the island at top speed to catch the ferry which was just about to pull away without us.

'You didn't take the elevator to the top and stand under the statue's face,' said Patsy, when we'd caught our breath. 'You should have done that for the tourists.'

'Why didn't you tell me?' I demanded. 'What do I have you along for?'

'I mentioned it,' said Patsy. 'You didn't hear me and I wasn't going to repeat it. My only childhood memory of the statue is of standing on that outdoor platform, three hundred and five feet above sea level, terrified out of my mind. I'm afraid of heights.'

We were hanging over the rail staring at the Lower Manhattan skyline at the time. And since the skyline is dominated by the twin towers of the World Trade Center, I realized I had a problem. I'd read somewhere that the World Trade Center's 110th floor Observation Deck is a quarter of a mile above the ground, and sooner or later I was going to have to get Patsy up there. It's an absolute Must for tourists, and I certainly wasn't going up there alone; I'm afraid of heights myself.

The ferry deposited us at the dock alongside Battery Park and we looked around for a restaurant. We didn't see any. Lower Manhattan, just ahead of us across an intersection, was full of restaurants but we didn't know where to find them.

'Where's Sloppy Louie's?' I asked Patsy. 'Isn't that around the docks somewhere?'

'I think it's further up,' said Patsy vaguely. If we'd had a map, we'd have seen that we were only a few blocks from Fraunces Tavern, which was not only a restaurant but one of the tourist sights on my list. But we didn't have a map. (Why would we have a map? We lived here.) We had lunch at the only place we could find, which was a dirty, dockside cafeteria.

'You'd think there'd be a downtown restaurant mentioned some-where in that four pounds of information you copied out,' said Patsy, as we slurped lukewarm coffee out of paper cups.

'There was,' I said. 'Fraunces Tavern, but I don't know where it is.'

'Has that re-opened since the Cubans bombed it?' Patsy asked.

'I thought it was Puerto Rican nationalists,' I said. 'I don't know whether it's open or not, I'll check it out.'

After lunch we toured Battery Park, a broad green strip along the bay at the tip of the island and one of the places guaranteed to bring out the historian in me.

'President Washington,' I told Patsy – though I knew from experience that the minute you start a sentence with 'President Washington' everybody stops listening – 'used to stroll here on summer evenings with his wife and the members of his Cabinet and their wives, back in 1789 when New York was the nation's capital.'

By this time, Patsy wasn't even within earshot. There are memorial stones in Battery Park, honouring immigrants who died in their adopted country's wars, and Patsy was darting from stone to stone, rapping out: 'Who's on this slab? Did you write him down? Who's on that slab over there? Did you read this one? Write it down. You're not writing anything down!'

'What do I want with every name on every stone?' I demanded.

'Well, I just think you're being very haphazard about this!' said Patsy. 'Somewhere in this book you'd better write: *Everything in this book is half-accurate.*'

It was mid-afternoon when we finally left the park, crossed the broad intersection and walked up into Lower Manhattan to look for a subway to take us home. But except for occasional jury duty – when you take a subway down to your designated courthouse, spend the day indoors and take the subway home – neither of us had ever really been to Lower Manhattan. Now, as tourists, we were seeing it for the first time and it struck us full in the face.

Lower Manhattan, which contained the original City of New York (and before that, the city of New Amsterdam) was once a town of small, upright houses on narrow, curving streets. The houses are long gone but the narrow, curving streets are still there, transformed into toy canyons by the row on row of jutting skyscrapers along them. And on every narrow street and alley, early skyscrapers have been joined by newer and higher ones, so that glass, steel and chrome towers rise above and behind the stone skyscrapers of the fifties, which themselves rise above the brick buildings of the twenties. The result is so dramatic that as we walked, Patsy would clutch my arm every few minutes and say: 'Look up there!'

And I'd look up and see three skyscrapers rising in a single vertical line, each built a generation later than the one below it, all three in wholly unrelated architectural styles, yet the three together somehow forming a single, harmonious composition.

We didn't notice what streets we were wandering along or what ones we passed; we just walked, open-mouthed, gawking upward. We did stop once. We came to a huge, heavy new building and stopped to stare at it, impressed, because etched in the stone was the name ONE WUI PLAZA.

'The Chinese are really booming!' said Patsy. 'One Wui Plaza is finished and Confucius Plaza is going up. Write that down.'

I was writing it down when I happened to notice, above the name of the building, the zigzag symbol used to denote electricity.

'Let me ask you something,' I said. 'Is Western Union an international company?'

(One Wui Plaza did a lot for my morale later on. It kept me from feeling guilty when I didn't write something down every single time Patsy ordered me to.)

We stopped at a Chock Full O' Nuts and climbed on stools and ordered coffee and Patsy ordered a doughnut. We were sipping our coffee peacefully when Patsy said:

'Were we on Wall Street?'

The question filled me with mild hysteria which I hoped I kept out of my voice.

'Of course we were on Wall Street!' I said. 'It was that canyon!'

'They're all canyons,' said Patsy absently, chewing her doughnut. She broke off a corner of it and handed it to me. 'Taste that.'

I tasted it.

'Ambrosia,' I said.

'So's their coffee,' said Patsy. 'Write it down.' I looked at her and she said: 'I'm serious! All tourists aren't rich. They'll see Chock Full O' Nuts places all over town; they should know you get great coffee and doughnuts there, and good sandwiches, and the service is quick and the places are always clean.'

'I'll use it,' I said. 'I just hope it doesn't go to their head.'

We found a subway we could both take as far as Grand Central, and as we went down the steps, Patsy said:

'You'll have to come down here again; we didn't see anything.'

'Of course I'm coming down again!' I said as we put tokens in the turnstile and joined the people on the platform. 'I have to do Wall Street, I have to do Fraunces Tavern – and I certainly have to go to the top of the World Trade Center! That's the one Must in a *new* tourist book about New York!'

Patsy studied the subway floor.

'I'm afraid of heights,' she said.

'So am I,' I said.

'No, I mean really afraid,' said Patsy. 'It's a phobia.'

'I'm just as afraid as you are. Don't give yourself airs,' I said. Then it occurred to me that she didn't have to go there with me if she didn't want to, and I added hastily: 'I probably won't get to it for a while. There are so many other places I have to see.'

'Where are you going next?' Patsy asked.

I had no order of preference, and I was so anxious not to press the World Trade Center that I fled clear to the other end of the island.

'The Cloisters,' I said.

'Oh, I haven't been up there in years, I used to love that place!' said Patsy.

'I thought I'd go next Thursday,' I said casually.

Patsy looked stricken.

'I can't make it, Thursday,' she said.

The subway screeched into the station and there was no way I could shout 'How about Friday?' without seeming pushy. We squeezed into a subway car and rode to Grand Central without trying to talk. As she left me to change to a West Side subway, Patsy mouthed 'I'll call you.' During the rest of the ride home, I looked over my notes and discovered I'd taken no notes at all on Lower Manhattan. That discovery marked the beginning of a very moody weekend.

On Friday night at two in the morning I got out of bed to look up Cartier's in the phone book. (It's at Fifty-second and Fifth.) On Saturday, as I cleaned the apartment, I seesawed between deep gloom and high panic. Instead of being in command of a large project with an admiring Patsy at my side, I saw myself taking solitary trips to places I knew nothing about and – if Lower Manhattan was any criterion –

wouldn't know anything about after I'd seen them.

On Sunday, I tried to bury myself in the *Sunday Times* as usual. But it's the *New York Sunday Times*, and everything I read pointed an accusing finger at some New York sight I'd forgotten to include in my plans. On Sunday night came the climax. I went to sleep and dreamed I was in the publisher's office. My finished manuscript lay on the desk between us as the publisher, with a sorrowful look, handed me a large, beautifully bound volume, its title in gleaming gold letters reading: BROOKLYN BOTANICAL GARDENS.

On Monday morning, I got out the 1975 World Atlas and just in case my editor should ask why I hadn't researched all five boroughs, worked out the following reply.

Brooklyn has a larger population than the city of Paris.

Queens has more people than Vienna.

The Bronx contains more people than the city of Warsaw.

Staten Island has a larger population than Cardiff.

That leaves New York, New York, the city jazz musicians first dubbed 'the Big Apple,' situated on a strip of island twelve miles long by less than two miles wide at its widest, which contains more people than live in Greater Liverpool with all its suburbs included, and that's enough territory for one book to cover.

Over lunch I calmed down. I reminded myself that I'd been hired to write copy for photographs which somebody was collecting for me and would eventually send me. The Cloisters was way up at 186th Street, and I had no guarantee the book would include a photograph of it. (I was prejudiced against the Cloisters anyway.) I decided to postpone the trip, and all other sightseeing trips, till the photos came; and after lunch I fled thankfully back to the safe haven of my library books.

At five o'clock, Patsy phoned:

'Hi,' she said. 'Listen, I changed my dentist date, I can go, Thursday. Where do you want me to meet you?'

Patsy came east, I walked north and we met on the corner of Seventy-ninth and Madison for coffee before taking a Madison Avenue bus up to the Cloisters. It was a sunny April morning and we ordered coffee-to-go and carried our containers over to Fifth, to the Seventy-ninth Street park entrance. We sat on one of the benches beside the lawn that rolls up to Dog Hill. We were therefore sitting with our backs to the Metropolitan Museum of Art, which is the only way I will ever consent to sit.

The Metropolitan Museum of Art is one of the world's great museums. It is also a sprawling, ugly pile of grey stone, which you won't realize when you go there because you'll enter through the front doors on Fifth Avenue, and the museum's Fifth Avenue façade is impressive. It extends from Eighty-first to Eighty-fifth Street and is New York's answer to Trafalgar Square: on any fine day, you'll see fifty or sixty people sunning themselves on the broad front steps. Flanking the steps are fountains, and at night when the façade and the fountains are illuminated, the museum looks seductively beautiful.

The Metropolitan Museum has great European and American collections, great Egyptian collections, Greek and Roman collections, medieval collections and Far and Near East collections. It has a concert hall, courtyard cafeteria on the ground floor and a private parking lot. All of this occupies thirty-seven acres, and I don't know how many additional acres the museum will occupy when its two new buildings, one to the north of the main building and one to the south, are completed. What I do know is that all of its acres were torn out of Central Park, which does not belong to the Metropolitan Museum of Art, it belongs to me. Me and a million other New Yorkers for whom life in New York would be unthinkable without it.

Wherefore, when Patsy glanced over her shoulder at the museum, barely visible behind the ugly wall around its huge construction site, and asked: 'Have you been in the Lehman Wing?' I said: 'I have not. I spent a solid year watching the museum's bulldozers and derricks trample down old trees and rip huge, gaping holes in one of the loveliest park stretches to put that wing up. Now I'm watching a newer and bigger demolition starting all over again.'

'Do you ever go to concerts in the Grace Rainey Rogers?' Patsy said. 'It's a perfect size for chamber music, I love that hall. And I love the Islamic collections. And the costume exhibits. I guess I love a lot of it.'

'Most people do. So would I, if it had a heart,' I said. 'Will you tell me why, in this skyscraper city, a three-story museum can't build *Up*? Why does it always have to build on the ground, destroying more and more of Central Park?'

'The Cloisters,' said Patsy neutrally, 'is part of the Metropolitan Museum.'

'I know it is,' I said. 'And I consider it very broad-minded of me to be going on a day's outing just to visit it.'

We went back to Madison and got on a Number 4 bus and looked out the windows at the shops. Madison Avenue is an incredible street; there's nothing you can't buy on it, from designer clothes to housewares, from pastry to paintings. The most expensive stores are in the Sixties and Seventies, but there are shop windows to look at out of a bus window all the way up through the Nineties.

It wasn't till the bus crawled up through the early hundreds that I said to Patsy:

'I don't work on weekends – Saturdays I clean and Sundays I lie down – but I should've made an exception for the Cloisters. The Culture bus would have got us up there much quicker.'

'Does it go up as far as the Cloisters?' asked Patsy. 'Wait a minute!' And she darted down to the front of the bus and spoke to the driver, and came back with the Culture Bus Loop I folder in her hand. She was right: the Culture bus doesn't go uptown as far as the Cloisters. But it will take you everywhere else mentioned in this book, and it's the greatest New York invention since the Mets.

There are two Culture Bus routes: Loop I goes uptown and stops at twenty-two tourist sights; Loop II goes downtown and makes twenty-nine stops in Lower Manhattan and Brooklyn. This is how they work:

There's a Culture Bus stop at every few blocks along the major avenues. You get on and buy one ticket which is good for the entire day. When the bus comes to the first sightseeing spot you want to visit, you get off the bus and see the sight at your leisure. Then you go back to the bus stop and another Culture Bus comes along and takes you to the next sight you want to see. A bus comes by every twenty minutes, and your ticket entitles you to get on and off at as many stops as you like.

At 110th Street, the bus turned west along the northern boundary of Central Park and as it turned north up Riverside Drive, Patsy got galvanised and started rapping out sights for me to write down.

'Hundred-and-twelfth Street! If they sit on the right, and look over that way, they can see the spires of the Cathedral of St John the Divine ... Hundred-and-fifteenth! Columbia University. Well, you can't see much of it from here but put it down anyway ... Hundred-and-twenty-fifth! Riverside Church. No, wait. Tell them to look out the back window till the bus gets to ... to ... One-twenty-eighth. If they look out the back window at a Hundred and twenty-eighth, they can see the Riverside Church bell tower.'

I didn't say anything. The Columbia-Riverside-St John's-Grant's Tomb area was a separate day's outing and I had no intention of going on that dreary safari by myself.

The bus rolled on up into Washington Heights and Patsy said:

'Hundred-and-seventy-ninth? George Washington Bridge!'

'Listen, I'm supposed to make a big thing out of that bridge, it's a Top Ten Sight,' I said. 'It's beautiful at night, but what else can you say about the George Washington Bridge?'

'It gets you home from Jersey,' said Patsy.

An hour and a half after it had left Seventy-ninth Street the bus turned in at a parking lot at the foot of the Cloisters. We stepped out and had to crane our necks to look up at the rambling stone structure. The museum is set on a high eminence overlooking the Hudson, and from the bus parking lot it is only reached by several flights of high, steep stone steps. We were halfway up them when Patsy suddenly said: 'I'll be right back,' and shot back down the steps and disappeared. I went on climbing and waited for her at the top. Standing there, looking through the entrance to an ancient monastery, it occurred to me that the Cloisters would be preposterous anywhere in the world but in a country as new as my own.

Financed in the nineteen thirties by John D. Rockefeller Jr, the museum contains a thirteenth century cloister from an abbey in the south of France; a chapter house from a twelfth century abbey in Gascony; a reconstructed twelfth century cloister from the eastern

Pyrenees; a thirteenth century Gothic portal from Burgundy and stonework from a twelfth century church in south-western France. All of these sections and fragments of ancient buildings were pulled down, stone by stone, shipped across the Atlantic, reassembled and reconstructed and set on a high hill in New York, New York. To Europeans watching the dismantling of ruined abbeys and chapter houses, it must have seemed a Mad Scientist project only an American billionaire would finance.

But no European can imagine being born in a country which was a wilderness three hundred years ago, in which a building seven hundred years old is literally unimaginable. John D. Jr knew that millions of Americans had no hope of seeing Europe, but might manage to see New York. Since his countrymen couldn't travel abroad to see medieval architecture, he brought medieval architecture to them.

Patsy came running back up the fifty or sixty stone steps and when she had caught her breath, said:

'I talked to a guard. People driving up don't have to worry about the steps. There's a ramp for cars that goes up to the Cloisters. Anybody coming by bus who can't climb steps should call in advance, and somebody here will meet them and take them up in an elevator.'

We went through the entrance hall and up to a desk where a woman sat behind a pile of folders. Next to the pile of folders was a sign. Patsy and I stared at that sign.

Most New York museums these days are reduced, by inflation and rising costs, to asking a small admission fee or voluntary contribution. The Cloisters, like the Met, is listed in the Convention & Visitors' Guide, as requesting a voluntary contribution. 'Pay what you wish,' says the Visitors' Guide. But what the sign on the desk said was: Suggested Contribution: $1.75.

Patsy was shocked.

'That's too much!' she said. 'Suppose a tourist family comes up here? Say a man drives up with his wife and three kids and maybe the kids' grandmother. He could get all the way up here thinking it's a free museum and then get cleaned out of ten or twelve bucks! For the smallest museum in town.'

I was too angry to answer. I took out two one-dollar bills and laid them down on the desk. The woman behind the desk looked at them, and then coldly at me, and then coldly at Patsy.

'Is this for *both* of you?' she asked.

'It is,' I said, stonily refusing to let her intimidate me. But I live here and I hate the Metropolitan Museum with a passion and she couldn't intimidate me. She could intimidate you. DON'T LET HER. The Cloisters is a free museum. If you want to make a contribution, it will help the museum to stay open. But remind yourself that your contribution is voluntary. If the woman at the desk forgets that, remind her.

The dark monastic interiors calmed us down. The chapels are starkly bare, their ancient stone walls, altars and tables unornamented except for a few sculptured figures of saints, and high, narrow stained-glass windows. On a few of the walls were medieval French and Flemish tapestries borrowed from the museum's Tapestry Room. The arched doorways of the chapels led out into the cloister gardens and the airy grace of the gardens accentuated the austerity within.

There was one exhibit which rather haunted me. Referred to in the official booklet only once, by the unamplified word 'reliquaries', there stood on display on the bare floor of one chapel several ancient stone coffins. Each coffin bore on its lid a full-length effigy of the man or woman buried in it. One, for instance, bore the effigy of a young woman identified as:

MARGUERITE
d.1277
daughter of Robert
Second Baron of Neuberg
Normandy

She was probably laid to rest in a monastery near her father's estates. And you suddenly think how bizarre it is that seven hundred years later, she should have been uprooted and transported thousands of miles to a continent she never knew existed, to be put on public display in a city and civilization she could never have imagined. I'm very grateful to John D. Rockefeller Jr. But is she?

It was one-thirty when we finally left the main building to look for the cafeteria Patsy remembered was somewhere on the grounds. We asked a guard for directions and he said:

'Just walk down that way about a quarter of a mile. You can't miss it.'

And he pointed the way. But he was pointing to two parallel paths. The inner path, next to the Cloisters, was crowded with tourists, so we took the empty, outer path nearer the river. (The inner path was crowded because it led to the cafeteria; but that was the kind of horse-sense conclusion neither of us in all our travels ever managed to reach, let alone jump to.)

People tend to think of this island as being level ground. It is not. In New York, 'downtown' and 'uptown' are literal words, and if you're a walker you're well advised to remember that 'downtown' is downhill and 'uptown' is uphill. You won't notice this in midtown Manhattan where the incline is very gradual. In uptown Manhattan, the incline can, without warning, become surrealistic. Patsy and I, being deep in conversation as we walked, didn't notice that our path was running gradually downhill while the adjoining path was running gradually uphill. We were still gravely discussing the significance of the Cloisters and I was making a few more notes, when Patsy said:

'Something's wrong. We've been walking for half an hour and he said it was only a quarter of a mile.'

We peered ahead and saw nothing that looked life a cafeteria. Then I happened to glance to our right.

'Where's the other path?' I said.

The inner path had entirely disappeared. We were walking along a single path by the side of a fifteen-foot-high stone cliff. A man came walking toward us on the path and Patsy stopped him.

'Can you tell us where the cafeteria is?' she asked him.

'What cafeteria?' he said.

'They told us there was a cafeteria on the Cloisters grounds,' I said.

'Oh, the *Cloisters*!' he said. 'The Cloisters is up there.' And he pointed up at the top of the cliff.

'How do we get there?' Patsy asked him.

'You're walking away from it,' he said. 'The Cloisters is back that way.' And he pointed us back the way we'd come. We turned around and went back to Square One and started over, along the inner path, and by the time we finally reached the cafeteria we'd had a healthy two-mile hike.

We revived over sandwiches and coffee, at an outdoor table in the sun, and then set off on a tour of Fort Tryon Park.

'This must have been an old fort,' I said. 'It's named for William Tryon, he was one of the British governors of New York.'

Fort Tryon park is a pleasant green rectangle overlooking the Hudson, with recessed stone benches along stone paths. Today, the benches were all occupied by elderly women reading or knitting in the sun. Most of them probably remember the park long before the Cloisters arrived in it. The land surrounding the fort was owned by the Rockefellers who gave it to the city for use as a park, back at the time of World War I. By the early thirties it included a promenade, a playground and a pool. Then in 1938 came the Cloisters, and took up most of it, and the park is now very much smaller. (See Metropolitan Museum.)

Across the Hudson from us were the opulent new apartment houses perched along the cliffs of the Jersey Palisades, built not to attract Jerseyites but to attract New Yorkers.

'People in this town are crazy,' I said. 'Thousands of them work in New York all day long, and then trek all the way up the Hudson and across the river to New Jersey, just to look at New York at night.'

'Well, the views are spectacular,' said Patsy.

'I know, but isn't that going a little far for a view?' I said. 'You don't have to move to another state to get a good view of New York City!'

For a second, Patsy didn't answer. She was looking tense.

'All right,' she said finally. 'If you're determined to go to the top of the Trade Center we'd better go there next, before I lose my nerve.'

'Tuesday?' I said. 'It's supposed to be less crowded early in the week.'

'All right,' she said, and as we headed back to the parking lot, she added: 'I warn you I'm not going to like it.'

'Neither am I,' I said.

Throughout its construction, the World Trade Center was cordially detested by all New Yorkers. The unpopular Rockefeller brothers were so closely involved in the financing that for a while, the twin towers were known as Nelson and David; the giant buildings are owned by the even more unpopular Port Authority, which wasn't created to build and own huge office towers. Plus which, the financially desperate city didn't need two new 110-story office buildings and couldn't afford to supply them with services. And to cap it off, the rumor among the fifty thousand office drones who worked in the buildings was that the elevators shook, especially up around the 85th floor (a rumor I did not think it necessary to pass on to Patsy).

The bus followed the same route back and Patsy said:

'Make a note: they can take a subway home from the Cloisters.'

'They have to take one subway ride anyway,' I said, 'just for people-watching.' (The variety of human sizes, shapes, colors and faces you'll see on one New York subway car is a living, breathing World Atlas.) 'Listen, should we make a list of one-way Avenues? Fifth-Avenue-buses-go-down, Madison-buses-go-up and so forth? – so visitors won't stand on an Up avenue waiting for a Down bus?'

'If they're standing on Fifth Avenue they'll see the traffic's all going one way,' said Patsy. Then she said: 'What are you going to do if you have to mention Sixth? What are you going to call it?'

'I'm going to call it Sixth Avenue,' I said. 'Did you ever hear anybody call it anything else?'

'Then you'll have to explain it,' said Patsy.

'Okay, I'll explain it,' I said.

The late, great Mayor of New York, Fiorello H. LaGuardia, once remarked: 'When I make a mistake, it's a beaut.'

Well, Hizzoner's most enduring beaut was committed against Sixth Avenue. Back in the forties, Fiorello got carried away one year by Pan American Day – or maybe it was Week – and announced that in honour of Pan America, Sixth Avenue was henceforth to be known as The Avenue of the Americas. Nobody thought he meant the change to be permanent, but he did.

All the Sixth Avenue street signs came down and new signs went up reading: AVE. OF AMERICAS. Every place of business on the avenue had to change the address on its stationery and in the phone book. A couple of decades later, when new skyscraper office towers went up along midtown Sixth Avenue every corporation in every building naturally had to list its address as *Avenue of the Americas*.

But somehow the name didn't take. To the people who lived here, Sixth Avenue flatly declined to be known as the Avenue of the Americas. It went right on being Sixth Avenue. Thirty years later it's still Sixth Avenue, and it's obviously never going to be anything else. The chief sufferer from Fiorello's beaut, therefore, is the hapless visitor.

You'll come to New York one day and go shopping in Saks, Fifth Avenue, and when you come out of Saks you'll stop a passer-by and ask him if he can direct you to Radio City Music Hall. And the passer-by will point west and say: 'One block over, on Sixth Avenue.'

And you'll walk one block over, and when you get there you'll check the street sign, and the street sign will say – AVE. OF AMERICAS. So you'll stop another passer-by and say: 'Pardon me, can you tell me where Sixth Avenue is?'

To which there is no possible answer except: 'You're standing on it.'

Tuesday, April 20

The night before we were to go down to Lower Manhattan, I called Patsy and gave her the itinerary:

'Wall Street, Trinity Church, the World Trade Center and Fraunces Tavern,' I said, slipping the Trade Center in as if it were just one more ground-level attraction.

'How do you want to go down?' Patsy asked. 'We've taken one West Side bus. Do you want to take an East Side bus down and see the Lower East Side?'

'I have to do that on foot,' I said. 'I want to go down to Orchard Street on a Sunday, it's one of those sights I've heard about all my life and never seen.'

'Oh, great!' said Patsy. 'And we can walk down and see Wall-Street-on-a-Sunday, it's supposed to be a ghost town. Make a note.'

And I made a note, laying the groundwork for what we would look back on as Blockbuster Sunday.

'What about tomorrow? You want to take a Second Avenue bus anyway?' Patsy asked. 'Is there anything for tourists to see on Second?'

'Not much,' I said. 'It's mostly for people who live on it or near it. You know: supermarkets, neighbourhood stores, thrift shops.'

'Nothing else?' Harvard probed.

'OTB parlours,' I said.

OTB stands for Off-Track Betting. It's a legal way for New Yorkers to bet on the horses, and was devised by the city as a painless way to extract from its citizens the extra dollars it so badly needed. (Then the state discovered OTB was profitable and took it over, and now the state runs it and hogs the money.) OTB parlours are store-fronts and some neighbourhood block associations wage battles to keep the gambling parlours from opening in their neighbourhoods, and while I don't mind them that much, they don't exactly beautify the landscape.

'Let's save time and take a subway down,' I said to Patsy, 'and get off at the Wall Street station so we won't miss Wall Street again.'

We got off at Wall Street and when we came up the subway steps we found ourselves on the sidewalk in front of Trinity Church. The church, on Trinity Place, faced the beginning or end of Wall Street, we weren't sure which.

Trinity was one of the city's fashionable Anglican churches back in pre-Revolutionary days (becoming Episcopal after the war). The building has been twice destroyed and rebuilt since then, and is a simple Gothic church, with a narrow steeple that was once the city's tallest spire and tranquilly refuses to look either shrunken or out of place among the towering skyscrapers. But it wasn't the church, it was the churchyard I'd come to see. Alexander Hamilton is buried there. So is Albert Gallatin, whom I'm much fonder of. (He was Jefferson's Secretary of the Treasury.) So when we came out of the church and I tried the churchyard gate and found it locked, I was very disappointed and glad I hadn't told Patsy who was in there. (I keep assuming other people *care* where dead statesmen are buried.)

'Would One Wall Street be at this end?' I asked Patsy.

'I don't know,' she said. 'What's there?'

'Wall Street got its name from a wall Peter Stuyvesant built to keep out pirates. We all know it never did keep out pirates and it was torn down a couple of centuries ago, but there's a plaque on the building at Number One Wall Street marking the spot where the wall began.'

'Let's find it,' said Patsy, starting across the street.

We found the building on the corner directly opposite Trinity Church. It was a huge bank building, home of the Irving Trust (and I hope Washington Irving had nothing to do with the founding of it). Next to the name was the address: Number 1 Wall. We hunted along the walls for the plaque and didn't find it. But on the side wall, we found a large, pale square in the stone, with four holes at the corners, marking the spot where the plaque had been.

'Somebody stole it,' I said.

'Let's go ask,' said Patsy, and sprinted around the corner and in through the imposing front doors. I followed her as she stepped up to the first desk she came to, and asked the dignified gentleman behind it if he knew anything about the missing plaque.

'Vandals took it, I'm afraid,' he said regretfully.

'How long ago?' asked Patsy.

'Oh, quite some time ago,' he said.

'Well, the plaque had no historical value,' I said. 'It was just a plaque. Couldn't the bank afford to replace it?'

He gave me a gently reproving look.

'I'm sure that's being done,' he said.

When we came out, Patsy said: 'Make a note to come back next month and see if the new plaque is up.'

'You mean you believe him?' I demanded. 'You think a bank is going to run out and have a new plaque made? A *bank*?'

'Make a note,' said Patsy implacably. 'We'll come back down and see.'

I made a note.

One thing about the World Trade Center: you don't need a map to find it. With our eyes on the severe twin towers jutting skyward, we steered a zigzag course through winding streets until we came to an intersection seething with traffic, across the street from it. As we waited for a green light, we looked across the street and saw, in front of the Trade Center and blocking the entrance to it, cement mixers, mounds of earth, piles of wooden boards and the rest of the construction mess out of which the Center's landscaped plaza will have emerged by the time you read this.

'You know the problem with this book?' I said to Patsy. 'I want to write about the Trade Center Plaza and I can't because it isn't there yet. I want to write about Radio City Music Hall and I'm not sure it'll still be there when the book comes out. No other city on earth has such a mania for tearing down the old to build the new – which I approve of. My theory is that since New Yorkers mostly come here from somewhere else, they have no interest in the city's past, they come with big plans for its future. And on a narrow strip of island, you can't build the future without tearing down the past first; there isn't room for both. But it's a headache when you're writing a book about it.'

We crossed the intersection and picked our way through the mess to the unfinished door of World Trade Center Two, where the Observation Deck is. We walked into the lobby and I said: 'Welcome to the Twenty-first Century.' (And what's startling about that, is that in the next two weeks I was to read the same words in two descriptions of the Centre lobby.)

The lobby is mostly white marble and seven stories high. Far up on the walls are Gothic oval windows, bizarrely churchlike; and the height and depth, and the whiteness and the church windows, create the effect of a science-fiction interior. Two or three stories above the lobby floor is a mezzanine deck which encircles the lobby; you take an escalator up there to buy tickets to the 107th Floor Observatory, from which an escalator takes you on up to the tallest outdoor observation platform in the world, on the 110th floor.

It was a cloudy day and the sign over the ticket booth warned: Visibility – 5 miles. There were very few people on line and I said to Patsy: 'Should we wait and come back on a clear day?'

'We're here,' said Patsy grimly. 'We're going through with it.'

Fifteen or twenty of us were herded into an elevator, and the door slid shut. The elevator shot up to the 107th floor in a matter of seconds – and they're right, it shakes; and your ears pop. At the 107th floor the door opened and relief flooded us: the vast floor was enclosed by an unobstructed expanse of heavy windows that ran clear round the deck. Hand in hand, bravely, we approached the windows.

There's a bench inside every window. Between the bench and the window is a heavy brass railing you can hang onto as you look down (and you'll hang onto it). Stencilled in each window is a small map of the street below it, with the sights and buildings labelled. You grasp the railing and look straight down a quarter of a mile, into Wall Street or Battery Park or whatever is below your particular window. And then you look up and out, at eye level, at all five boroughs and all five great bridges, but mostly at the city itself. From this bottom-most tip of the island the whole of New York is spread out before you, its thousand skyscrapers fused into a single, improbable vision of 'topless towers'. For us, they shone against the grey sky as if the sun were on them.

Seen from those windows, the New York skyline was more an entity than Wren's London or L'Enfant's Washington. No one could look at it without asking: 'Who built it?' If you consult the library books, you'll be told that the Empire State building was designed by Shreve, Land & Harmon, and that Rockefeller Center was created by Corbet, Harrison & MacMurray, Hood & Foulhoux, Reinhard & Hofmeister. Yes, but who? What senior member of the firm drafting plans for the Lever building said: 'Suppose we used green glass . . .?' Who of the Seagram architects first said tentatively: 'What about bronze . . .?' Whose pencil drew the spectacular sweeping curve of 9 East 57th Street? Who built it? Anon, that's who. Nobody built the New York skyline. Nobody by the thousands.

We stared out with no sense of height, just awe.

'That's some dying city,' I said.

And suddenly, irrationally, I gloried in the high-handed, high-flying, damn-your-eyes audacity that had sent the Trade Center's twin columns rising impudently above the skyline at the moment when New York was declared to be dying, and so deep in debt it couldn't afford workers to dispose of the Center's trash, police its plaza or put out its fires.

We moved from window seat to window seat, silently gawking, except when Patsy, sitting before a window map that included Fraunces Tavern, announced that she had studied the location and knew exactly how to find it, so the afternoon would present no problems.

There are telescopes by the windows and several tourists were glued to them, probably hunting the block in Queens they lived on. (Locating Uncle Harry's house in Connecticut would have to wait for a clearer day.)

Next to the elevators was the steep escalator which led up to the 110th floor Observation Deck. Patsy circled it warily and said: 'Let's wait and get on behind other people.'

We stepped on behind a broad-backed man and his broad-backed wife. Patsy was so ashen with terror that I forgot my own in my obligation to reassure her.

'Did you know,' I said conversationally, 'that in 1770, New York City went bankrupt? Governor Colden had to write to London for permission to float a loan.'

'Keep talking,' said Patsy.

'The Crown,' I said, 'vetoed the loan.'

'Oh, right,' said Patsy.

'Well, what with all the taxes New York was paying to London, the town got very worked up,' I went on, 'and the Crown grudgingly reconsidered and said: "All right, you can have a loan. But just this once. After this, if you're still in trouble, you can drop dead." Well, after that, the Revolutionary War broke out and the Crown lost all its colonies.'

We stepped off the escalator onto an outdoor platform sensibly designed to prevent suicides and provide a needed anticlimax to the Observatory three floors below. The platform we stood on reminded both of us of a resort boardwalk. It's a broad wood and cement floor, the railing hidden behind thick shrubbery. A few feet below it is another broad boardwalk extending further out on all sides, so that when you look down, the lower boardwalk is all you can see. Then you look out, and the splendour of the city smites you all over again with 'astonishment of the heart,' as it says in the Bible.

It was one-thirty when we finally took the elevator back down to the lobby to look for a restaurant open to the public. A new restaurant had just opened on the 107th floor of Tower One, but we knew we wouldn't be admitted to it. (That restaurant – 'Windows on the World' – is now New York's most celebrated restaurant. But it was an added source of irritation when it first opened, because it opened as a private club from which the general public was excluded at lunchtime. This caused such public fury that the restaurant backed down later, and today, non-club members are admitted to lunch on payment of a steep cover charge in addition to the cost of the lunch. At night, dinner at the restaurant is like a ticket to a Broadway hit musical: you have to reserve your place months in advance. If you're not rich, go there for Sunday brunch, when there's no cover charge; or better still, stop at the cocktail lounge after dusk – it's open from four to seven – and see the diamond-studded night city.)

We found an attractive coffee shop in one of the two lobbies, I forget which. It had small tables along cushioned banquettes. We found an empty table and a waitress brought us menus. After studying mine, I was happily watching attractive lunch platters go by on trays when I realized that Patsy, her menu unopened was staring at me.

'What's the matter?' I asked.

'You're writing this book for tourists,' she said. 'We cannot eat lunch in the basement of the world's tallest building.'

'It's not the basement, it's the ground floor,' I said.

'It's the basement,' said Patsy. 'We are sitting in the basement of the tallest building in the world.'

'The 110-story Sears building in Chicago is taller,' I said.

Patsy went on staring at me like a stony conscience.

'In Toronto,' I said, 'there's a Needle that's taller than the Sears building in Chicago.'

Nothing. Patsy's accusing eyes never left my face. So I sighed and gave in and put my shoes back on, and we left the coffee shop and went past a maze of lobby shops and on into the other lobby and up to the information desk, and then around to a bank of elevators which would take us up to the 44th floor 'Sky Lobby' where, we were told, there was a restaurant.

There is definitely a restaurant on the 44th floor. I'm told it's very pleasant and you will probably find it without difficulty. We couldn't find it. We went down a long hall which turned more corners than I thought there were. We went past rabbit-warren office doors and past two of the Center's seven banks of elevators. Finally, when an office worker came along, Patsy stopped her.

'Do you know where we can eat up here?' she asked. And the office worker said:

'One flight down, through that door.'

We pushed open the door and walked downstairs; and that's how we happened to have lunch in the dirtiest, drearist office-workers' cafeteria that ever closed for the day just as we were ready for our second cup of coffee.

Of course, when we got out on the street, Patsy not having the stencilled window map with her, didn't have any idea where Fraunces Tavern was. However, on our walk from Trinity church to the Trade Center, we had noticed the wall maps which are a charming feature of the Lower Manhattan landscape. On lamp-posts and on the walls of buildings, at three- or four-block intervals, is a small map of the immediate area with all the chief points of interest marked, and a bright, black arrow pointing to one spot on the map, with the legend: YOU ARE HERE. We found one such map near the Trade Center and Patsy studied it.

'This map,' she said finally, 'is upside down. I think we go that way.'

We went that way, through small streets we hadn't been on before, and I began to wish somebody we knew would come along. There are two groups of professionals who work in Lower Manhattan: 1 the stockbrokers, bankers, underwriters and accountants who work in the financial district, and 2 the city officials, judges, law clerks and attorneys who work in the City Hall and Courts district. We knew a sprinkling of people in the second group, but of course no none of them came by. Finally we stopped a man hurrying by with a briefcase.

'Can you tell us where Fraunces Tavern is?' Patsy asked him.

'I'll be glad to,' he said. and he put down his briefcase, took his wallet out of a breast pocket and extracted from the wallet a small map. As he studied it, I was comforted to realize that Lower Manhattan was just enough like London for even the regulars to carry maps. So Patsy and I weren't as dimwitted as we felt.

'Here we are,' he said finally, and pointed us down toward Battery Park and then east of it.

We walked down till we came to the broad intersection where, from the Battery Park side, we had first seen Lower Manhattan. But the approach from the upper side was dramatically different. With the skyscrapers behind us, we looked across the intersection to a row of eighteenth-century houses on a street that was like a little island standing by itself, a forgotten relic of the past. Fraunces stood on the corner nearest us. Being both a historical museum and a popular restaurant, its red brick and white moulding looked freshly painted, and its windows, brightly clean, were flossy with white curtains. By contrast, the four houses alongside it looked decayed and abandoned and there was something touching about them, empty and neglected but still stubbornly standing where they had always stood. Then we noticed the last house in the row. Dingier and more dilapidated than its neighbours, it had a sign of life in its bleary ground-floor window. The sign read: OTB.

And Patsy was waving at it wildly and I was laughing and crowing 'I love this town!' and we almost got run over crossing to Fraunces.

All traces of the bomb damage were gone, and the tavern seemed intact. It's an attractive restaurant, 'restored' and self-consciously charming like the Dickens pubs in London.

We went upstairs to the celebrated room from which General Washington said farewell to his officers. According to an eye-witness, Washington 'filled his glass and lifted it and said: "With a heart full of love and gratitude I now take leave of you".'

'The officers who were present at the leave-taking,' I told Patsy, 'very probably included Kosky-Osko.'

The museum contains military despatches, and a few letters and artifacts from the Revolutionary War, as well as the history of Samuel Fraunces, the West Indian who owned the tavern before, during and after the Revolution.

('Race prejudice is a remarkable thing,' I said to Patsy. 'When the British invaded New York and the patriots fled, the British confiscated all patriot property. When the British marched out and the patriots returned, they confiscated all Tory property. But neither side ever confiscated Sam Fraunces' tavern: he was black so he didn't count as Tory or patriot. You get the feeling nobody ever thought to ask him which he was.')

It was ten minutes to five when we left Fraunces, so we were just in time for the five o'clock subway rush hour. Maybe, just once, you ought to take a New York subway during the five o'clock rush, to see how the other side of insanity lives. Every subway car is wall-to-wall people. I was pushed nearly to the middle of the car by the crowd entering behind me; and though I had nothing to hang on to, and the train lurched round every bend, the solid wall of bodies kept me upright. I finally managed to work my right arm through enough coats and elbows to get three fingers around the center pole and I counted eleven unrelated hands or parts of hands above and below mine on the pole. Then the train stopped at Grand Central and two thousand more people pushed into the car and I lost my hold entirely. It's not an experience I am up to twice in one week, so when Patsy phoned on Wednesday and said: 'I've got tomorrow free. Where to next?'

I said: 'Midtown Manhattan. We're entitled to a nice easy one. We're going to spend the day with millionaires.'

'Would you believe,' I said to Patsy when I met her the next morning, 'that there are forty-five museums listed in the Manhattan telephone book?' I consulted my notes and added: 'in addition to the Irish, Chinese, Jewish, Hispanic, American Indian, Black, Primitive and Folk, there are museums of Fire-fighting, Numismatics, Sports, Jazz and Oceanography. And that's not counting any of the art museums, not even the most famous ones – the Met, the Guggenheim, the Whitney and Moma.' (The Museum of Modern Art is on Fifty-third Street, and when you pass it you'll see an enormous navy blue banner floating in the breeze with the acronym MOMA on it.)

'How many do we have to go to?' Patsy asked dubiously.

'I picked out four,' I said. 'Three have a common denominator: even tourists who are bored by museums have to see them. They can ignore the museum when they get there. It isn't the museum I want them to see.'

'Oh,' said Patsy. 'Like this one.'

We were standing in front of a mansion on Thirty-sixth Street between Park and Madison. Its official name is the J.P. Morgan Library. It's a two-story mansion built by J.P., to house his private library and his priceless collection of art objects. And let's say you have no interest in J.P.'s rare porcelains, illuminated medieval manuscripts, Gutenberg Bibles or early children's books, and that since you're not a scholar or collector, you won't be admitted to the reference library. Go anyway. Go there to meet J. Pierpont Morgan.

The mansion was designed as 'a Renaissance palazzo built of fitted marble blocks in the classical Greek manner,' it says in the brochure. Inside, however, the house abandons the Renaissance and classical Greek in favour of Queen Victoria and Edward VII. You enter a dark, airless hall with heavy mahogany doors opening into two exhibit rooms. After you've seen whatever interests you – the medieval manuscripts in glass cases or the portable Flemish altar on the mantel – climb the dark, heavy mahogany stairs to the second floor, to the East and West Rooms. Do the East Room first. This was J.P.'s private library.

The long gallery above the room is lined with rare and

magnificently bound books (which you can't go up the gallery stairs to look at, because you're not a scholar). You'll find a few more books in glass cases and more rare art objects on display. Then go into the West Room, which was Morgan's private study and has been preserved just as he left it. In the West Room, you are in the palpable presence of the owner of the house.

The room is suffocating with mahogany and red plush: heavy dark mahogany tables and chairs, red plush sofa and drapes, and red silk wallpaper. The carved ceiling was imported from a Florentine cathedral. The stained-glass windows were imported from a German cathedral. I don't remember where the massive fireplace was imported from. Dominating the room, extending from the ceiling down to the mantel above the fireplace, is a huge, standing portrait of J. P. Morgan, wearing a red dressing gown that matches the red silk wallpaper. Beneath the enormous canvas, several small items on the mantel pale into insignificance, including a priceless miniature portrait of Martin Luther. Straight-backed mahogany armchairs are set at a respectful distance from the imposing desk they face.

'From behind that desk,' the guard on duty informed us proudly, 'Mr Morgan made all the major financial decisions for the Allies in World War I.' Kings and queens and heads of state, he told us, came to this room, hat in hand, to negotiate loans with the great J.P.

The room gave me the cold horrors. But history, as somebody once remarked, is not a rummage sale. If you come to New York looking for the history of the United States, the pretty candy-box of Fraunces Tavern is not chiefly where you find it.

It was a relief to get out of that oppressive mausoleum into the sunny April morning again.

'Did you know that J. P. Morgan was born in Hartford, Connecticut?' I asked Patsy.

'If that's the beginning of one of your long-winded stories I don't want to hear it,' said Patsy. 'Let's start walking toward the Frick even if we don't make it.' The Frick Collection was nearly forty blocks away, up at Seventieth and Fifth. 'We can stop for coffee on the way.'

'Of course we're stopping for coffee on the way,' I said. 'We're going to Paley Park. I told you we're spending the day with millionaires, I didn't say they were all dead.'

Paley Park is on Fifty-third Street between Madison and Fifth, but it's not the open green space the word 'park' implies and you have to look sharp or you'll pass it by. It's a narrow hole-in-the-wall park, sandwiched in between two dark buildings, a green oasis where you can get coffee and a sandwich to eat at one of its picnic tables, or just sit on a park bench and enjoy the greenery and the waterfall which is the back wall. I read somewhere that William Paley (whose CBS building is only a couple of blocks away on Sixth Avenue) built it for the city's midtown office workers. Those who brought their lunch from home needed a pleasant place to eat it; those who didn't, needed to buy sandwiches and coffee at a place less dreary than the cafeterias they could afford. As we got our coffee and took it to a table, I told Patsy:

'William Paley was born in Philadelphia, like me.'

She wasn't listening. She was fishing two newspaper clippings out of her handbag. She pushed them across the table to me and said:

'I thought you might have missed these.'

Both were from the *Times*. I hadn't missed them, I'd ignored them. One was about the house down in the Twenties somewhere, where Teddy Roosevelt was born. The other was about the Morris-Jumel mansion up at 160th Street and St Nicholas Avenue. Looking at those clippings I realized that Patsy's Harvard background could be something of a problem.

'With all there is to see in New York,' I said, 'do you really think tourists are going to want to run down to the Twenties to see Teddy Roosevelt's birthplace? FDR had a town house on East Sixty-fourth Street and I wasn't even going to bother with that.'

'Herbert Hoover,' said Patsy thoughtfully, 'had a suite at the Waldorf Towers. Well, all right, I guess you can skip presidents' houses. But the Jumel mansion is a landmark, it was Washington's headquarters during the Revolution.'

'I know,' I said. 'He was there just long enough to lose the Battle of Harlem Heights and abandon New York City,' and I changed the subject. I thought I'd disposed of the Jumel mansion and when we rose to go, I left the clipping on the table. But Patsy, with one of her stony glares, picked it up and stuffed it into my shoulder bag and I knew I hadn't heard the last of it.

The Frick Collection was the finest private art collection in the country, when Henry Clay Frick died and left it – and the mansion that houses it – to the people of New York City. (He was born in Pittsburgh.) It's another 'palazzo' but entirely white – white stone outside, white stone and marble inside. And as often as we'd both been there, entering it today was almost a shock, coming to it as we did from the sombre darkness of the Morgan. The Frick house is all light and air.

You enter a foyer where an oblong stone pool of very clear green water is flanked by white garden benches and potted trees. You go on into a central hall, the white marble floor as spacious as the gallery rooms opening off it. At the far end of the hall, there's a great marble staircase with the pipes of an organ on the landing. (The keyboard is in a niche by the foot of the staircase.)

I read in S. N. Behrman's 'Duveen', that Frick used to hire an organist to come and play to him on Saturday afternoons. Frick sat in his long gallery, reading the *Saturday Evening Post*, while the organist played 'Silver Threads Among the Gold.' Never mind: today, you can hear lovely chamber music concerts at the Frick on Sundays at four.

We entered the gallery rooms where white walls leave all the colour to the paintings – and even if (like me) you know nothing about painting, the blaze of colours on the Frick walls will dazzle you.

'Harry Truman,' I said, 'once said that the Carnegie libraries were steeped in the blood of the Homestead steel workers.'

'Did you see the Goya over the mantelpiece?' said Patsy. 'It's incredible.'

'The steel workers at the Homestead plant had gone on strike for a union contract. So of course the plant hired scab labor,' I said.

'Look at the little Memling,' Patsy murmured. 'The light takes your breath away.'

'The manager of the Homestead plant brought in three hundred armed Pinkerton guards to protect the scabs. He smuggled them in at night by boat. When the Pinkerton guards' guns weren't enough to break the strike, the governor sent in the state militia.'

'Where's the Rembrandt self-portrait?' asked Patsy.

'The guards and the militia cut down the steel workers in cold blood, and that finally broke the strike,' I said. 'And for years afterwards, the steel companies didn't have to pay union wages; and Carnegie and the Homestead plant manager lived happily ever after.'

'Why do you have to tell me a story like that when I'm trying to see the most fabulous collection in town?' Patsy demanded.

'Because that's how this fabulous place got built,' I said. 'the manager of the Homestead plant was Henry Clay Frick.'

We left the Frick and when I said: 'Next stop: the Cooper-Hewitt Museum of Interior Design,' Patsy gave me a sour look.

'I love the Cooper-Hewitt,' she said. 'I love the Meissen china and the antique wallpaper and the antique textiles – and after your terrible story, I won't be able to enjoy it!'

The Cooper-Hewitt museum is at Ninetieth and Fifth, in the Carnegie mansion.

As we walked up Fifth Avenue, passing all my favorite East Side streets at intersections on the way, I said:

'How can I get visitors to turn off Madison or Fifth and walk East and explore the side streets in the Sixties and Seventies? When my friend, Nora Doel, came here from London she was bowled over by them. She said the only pictures she'd ever seen of New York were of skyscrapers; she couldn't believe the rows of beautiful houses along the East Side streets.'

'I gather,' said Patsy politely, 'you're not planning to include the West Side in your book.'

'I'm doing the West Side next, as a matter of fact,' I said virtuously. 'I'm going to do Rockefeller Center.'

Patsy stopped in her tracks.

'Do you mean to stand there and tell me you call Rockefeller Center the West Side?' she demanded. 'Your idea of the West Side being the west side of Fifth Avenue?'

'Rockefeller Center runs west of Fifth almost to Seventh,' I said. 'And you didn't let me finish. We're going to do Rockefeller Center and Lincoln Center, and I'll mention the theatre district. I'm not chasing all the way over to Duffy Square just to look at it, but I'll mention that Duffy Square is at Forty-seventh and Broadway, and there's a booth there called TKTS where you can get half-price theatre tickets for any show on Broadway that isn't sold out for that day's performance. And unless you really insist on dragging me through the Natural History Museum to stare at reconstructed dinosaurs I don't know what else there is to see on the West Side.'

'If you can lower yourself to come to my house,' said Patsy, 'I'll show you.'

We turned into the side entrance of the Carnegie mansion, to be met by a locked gate and a huge sign telling us the museum was closed for the summer 'for renovation' and would re-open as a branch of the Smithsonian Institution. By the time you read this, it will have become a much larger and more impressive museum of interior design, with medieval and Byzantine textiles and collections of drawings, ancient and modern. And maybe the remodelled Carnegie mansion will have an interior less grim and forbidding than it used to be.

'Okay, now where?' asked Patsy as we turned away from the locked gate. 'Gracie Mansion?'

Gracie Mansion, up in the eighties next to the East River, is not a museum, it's the official residence of the Mayor of New York. Technically, its'a tourist attraction but it's surrounded by a wall.

'What can a tourist see of Gracie Mansion but the wall and the driveway?' I said. 'Do you want to know the only way an ordinary citizen can get a really good view of Gracie Mansion? Have a baby. A couple expecting a baby should reserve a room at Doctors Hospital and ask for a room with a river view. As soon as the baby's born, the parents can hang out the window and watch the goings on in the Gracie Mansion garden and living-room and dining-room and even a couple of bedrooms.'

We were walking up Fifth and Patsy said:

'Well, do you mind if I ask where we're going?'

'I thought after all these millionaires,' I said, 'we'd go visit one pauper.' And we went on up to 104th Street and Fifth, to the Museum of the City of New York.

'It's a small, manageable museum in a brown-and-white brick house, recording the city's history from the Dutch days onward in four floors of engaging artifacts. (The top, fifth floor contains rooms from the old Vanderbilt mansion but is closed to the public these days because the city can't afford guards to keep it open.)

Everybody's favorite exhibit is the display of antique toys and dolls, together with a group of marvelously detailed dolls' houses, complete down to handmade linens in the hope chess. Patsy, being a rabid theatregoer, had to be dragged away from the Broadway theatre exhibit. (It changes every few months and may deal with an era or just a single personality in the theatre, and is always complete with three-sheet posters, programmes, costumes, photographs and recorded songs.)

There are period rooms from every quarter-century, and until you see the life-size mannequins in each room, you don't know how tall mankind has grown in three hundred years.

There's one exhibit which I love and which ruined my day. It's a group of dioramas depicting the history of the New York Stock Exchange, from the famous first meeting of merchants under a buttonwood tree to the nineteenth century day when ticker-tape replaced runners, and including a spectacular three-dimensional view of Wall Street during the Blizzard of '88. And it was as we were peering into this one that the hideous oversight struck me. I must have turned a sickly color because Patsy asked:

'What's the matter?'

'I made sure we saw Wall Street because it's on every book's Must See list,' I said. 'And I forgot that the reason *why* it's on every Must See list is it's the home of the world-famous New York Stock Exchange. Which we didn't even look for, much less take a tour of.'

'Oh, right,' said Patsy. I looked at her and she looked pleased. 'I guess we'll have to go back down there,' she said.

'To tell you the truth,' I said, 'I was going back down anyway. Alexander Hamilton and Albert Gallatin are buried in Trinity churchyard and I want to see their graves. The cemetery was locked when we were there but I thought I'd phone Trinity and ask when it's open.'

'It wasn't locked,' said Patsy. 'The side door was open. I wondered why you didn't want to go in.'

I had two martinis that night before dinner instead of my usual one and a half. I didn't mind having to go back down to Lower Manhattan again (and wouldn't have minded if I'd known we'd have to go back down there not once more but twice). What I minded was the discovery that I was no more in command of the project than I'd been when we started.

Wednesday, April 28

Like most cities, New York is a collection of small neighborhoods. I live in Lenox Hill, surrounded by colleges (Hunter, Marymount Manhattan, Mannes Music), singles (young and old), monster new apartment houses and dogs. Above Lenox Hill is Yorkville, old and formerly German, with a main street – Eighty-Sixth Street – that looks like any small town Main Street except that the bakeries, restaurants and small stores along it are German, Swiss and Hungarian as well as American. Below me is Sutton Place, small and rich and quiet, and below that Beekman Place, even smaller and richer and quieter. Then, you come to Murray Hill and then to Tudor City – a compact small town built above the city and reached by high stone steps – and then Madison Square and Gramercy Park, and so forth. Most of these neighborhoods have their local free weekly newspaper, their political clubs, block associations and Community Planning Boards.

Patsy lives on Central Park West, in a section of it which is also a neighborhood: a row of old and famous apartment houses, now co-operatively owned by the families who live in them. Above her neighborhood and slightly west of it is the Riverside Drive neighborhood, thick with Columbia professors' families, and above that is Morningside Heights. (See next chapter.) Below Patsy's, there Lincoln towers – an apartment house complex behind Lincoln Center which is its own self-contained community – and below that you come to Chelsea and Clinton and the Village, and so forth. They, too, have their throwaway newspapers and political clubs and block associations and Planning Boards.

BUT: all the neighborhoods above and below and including mine, are strung together into a psychological unit and share a common attitude and common rules of behaviour. And all the neighborhoods above and below and including Patsy's, are strung together into a psychological unit and share a common attitude and common rules of behaviour. And the two units are poles apart and don't understand each other. Because unlike other cities, New York is literally split down the middle by Fifth Avenue, into East and West Sides. And never the twain shall meet on any common ground but Saving New York City.

Fifth Avenue itself, which runs through the center of town from Seventh Street to a Hundred and Tenth, is neutral territory. But the street signs at intersections along the Avenue mark off the separate sides for you. Say you're standing in front of St Patrick's Cathedral and you see a sign on the downtown corner reading E. 50 St. Cross the avenue and you'll see a sign on the corner reading: W. 50 St.

And just so you'll know what Side you're on at any given moment, if you're on Fifth and you walk East, you'll come to Madison, Park, Lexington, Third, Second and First, in that order. If you're on Fifth and you walk West, you'll come to Sixth, Seventh, Broadway, Eighth, Ninth and Tenth. That's in midtown. When you go up to Fifty-ninth, where the park begins, you'll see that Central Park itself separates East from West, being bounded on the East by Fifth Avenue and on the West by Central Park West (an extension of Eighth Avenue) where Patsy lives. Both Fifth Avenues and Central Park West have fine views of the park, which is very even-handed. Today, the East side is basically richer that the West, fifty years ago it was the other way round, which is also even-handed.

What the West Side has always had, that the East Side has never had, is a concentration of the city's great performing arts centers: the Broadway theatres, Carnegie Hall, Lincoln Center, the giant television network centers in skyscrapers along Sixth Avenue, and Rockefeller Center, which begins at Fifth Avenue and mushrooms west.

That's the background. The underlying differences between East and West Siders can wait till we get over to Patsy's.

Patsy and I met that morning at 30 Rockefeller Plaza ('30 Rock' to the people who work there) and went up to the tour desk in the lobby and discovered there are two separate tours: Tour 1, a guided tour of Rockefeller Center and Tour 2, a backstage tour of NBC's radio and television studios. Tour 1 tickets were available. Tour 2 was on strike.

'Should we do the Center tour now and come back for the NBC tour when the strike is over?' I suggested.

'– and we'll get home tonight and hear on the six o'clock news that the strike's just been settled,' said Patsy. 'Let's wait a week.'

So we left Rockefeller Center and walked up to Fifty-seventh and then turned west, toward Lincoln Center which starts at Sixty-fourth Street. We turned west on Fifty-seventh partly because it's a beautiful street to walk along: it has fine shops and art galleries and Carnegie

Hall. But there was another reason – and I promise this is the last time I'll bore you with street directions, but this one is something nobody ever warns visitors about, and it always gets them into trouble.

If you're standing in front of One East Fifty-fourth Street and you're looking for One West Fifty-fourth Street, you'll find it right across Fifth Avenue or, as they say, right-across-the-street. But if you're standing in front of One East *Sixty*-fourth Street and you're not looking for One West Sixty-fourth Street, it's not across the street, it's clear across Central Park, and you ask somebody where you get a crosstown bus to take you over to the West Side. Patsy and I avoided this by turning west before we got to Fifty-ninth where the park begins.

'We get the tour tickets at Avery Fisher Hall,' I said, as we came within sight of the Lincoln Center buildings.

'Philharmonic Hall,' Patsy corrected grimly.

We got our tickets for the tour which took us through most of the main buildings – a two-level theatre for stage plays known as the Vivian Beaumont Theatre upstairs and the Mitzi Newhouse Theatre downstairs; the New York State Theatre (home of the New York City Ballet and the New York City Opera companies); Avery Fisher/ Philharmonic; and the Metropolitan Opera House. (The best Lincoln Center tour is the backstage tour of the Met which you can only take during the opera season, October to March, and which includes rehearsals.) The tour didn't include the Julliard School of Music and its adjoining concert hall, alias Alice Tully Hall.

'The trouble with this tour,' said Patsy as we hung over the rail of one of the Met's promenade decks, 'is that it's in the daytime, and these buildings have to be seen at night. You have to be part of the audience. You have to see the chandeliers lit, and the promenade decks during intermission – when you look down at all the marvellous people in the lobby, all looking the way you'd like to look.'

'I'll tell you a story about this place,' I said. 'My friend Arlene ran a political fund-raising party here a few years ago. There's a lobby on the Met mezzanine big enough for a cocktail party for two hundred people and that's where she had it. I was volunteer ticket-taker – the party was for a candidate our club was backing – and my ticket table was at the top of the grand staircase. The party was on a rainy winter Thursday, at five, and people came direct from their offices without going home to dress. You know how they look – the lawyers and law-clerks and local officials and club workers who go to that kind of party. I sat at my table at the top of the staircase and watched them push through the Met doors in bunches, in a hurry to be out of the rain, all of them looking wet and frazzled and out of sorts. When they started up the sweeping marble staircase they were all hunched forward, the way people do when they're climbing steps.

'But when they reached the third or fourth step, they began to change. Coming up that staircase they straightened, almost imperceptibly at first. They became erect, they began to climb more slowly – and about halfway up, every man almost unconsciously took the arm of the woman next to him. By the time they reached the top, the men were stepping aside to let the women pass, and the women were sweeping regally up to my table and smiling at me and saying "Good afternoon", which they don't normally say to a ticket-taker. It was extraordinary.'

Outside the Vivian Beaumont theatre, on a wall beyond the long reflecting pool, there's a plaque honoring John D. Rockefeller III, identified as 'the prime mover' behind the creation of Lincoln Center back in the early sixties. On the plaque is a statement by Rockefeller which begins: 'The arts are not for the privileged few but for the many.'

'That's what's special about New York,' I said. 'The concern for "the many" that people have when they come here, or acquire after they get here. That's why a handful of rich men and women have done so much for the city.'

'Like Frick,' said Patsy.

'Like Frick and Carnegie,' I agreed. 'This overcrowded city is where they lived; and it's the hordes of people of all kinds, which Rockefeller delicately called "the many," that they left their great collections to and build concert halls for. In view of which, we shouldn't resent the new names on all these buildings.'

'Personally,' I said, 'I wish Avery Fisher had declined to have Philharmonic Hall renamed in his honour, no matter how much money he spent to have the acoustics corrected. And I wish Alice Tully had said: "No, no, just call it Julliard Hall." But let's face it: you and I both know that while art may be for "the many," it always has to be financed by the few. And fair's fair: readers of a book about New

York have a right to know what Avery Fisher and Vivian Beaumont and Mitzi Newhouse and Alice Tully have in common.'

After lunch we walked up Central Park West to Patsy's apartment house, passing side streets lined with large Victorian brownstones and greystones as we went.

Back in the early years of the century, the West Side was a middle- and upper-income residential area. The East Side in those days was most famous for its slums, where railroad labourers lived and died in Old Law and New Law tenements. (Old Law tenements had air shafts; New Law tenements had to have windows.) Those were the days when the West Side was the opulent New York of Lilian Russell and Diamond Jim Brady, of majestic hotels and fine town houses. Today most of the hotels are ancient and decayed and house welfare families. The rows of Victorian houses, having long since become mouldering rooming-houses, are still largely rooming-houses; but more and more young families have begin buying them, ready to spend years remodelling and rewiring to convert them into modern one-family homes. The old houses have high ceilings, fireplaces, long halls and spacious rooms all reminiscent of an earlier age which, to West Siders, is the secret of their charm.

'A friend of mine lived over here for ten years,' I told Patsy. 'She had a floor-through in an old brownstone. Then I met her in my supermarket one day and she told me she'd moved into a new building up the block from me. She said: "I got up one morning and thought: Enough of this Old Charm, I want a modern kitchen".'

Patsy nodded.

'We lived on the East Side for six years,' she said, 'before I suddenly knew I didn't care if the moulding peeled, I wanted to live where I could feel roots and a sense of the past around me.'

By this time we were approaching the American Museum of Natural History which runs from Seventy-seventh to Eighty-first Street and has a 67-foot long, 16-foot high, 30-ton reconstructed brontosaurus in Brontosaurus Hall, if that interests you. Also stuffed elephants, stuffed lions and stuffed rhinoceroses.

'Do we have to do the monsters?' I asked.

'They have a fabulous jewel collection,' said Patsy. Then she said: 'No, forget it, you could spend a month in there and not see everything, and not find your way out again.'

'I'll tell you what,' I said. 'We'll skip Natural History and go see the Hayden Planetarium Sky show. There's a show at three, I made a note of it. We can just make it.'

Patsy threw me a non-committal look.

'Our class went there when I was eight,' she said. 'My kids both had to go with their classes when they were eight.'

'Well, I've never been,' I said – and we went.

We were ushered into the Sky Theatre, where the ceiling was a simulated sky full of stars, and we took seats among the twenty or thirty school children waiting for the show to begin. A lecturer came out on stage and welcomed us. Then the theatre darkened, the overhead sky-ceiling brightened and the show began.

'Twinkle, twinkle, little star, How I wonder what you are!' said the lecturer, and then proceeded to explain what a star was, in terms nobody without an M.S. in Astronomy could understand.

The children squirmed and looked up at the star-studded ceiling with relief whenever the patterns changed. At the end of an hour, the lecturer recited triumphantly: 'Twinkle, twinkle, little quasar, Now I know what YOU are!' and the house-lights came up and we got out of there.

'You could have warned me!' I said. And Patsy said: 'Well, you go back every fifteen years thinking maybe it's got better.' We adjourned to her house for coffee. And you need only walk into her foyer to know why families live on the West Side.

My own apartment is listed by the landlord as a '2½-room studio' and is actually a living-room with a small alcove. The living-room counts as one room, the alcove is a second room because it has a window, and the kitchen is half-a-room in because it doesn't have a window. The bathroom they throw in free. Real-estate arithmetic. And the statement I am about to make is not an exaggeration and not meant to be humour, it's a flat fact: You could put my entire apartment in Patsy Gibbs' foyer. In the *foyer*. Opening off the foyer are more rooms and bigger rooms than you'll find in a modern ranch house. There's a large living-room, an equally large library, a dining room that seats twelve easily (eighteen if it has to), three bedrooms, three baths, a large bedroom for the housekeeper (remodelled from two small rooms), and a kitchen, which includes a former butler's pantry, where eight people can sit down to breakfast.

'Anne Jackson and Eli Wallach have an apartment the size of yours, if you'll pardon my name-dropping,' I said, as Patsy made coffee. 'I got lost in theirs once. I could hear Annie calling me and I went from room to room and couldn't find her; she had to come and get me.'

'When we first moved in, we had a babysitter coming one night,' said Patsy, 'and we waited and waited for her, and finally I called her house and her mother said she'd left forty minutes before. So we went looking for her. She'd been sitting in the library for half an hour.'

Though living space is mainly what families move to the West Side for, you find singles and childless couples over there, too; and living space and charm are not what chiefly attract them. The real difference between the East Side and West Side is in the people. They not only think and behave differently from each other; they look different.

Generally speaking, West Siders look dowdy, scholarly and slightly down-at-heel, and the look has nothing to do with money. They look like what a great many of them are: scholars, intellectuals, dedicated professionals, all of whom regard shopping for clothes as a colossal waste of time. East Siders, on the other hand, look chic. Appearances are important to them. From which you'll correctly deduce that East Siders are conventional and proper, part of the Establishment and in awe of it – which God knows, and God be thanked, West Siders are not.

I'll give you an example. Suppose tomorrow's *New York Times* prints the news that JFK airport is building new runways for supersonic jets. The West Side Democratic clubs will charter buses, ride out to JFK and march around the airport with placards reading: NO SST FOR NYC and SAVE THE ENVIRONMENT FOR OUR CHILDREN. They'll sing fight songs, have a couple of clashes with the police and turn up on the eleven o'clock TV Evening News. The East Side clubs will hold a dignified debate and then send a telegram to the governor telling him they're against air pollution.

But since families need living space and may move to the West Side to get it, and since singles want modern kitchens and may move to the East Side to get them, both sides have a certain number of fish-out-of-water. Which explains why Patsy and her husband never joined a West Side club when they moved over there and why I periodically drift away from mine. I love the East Side streets and buildings; but my Establishment neighbors occasionally drive me up the wall and I read wistfully about West Side demonstrations because, psychologically, I belong over there. And Patsy, who loves the West Side for its space and charm, has never set foot in a noisy West Side Democratic club because, psychologically, she belongs over here. (Though Patsy is special: she was born on the West Side, so it's not a Side to her, it's her Old Kentucky Home.)

Still, the Side you live on influences your thinking and behaviour if you live there long enough. I've accepted the Establishment name of Avery Fisher Hall. Patsy will call it Philharmonic Hall for the rest of time.

We had coffee in the living-room, before picture windows looking out over Central Park with a breathtaking view of the Central Park South skyline beyond. then I said:

'It's after five, I have to get home.'

'We have one more stop to make,' said Patsy.

'Where?' I asked.

'Zabar's,' said Patsy.

I'd heard about Zabar's from all my gourmet friends but I'd never been there, so I said:

'I'll go there with you some time. Not today. I'm tired.'

Patsy's face registered instant outrage.

'Zabar's is one of the most famous Sights on the West Side!' she said. 'Do you realize people like Frank Sinatra have pastrami and bagels flown to them in Europe so they won't starve? You are going to put Zabar's in your book!'

'I'll tell you what I'll do,' I said. 'I have to tour Morningside Heights – Columbia, Riverside, Grant's Tomb, all that – which is another West Side tour. If you go with me, we'll take a Broadway bus back down and stop off at Zabar's on the way home.'

'All right,' said Patsy, 'but this time you're not going to weasel out of it.'

And just like that, I had her committed to the only wearing uptown junket left on my list.

Monday, May 3

I'll say this for our tour of Morningside Heights: every sight we saw bore the unmistakable stamp: Made in the USA.

We got off the Broadway bus at 112th Street, at the (Episcopal) Cathedral Church of St John the divine which is 'the largest Gothic cathedral in the world', according to the church booklet. It is a permanently unfinished cathedral.

The cornerstone was laid in 1892, and for three decades the work went steadily forward, until the completion of the great bell tower in 1930. Then came the Depression, followed by the war decade and war shortages, and in the fifties the great middle-class exodus to the suburbs. By the sixties, the neighborhood had changed from rich to poor, and today there are no plans to finish St John's. As a clergyman we met there said simply: 'You don't spend millions on a cathedral when people around you are hungry.'

The magnificent church seats ten thousand, but since it's a bishop's seat and has no parish, the nave is roped off for great occasions and the average Sunday congregation of three hundred worships in a vestibule chapel inside the front doors.

Patsy and I went down the side aisles to look at the rare tapestries hanging from the scaffolding which still supports one church wall. Then I moved down to look at the stone pulpit, and Patsy went out onto the altar floor to look at the three fine chairs, two white ones flanking the bishop's red one, all three set against the right-hand altar wall. Suddenly she turned and beckoned me violently, her face purple. I went up and joined her, and Patsy pointed to the wall behind the three chairs. Halfway up the wall hung a telephone. Next to the phone was an intercom board. On the intercom board was a list:

1 Console
2 Power Amp. Room
3 Panel Room
4 Dean
5 Precenter
6 Pulpit
7 Organ

8 Bishop's Throne
9 Recording.

'Operator, gimme the Bishop's throne.'

There may be an equally efficient intercom system operating off the wall of the high altar at Chartres or Westminster Abbey but somehow you doubt it; it just reeks of American know-how.

We left St John's and started walking toward 115th Street and Broadway and the entrance to the original quadrangle which once contained Columbia College and now contains a fraction of Columbia University's undergraduate buildings. Since Morningside Heights is also the home of the Union Theological and Jewish Theological seminaries, it's very much a Town-and-Gown community; and what startled Patsy and me, in view of all the horrific crime stories we'd read about the area, is that a Town-and-Gown community is exactly what it looked like.

We were walking in a spacious neighborhood of tree-lined avenues, the solid, substantial fronts of old brick houses hiding the poverty and desperation of both the black and Puerto Rican newcomers and the elderly white holdovers who live there. The lovely green stretch of Riverside Park along the Hudson concealed the fact that the park is considered one of the city's most crime-ridden. Maybe crime only comes out at night there. All I can tell you is that Patsy and I wandered all over the area all day long, and saw only students, professors and clergymen hurrying by, a class of small boys filing into a church school, black and white children playing at the foot of Grant's Tomb and elderly men and women sitting on park benches.

Entering the Columbia quadrangle was like stepping into the set of a nineteen forties college movie. The ivy-covered buildings and flagstone walks, the students lying on manicured lawns with their noses in textbooks (it was final-exam season) seemed unreal.

We were walking along a stone path, with college buildings on both sides of us, when Patsy announced:

'I have to find a ladies' room.'

We stopped a passing student who pointed to an administration building and said:

'Right over there.'

We went into the building and wandered about without seeing a washroom. Patsy stopped another student, who sent us through a courtyard and into an annexe where we were directed up a flight of steps to an elevator and told to get off at the seventh floor. We went down the seventh floor hall and around a corner and there at last was a washroom. When we came out, we saw an elevator next to the washroom and we rode down to the ground floor and went out into the quadrangle, unaware that while we had entered the building through the front door we'd left it by the back door and that furthermore it wasn't the same building.

You remember those parallel paths at the Cloisters? Well, the Columbia quadrangle also has parallel paths. But since the paths are on opposite sides of college buildings, you only see the one you're walking on. Patsy and I went our way along a flagstone path, looking at the buildings; and if the path was taking us gradually uphill, we didn't notice it. We just strolled on, admiring the academic scenery, until, with great suddenness, we saw the end of the quadrangle looming ahead and apparently suspended in space. We found ourselves on an open parapet above a fifteen or twenty-foot drop to a stone courtyard below. If you're afraid of heights, this is not a good place to find yourself. Looking around, I discovered that we were entirely alone. There wasn't a student in sight and the only building near by presented its windowless back to us. Next to the building I noticed the top of a flight of steps leading down from the outside of the parapet and, without looking at Patsy, I made myself walk over to it and look down.

'It's okay,' I called to her. 'It's a short flight of steps going down to a landing and there's a building down there.'

We ran down the steps, our eyes glued to the landing so they wouldn't stray off to the side and see the twenty-foot gorge.

On the landing we found a large glass door and peering in, we saw that it was the back door to a gym. The gym was empty. The door was locked. We turned to go back up the steps and saw, for the first time, that they were open, ship's ladder steps. Patsy went white.

'I can't go up there,' she said.

Since the only alternative was to throw ourselves off the parapet, I heard myself say:

'I'll go first.'

Sheer guilt drove me up those steps: it was my book we were up there researching (if that's the word for what we were doing). I started up the steps, Patsy close behind so she could keep her eyes on my back. I could hear my breathing. Patsy had stopped breathing altogether; she held her breath till we got safely back up onto solid stone ground. By this time I was too far gone for fear, and throwing off caution I walked close to the end of the parapet – and saw a long, steep but solid flight of stone steps leading down to the courtyard.

Columbia University has new science buildings and playing fields down on the courtyard level, and there was new construction going on which we ought to have investigated, but by that time we'd lost our taste for Columbia.

What Columbia does not have, as far as we could discover, is a place where non-students can eat. Anything. We wandered up and down Broadway and up and down the side streets and finally Patsy stopped a girl going by with books under her arm, and asked if she could tell us 'where there's a place to eat around here.' The girl recommended Mom Somebody-or-Other's Delicatessen.

'It's the best deli in town,' she said earnestly, and pointed us a few blocks further down Broadway.

'Do you want to try it?' Patsy asked when the girl had gone on her way.

'I just want to sit down,' I said. Since most delis don't have tables, I thought this meant 'No,' but Patsy decided it meant 'Yes,' and she started back down Broadway toward the deli. I followed her, repeating every now and then: 'I just want to sit down.'

In every New York neighborhood there's one deli which the local residents believe is the best in town. Since all of Morningside Heights, including the entire populations of Columbia, Union Theological and Jewish Theological, believed Mom Whatsername's to be the best deli in town, there was a long line of customers waiting for service. The line was jammed in between grocery shelves on one side and glass cases of cold meats and salad on the other. Everybody on line was waiting to step up to the glass cases and give one of the two countermen a lunch order for sandwiches and coffee. To go. There weren't any tables.

Patsy streaked back to the end of the line, I followed her fuming, and as the line inched forward, she turned to me now and then to say brightly:

'The line's moving very fast, considering.'

After twenty minutes of Considering, we finally got our sand-wiches, cole slaw, one milk and two coffees and then carried the bags two blocks to a Riverside Park bench. I was carrying the bag with the cole slaw in it, and the cole slaw dripped all the way over.

We sat on a bench and I chewed my turkey-on-rye-with-Russian in simmering silence until Patsy turned to me, hesitated, and then asked tentatively:

'Do you want me to keep on with this? This sightseeing?'

My bad humor dissolved in shock.

'What kind of question is that?' I demanded. 'Here I'm in the middle of giving birth to this important book, and the midwife asks if I want her to keep on with what she's doing!'

'Well, I just realized this morning it's May,' said Patsy. 'We go away in June, when the kids come home from college. I thought I'd better ask how much time you want me to save this month.'

'All of it!' I bleated. 'We haven't seen anything yet! We have all the major tours to do!'

After lunch we stopped at Riverside Church – known colloquially as 'the Rockefeller church' because John D. Rockefeller Jr supplied the funds for it. Riverside is another beautiful Gothic church, less ornate and imposing than St John's. It's probably no more beautiful than the big midtown churches – St Patrick's, St Thomas's and St Bartholo-mew's – but then, it isn't the building that makes Riverside Church the pride of New York.

As its brochure proclaims, Riverside is 'an interracial, interdenomi-national and international' church. Along with the standard church groups, its three thousand parishioners include a Black Christian Caucus and a Chinese Christian Fellowship. From the days of Harry Emerson Fosdick, its most celebrated preacher, to the present, Riverside has involved itself in every battle for human rights from anti-war protests to migrant labour legislation to prison reform. And since Martin Luther King graced its pulpit as guest preacher in the sixties, we weren't surprised to find that its current roster of ministers includes a woman.

'And I'll bet you,' I said to Patsy, 'that men who've never had any trouble at all saying "charwoman" or "cleaning-woman" will find it absolutely impossible to say "clergywoman".'

Catti-corner from Riverside Church is the tourist attraction which dominated the landscape of Morningside Heights. Grant's Tomb, with its immense granite dome, sat on its hill above the Hudson looking impressive, beautiful and deserted, and we trudged staunchly across the street to it. We went up the broad marble steps and in through the imposing doors, to pay our respects to Ulysses Samuel Grant, the great Union general who won the Civil War, whose military memoirs have been compared with Caesar's, and who, as President of the United States a century ago, presided over the most corrupt and scandal-ridden administration in the country's hundred-year-old political history.

You enter a vast, empty white marble hall, feeling dwarfed by the huge dome above you. You walk to the center of the floor to the rim of a great marble basin. You peer over the rim of the basin down to a floor below, and see two bronze coffins containing the mortal remains of U.S. Grant and his wife, Julia Dent Grant. This is the sight you've come to see, and almost all there is to see.

'It looks like Les Invalides,' said Patsy. 'Napoleon's tomb.'

'I don't know whether that makes it more preposterous or less,' I said.

'Well, at least there are two of them in here, instead of just one,' said Patsy, looking on the bright side.

Beyond the great hall were two small rooms and we went back to investigate them. On the walls were framed newspaper clippings recounting the history of Grant's life and career, and framed newspaper photographs of the family. And it's nobody's fault that the bearded general and his wife were angular and rawboned, and stared woodenly into the newfangled camera with expressionless faces, but today they look like characters in an Ozark cartoon.

There was one photograph in particular, in which Grant and his wife and children were all sitting bolt upright on the porch of a bolt-upright frame house which, if it wasn't falling down, could at least have used a paint job. Underneath the photograph was a typewritten caption: *President Grant and his family on the porch of the Summer White House at Long Branch, New Jersey.*

Patsy and I had to support each other out of there.

A solitary guard was on duty at the door and when we came out, Patsy asked him if there were many visitors to the Tomb.

'Oh yes,' he said. 'Every year there's a big ceremony on General Grant's birthday.'

'How many people come to it?' Patsy asked.

'Well, the Union Army vets always turned out big for it,' he said. 'We'd have three to four hundred vets come very year.'

'How many people came this year?' asked Patsy.

'Well, they've all died off now,' he said. We waited, but he didn't add anything. We thanked him and went down the broad steps and left the deserted shrine and walked over to the Broadway bus stop. And the photographs had been funny and the tomb outlandish, but old lines were running in my head:

> *The tumult and the shouting dies.*
> *The captains and the kings depart . . .*
> *Lord God of Hosts, be with us yet,*
> *Lest we forget — lest we forget!*

Going from Grant's Tomb to Zabar's (pronounced Zaybar's) was going from the sublime to the ridiculous or from the ridiculous to the sublime, I'll never be sure which. And if Grant's Tomb was Made in the USA, Zabar's was Made in New York City. Definitely no question.

I don't think anybody's ever counted the number of delicatessens in New York, but there are four within less than two blocks of my apartment house and it's not an unusual number. Every neighborhood has a string of delis and almost all of them make excellent sandwiches, sell good rye bread and pickles and the usual cole slaw, pickled beets, potato, chicken and tuna salad. But Patsy was right: none of them can be remotely compared with Zabar's.

You go in through the front doorway and duck under ten or twelve different kinds of salami hanging on hooks from the ceiling. Way in the back, there's a cheese department it would take two jars of Air Freshener to neutralize. Between front and back, on the walls and on tables well away from the exotic food cases, there is every item of expensive gourmet kitchen equipment on the market, at considerably less than the market price.

None of which begins to convey the essence of Zabar's. Patsy went looking for the manager and conferred with him, and then came back to me, her arms full of outsized Zabar brochures. When I got home I culled from the brochures the following very incomplete summary of what you can buy at Zabar's, the pride of the West Side, at Eightieth and Broadway:

Fourteen kinds of salami; eight kinds of pâté; nine kinds of cooked fish; twelve kinds of salad; seven kinds of Hungarian sausage; thirty kinds of bread.

Also smoked beef jerky, fresh caviar, sturgeon, stuffed vine leaves, Hungarian peasant bacon, Polish and Yugoslav mushrooms, Romanian pastrami, and cheese 'from every country in Europe.'

Not forgetting eleven kinds of tea from every country that grows it, and coffee from Jamaica, Hawaii, Kenya, Tanzania, Guatemala and Mexico.

There's one more attraction to Zabar's. It is New York's only genuine *haute monde* delicatessen. A Zabar's shopping bag is a recognized status symbol. It tells the world you're a cultivated and discriminating gourmet, instead of just another New York shlemiel buying a hot pastrami on rye and a sour pickle to go.

Thursday, May 6

This was our only rainy day. And the rain cut short a tour we weren't all that crazy about, and sent us indoors on a tour we had both taken countless times and which somehow never palls.

Now that Patsy had committed herself, I dispensed with diplomatic overtures and phoned her and said bluntly:

'Thursday we're doing the Village.'

'Yich-ch,' said Patsy.

Greenwich Village is more than a neighborhood, it's a way of life. People who live there would be miserable living anywhere else. People who don't live there, see the Village as a kind of continuous theatrical performance interesting to visit for an evening.

Since the Village is on the West Side (the brief life of a potsmoking neighborhood called the East Village having begun and ended with the sixties), I said to Patsy: 'I'm taking a Fifth Avenue bus down, just to check out any Avenue sights I need to mention. Do you want to go down by subway and meet me?'

'Where?' said Patsy. 'Not in the Village?!'

'Meet me on the steps of the church at Twelfth and Fifth and we'll do Lower Fifth and the Square first,' I said.

'Oh, great, I love it down there,' said Patsy and we hung up.

It was sunny enough when I left home and walked to Fifth to catch the bus. One day while you're here, you ought to get on a Fifth Avenue bus up around the Carnegie mansion and ride all the way down to where the Avenue ends below Eighth Street; it's the best sightseeing bus I know of. You'll ride down along Central Park with all the museums and mansions on your left until you come to the Plaza Hotel at Fifty-Ninth Street, which marks the beginning of the midtown shopping district and from there on, you have to try looking out the windows on both sides of the bus at once.

Most of the famous shops are in the Fifties: Bergdorf-Goodman, Tiffany, Bonwit-Teller, I. Miller, Gucci, Cartier, Mark Cross, Saks. (Lord & Taylor is down at 37th Street, B. Altman is at Thirty-fourth and if you walk two blocks west of Altman's you come to R. H. Macy and Gimbel Bros., she-added-so-as-not-to-slight-anybody.) Spread through the Fifties and Forties you'll see the avenue's five mammoth bookstores: two Doubleday, one Scribner, Brentano and the beautiful Rizzoli.

The newest avenue sight at the moment is the glittering Olympic Tower, midtown Fifth Avenue's first apartment house. Olympic Tower, as Patsy succinctly put it, 'has apartments nobody can afford to live in, over stores nobody can afford to buy in.'

At Fifty-third on the uptown corner on your right you'll see St Thomas' Episcopal church, once New York's most fashionable church, now better known for its wonderful Wednesday noon choral concerts. Don't miss them on any account, if you're in town at Christmas or Easter time. Don't worry about how you're dressed. You'll see students pile into the church in blue jeans with their arms full of books, and women with their shopping bags flapping. The rector, John Andrew, is genuinely pleased to see the church jammed and gratified that you like his men's and boy's choirs, and he couldn't care less how you look.

Down below Thirty-fourth I saw one place I'd forgotten. It's just off Fifth, at One East Twenty-ninth Street. This one's also an Episcopal church with the official name of The Church of the Transfiguration. And the story has been told a hundred times but I feel like telling it again.

Back in 1871, when theatre people were beyond the pale of respectable society, a celebrated actor named Joseph Jefferson wanted to provide a funeral service for a fellow actor who had died penniless. Jefferson went to a fashionable Fifth Avenue church to consult the minister about arrangements.

'I'm afraid we couldn't possibly hold funeral services at our church for that sort of person,' said the minister, 'but there's a little church around the corner that might help you.'

So Jefferson went to the Little Church Around the Corner, and the church gave his friend Christian burial and has been marrying and burying actors and other disreputable folk ever since. If you stop in during the day and find a wedding in progress, you're welcome to assist at it. After six P.M., the weddings are private.

The church at Twelfth and Fifth, where I was to meet Patsy, and another below it at Tenth and Fifth, are both old-fashioned neighborhood churches and typical of Lower Fifth, a small, quiet residential neighborhood running from Thirteenth Street down to

Eighth, with its side streets extending into the Village.

I got there a little early, which was what I'd hoped to do. When I first came to New York, I used to go down to the New School on West Twelfth Street and the neighborhood is nostalgic for me. The New School – officially The New School for Social Research – is a college for adults. You can earn a B.A. or Ph.D. there and you can take day-time courses; but the New School's early fame stemmed from the fact that it was primarily an evening college for people more interested in an education than a degree. In the forties, its faculty was a haven for scholarly refugees from the universities of Hitler's Europe. Which may, or may not be what led Senator Joseph McCarthy to label the school 'Communist-dominated' in the fifties. This embarrassed the Eisenhower administration somewhat: it turned out John Foster Dulles had once taught at the New School.

I used to go down there two nights a week, for courses in such practical, everyday subjects as Ancient Greek and the Philosophy of Religion. (Our Greek professor was a German and like most Germans he couldn't pronounce *th*. So when pointing to the Greek letters zeta and theta, he'd say: 'Zis is a zeta and *zis* is a *zeta*.' And somebody in the class would pipe up: 'But professor, you said *that* was a zeta,' and he'd say, 'Yes, yes, quite right, zat is a *zeta* but *zis* is a *zeta*!') I was wandering along Twelfth Street remembering all this pleasantly, when Patsy came steaming toward me from Sixth Avenue.

We walked down Lower Fifth toward Washington Arch, stopping at Ninth Street to poke into Washington Mews, a cobblestone square lined with former carriage houses once attached to Washington Square mansions. The mews houses are quaint and charming and looking at them you know you're in, or near, the Village.

'Who owns these?' Patsy asked me.

'NYU,' I said, meaning New York University which is a private, not a state-owned, university. 'The only way you can get to live in a Washington Mews house is to be a big name on the NYU faculty.'

We went on down to Washington Square, created as a park setting for Washington Arch. The Arch was built in 1889 to commemorate the centennial of Washington's inauguration – because if Paris had an Arch and London had an Arch, why shouldn't we have an Arch? I-imagine-somebody-said.

We walked along Washington Square North looking at the fine

houses of Henry James's day and trying to decide which of them the heiress, Catherine Sloper, lived in. These houses are also now owned by NYU.

'I was in one of them once,' I told Patsy. 'They have one horrendous feature. They're all connected by interior doors. By which I mean you can be sitting in your living-room in your underwear on a Saturday morning when a door in your living-room wall slides open, and your next door neighbor walks in from his-or-her living-room and says "Hi, you busy?"'

We crossed Fifth Avenue to Washington Square West and walked on over to MacDougal Alley – 'where the effete meet,' said Patsy – which is another mews lined with quaint and charming carriage houses, these privately owned. At MacDougal Alley, you are in the village and you walk west to reach the heart of it.

With its center of activity around Seventh Avenue, the Village is a maze of short, narrow streets radiating in all directions, some of the streets cutting into each other and then disappearing to reappear a few blocks later way over that way. Patsy had brought a village map along and she looked up from it to inform me:

'There are two West Fourth Streets, one below Eleventh Street and one above Eleventh Street.'

So she put the map away and from then on we just wandered in and out of all the side streets, stumbling by accident on the more famous ones – Bank and Christopher and Morton and Waverly Place – all of them old and quiet with rows of small houses, looking as remote from the skyscraper city as if they'd been set down in it by mistake.

One of the most attractive streets we saw was St Luke's Place, the locale of the Audrey Hepburn film, *Wait Until Dark*, with neat four-story houses behind wrought-iron railings and high front steps. If you walk along it in the evening, you'll see glimpses of private libraries through the lighted windows of high-ceilinged living-rooms. We missed one famous house on West Eleventh Street but as far as I know it's still there, if you want to look for it. A gold plaque identifies it as the Great Garbo Home for Wayward Children.

Scattered along the avenues and through the side streets are the village shops, all of them remorselessly quaint-and-charming. I was taking notes on the items for sale in the shop windows – hand-woven

Mexican rugs, Indian sandals, unisex haircuts, Taro cards, astrology charts, handmade ceramics, handmade leather belts and shoes – when Patsy, reading over my shoulder, advised me:

'Just say the whole village is handmade.'

On Bleecker Street there are boutiques named 'Elegant Plumage', 'Second Childhood' and 'Marquis de Suede.' Also on Bleecker Street, a Spanish restaurant, an Italian, a Mexican, an Indian and a Moroccan restaurant – and that's on a side street. On Seventh Avenue we passed Greek, Indian, Chinese, Turkish, Japanese and Italian restaurants, all within a span of a few blocks.

HOWEVER: at noon it started to rain, and we thought we'd wait out the shower over an early lunch, and that's how we discovered that most village restaurants open at five P.M. You have to walk to Sixth Avenue to find a restaurant open for lunch. We found a Greek restaurant open and crowded with NYU Law School students.

'We made the same mistake with the Village that we made with Lincoln Center,' I said to Patsy as we waited for a table. 'The Village is another place that has to be seen at night. What tourists ought to do is come down late in the afternoon while it's still light enough to see the houses and shops, and then have dinner and go on to one of the off-off Broadway coffee-house theatres.'

'They don't serve coffee,' said Patsy gloomily. (She doesn't drink.)

'Well, whatever they're called,' I said.

Off-Off Broadway theatres (which differ from Off-Broadway less in professionalism than in the price of the ticket) specialize in new, experimental plays performed in any loft or hole-in-the wall available. But the ones that are the most fun are those in the back rooms or upstairs rooms of Village restaurants and bars, where the audience sits at small tables and watches the play while sipping Sangria or New York State wine. The play may bore you; the audience won't. Which is to say that the real sightseeing attraction of an evening in the Village is Villagers.

On a warm evening, Seventh Avenue and the streets near it are alive with Villagers, and with the young who live uptown and come down to the Village in the evening. The people – especially the not-so-young – seen on a Village street in the evening look completely unlike all other New Yorkers. They are colourful, flamboyant, unconventional and uninhibited. The atmosphere is of a friendly, integrated, liberated democracy, or an arty, intellectual Sunset Boulevard, depending on your point of view.

We got a table, and after the waitress took our order for a Greek shishkebab, Patsy fished out of her handbag a folded newspaper article from the *Sunday Times* and handed it to me. It was written by a *Times* architecture critic and was a lecture on How to Look at Buildings.

'I read this one,' I said. 'I did not think highly of it.'

Every time a new building goes up in New York, some critic condemns it in the *Times*, and every time an old building is to be torn down, the Landmarks Preservation Commission issues vehement demands that it be Preserved. Well, the chief New York building the *Times* writer had lectured me on How to Look At was Grand Central Station, which every now and then somebody suggests tearing down, only to be met with screaming objections from the Landmarks Commission.

'Do you know any New Yorker,' I asked Patsy, 'who personally looks on Grand Central Station with affection?'

'I hated that place when I was a kid,' said Patsy. 'We went away to camp from there. Going away you couldn't find the counsellors, and coming back you couldn't find your parents.'

'Exactly,' I said. 'You've put your finger on the difference between the experts who want to Preserve old railroad stations and the people who have to use them.'

Grand Central Station is a huge, squat stone building sprawling from Forty-second Street to Forty-fourth and from Lexington past Park Avenue and halfway to Madison, to a small avenue called Vanderbilt. It was built early in the century when architects believed that every building had to have a decoration on top. You see manifestations of this where Patsy lives: fine, tall old apartment houses with fancy cupolas and decorated Cupids on top. The author of the *Times* article admires that kind of architecture and is particularly fond of the statuary group on top of Grand Central Station, he says it pulls the entire station together. I hope there's a picture of it in this book. In case there isn't, the central figure is a Greek god (it might be Eros) wearing a hat, a loincloth and wings. He's standing by himself on top of the Grand Central clock. Near by, on both sides of him, reclining pseudo-Greeks are looking up at him. All of them sitting around on the roof of a mammoth railroad terminal, pulling it together.

'Do you remember the furor when the old Penn Station was torn down?' I said. 'That station was a gloomy horror of a building to come into at night, heavy and dark – and the lights so high overhead they threw deep, gaunt shadows on the stone floor. The Landmarks Preservers had a fit when it came down and a new, clean, light, easy-to-find-your-way-around-in station went up. What was it to them if the old station was a nightmare to people who used it? They didn't use it, they just rode around it in their cars staring learnedly at the architecture and advising us peasants to Preserve it.'

So now we're Preserving Grand Central Station. You'd better go look at it while you're here. God knows it's a sight.

We dawdled over lunch hoping the rain would stop, but it didn't.

We phoned Rockefeller Center and the NBC tour was still on strike.

'What other indoor tours do you have on your list?' Patsy asked.

'Only the UN and that's one tour I don't need to take,' I said. 'I know that place by heart. I love it.'

'So do I,' said Patsy. 'I take out-of-towners there first.' She sipped her coffee and added: 'I wonder how the new hotel is coming?'

'What hotel?' I said. 'Are they building a hotel over there?'

So we went out to the street and hailed a cab and told the driver to take us to the United Nations.

'A cab and a restaurant in one day?' Patsy said with an eyebrow raised. 'We're ruining our record.'

That was the only cab we ever took. But as we settled in the back seat, I said to Patsy:

'I'm tired of cafeteria lunches. From now on, we're going to eat restaurant lunches like respectable tourists.' And the cab driver must have heard this because he called back to us:

'You girls wanta see Bowery bums? You wanta see lesbians? I can show you everything! Where're you girls from?'

We told him we lived here and he spent the rest of the ride complaining about City Hall.

'Do you live here?' Patsy asked him as we got out of the cab.

'Nah!' he said. 'I live in Brooklyn.'

I never got to the UN without stopping first on the sidewalk to feast my eyes on the original buildings – the Secretariat and the General Assembly – with the hundred-odd member-nation flags flying in front of them. The UN occupies sixteen acres of land (mostly donated by the Rockefellers) and the years have seen the addition of a UN Library building, Dag Hammerskjold Plaza and the Eleanor Roosevelt Memorial. Across the way, we saw the construction mess which, by the time you read this, will have opened as One UN Plaza, New York's newest luxury-hotel and office building, in sloping blue-green glass.

As we got our tickets at the tour desk, I looked up at the Foucault Pendulum swinging above the grand staircase and told Patsy: 'Every time I come here, I make up my mind that this time I'll understand how that thing gives me "visible proof of the rotation of the Earth," as it claims in the booklet. And every time I come here, I don't.'

'If you come here early in the morning, the pendulum will be swinging one way,' said Patsy, 'and if you come back late in the afternoon it'll be swinging the opposite way. And you know the pendulum didn't turn around, so the Earth must have turned around.'

'Thank you,' I said. 'It pays to go to Harvard,' and we joined the tour.

Every time you go to the UN, you see something new. Every new country admitted to membership presents a gift to the UN. We hadn't been there since the admission of the People's Republic of China and our tour started with a look at China's spectacular gift. On a table almost the length of a wall, stood a replica of a railroad system winding through the mountains and cities of China, done entirely in hand-carved ivory, with every tree, house and inch of track intricately detailed.

Every time you take the tour you also learn something new. The young guides have fifty times as much information in their heads as they can convey in a one-hour tour, and each guide is free to choose which features of each room and which art works to tell you about. The guides, drawn from all the UN countries, speak perfect English and are awesomely well-informed.

'How do you know so much? How do you remember it all?' Patsy asked the attractive young woman from Sweden who was our guide; and the guide told us that all UN guides are required to attend a daily briefing on current debates and keep abreast of all the literature dealing with 'the Economic and Social Council's seven thousand projects, the UNESCO projects on behalf of children in one hundred countries and the administrative work of the Trusteeship Council.'

Unless a meeting is going on in one of them the tour takes you into all the main rooms – the Security Council chamber, the General Assembly room and the meeting rooms of the Trusteeship Council and the Economic and Social Council. They're still the most beautifully designed and constructed assembly rooms I've ever been in.

At the end of the tour, you're deposited in the basement, free to spend time and money in the UN Bookstore, Gift Shop and Souvenir Shop. The unique feature of the book store is its English translations of children's books from all the UN countries. And don't buy ordinary souvenirs in ordinary shops till you've seen the UN souvenir and gift shops. The shipments of gift items from member nations are continuous and unpredictable. One month you'll find Israeli jewelry and African wood carving, the next month silk scarves from India and moccasins from Iceland.

Patsy got carried away by all the exotica and bought a set of cushions labeled 'Four Peas in a Pod': four round green cushions shaped like peas, fitted into a long, split green cushion shaped like a pod.

Made in Vermont.

Wednesday, May 12

Even if you're not nostalgic about Hollywood, you have got to take the Rockefeller Center tour, the highlight of which is a tour of Radio City Music Hall, the super-colossal Zenith of movie palaces.

(The NBC strike hadn't ended, we'd just got tired of waiting. When it was finally settled, we went back and took the NBC tour and found it dull. Since television production is based in Hollywood, the NBC tour was confined to looking through glass windows at news rooms, soap-opera stages and the studios of NBC's local radio station. The only mild diversions were a demonstration of old-time radio sound effects and a chance to walk onto a TV stage and see yourself on a monitor.)

'Rockefeller Center' originally meant the group of low buildings clustered around the central seventy-story RCA building fronting Fifth Avenue at Forty-ninth Street and extending back to Rockefeller Plaza. Today the Center has grown to a mammoth complex of some twenty-odd buildings (they keep adding) mushrooming west from Fifth past Sixth almost to Seventh. The main buildings are connected by an underground concourse, and if you can find your way through the concourse – which mostly you can't – you can go from building to building and see most of the Center's two hundred shops, twenty-six restaurants and eighteen banks without ever going out in the rain.

But to most New Yorkers, 'Rockefeller Center' still means the original grouping, and you can see it best from across the street outside the doors of Saks: a group of buildings of graduated heights around a green plaza with the RCA building ('30 Rock') rising in the background. Cross the avenue to the Center and walk through the plaza and you'll see the two-level sunken plaza below it. The lower level is an ice-skating rink in winter and an outdoor restaurant in summer; the upper level is a kind of kibitzers' balcony from which to stare down at the skaters or diners, an essential amenity in a city where People-Watching is a favourite sport.

'Did you know,' I said to Patsy as we waited in the RCA lobby for the tour to start, 'that when Rockefeller Center first opened, it caused as much outrage as the World Trade Center? It opened in the thirties, and everybody said the city didn't need a huge office complex in the middle of a Depression.'

'Where'd you read that?' Patsy asked skeptically.

'They said,' I continued, 'that nobody'd rent enough office space to pay for the upkeep, nobody had the money to open shops, and nobody could afford to buy in them if they did open. And they said who needed a movie palace seating sixty-two hundred people, when every neighbourhood movie theatre had to give away dishes to lure families into buying tickets?'

'Who told you all that?' Patsy demanded.

'Cole Porter even wrote a line about it in a song,' I said. 'Sung by Fred Astaire. Nobody told me. I remember it. I was going to school in Philadelphia and I read about it in the *Evening Bulletin*.'

Patsy was regarding me with detached interest.

'You must be ninety!' she said pleasantly.

The tour took us through the RCA building first, and we stopped at a small, unlikely garden built outside the seventh floor windows and visible only from the upper floors of the building we were in and the upper floors of nearby office buildings.

'This garden is never used,' the guide told us. 'It is here for the psychological relief of office-workers on high floors.'

We were also, of course taken to the Seventieth Floor Observation Roof with its marvellous skyline views. Which reminds me: if you can't get a reservation at 'Windows on the World' (the World Trade Center restaurant), the next best place from which to see New York at night is the Rainbow Room on the sixty-fifth floor of the RCA building. BUT BE WARY: unlike 'Windows on the World,' the Rainbow Room has tables at narrow corner windows with almost no view. If you're stuck at one of these, get up and walk to the nearest broad window before you leave, and look out and see what Thomas Edison and New York's anonymous architects have wrought in the way of an incandescent miracle.

We went through the concourse and into the lobbies of the famous original buildings: the Italian building, with Atlas holding up the world on its façade; and the French and English buildings – and I would have been just as happy if the guide hadn't told us that the plaza gardens are officially named the Channel Gardens because they have the French building at one end and the English at the other.

From there, we proceeded to Sixth Avenue to the Largest Indoor Theatre in the World, containing the Largest Indoor Stage in the World, Radio City Music Hall.

The tour began in the great lobby from which we descended a sweeping staircase to the Lounge, a full city block long, thickly carpeted and furnished with chairs and sofas, and ceiling and wall decorations in the grand Hollywood style.

'Do you remember a ladies' room here where the toilet seat sprang up and glowed with violet light when you rose from it?' I asked Patsy. 'Ultraviolet disinfectant was common for a while later on, but at the time no other toilet in town lit up lavendar and it unnerved me.'

'No, the one I remember,' said Patsy, 'had mirrored walls on all sides. It was terrifying: you not only saw yourself from all angles but on into infinity.'

The tour guide's talk was entirely devoted to weights and measures: how many feet wide and high the stage was, how many tons of cable it took to raise the whale-sized orchestra from the pit to the stage on an electronic platform; how many acres of seats the theatre's vast tiers held; how many tons the World's Largest Indoor Organ weighed.

(The plans for the Music Hall were drawn up in 1929, when organ music accompanied silent films; and either the management was already stuck with the World's Largest Organ when the theatre opened, or didn't think the talkies would last.)

Patsy and I moved away from the tour group to wallow in our memories of Radio City Music Hall stage shows. And if I speak of them in the past tense, it's less because the Music Hall may have been converted to other forms of entertainment by the time you come, than because the place itself is so firmly part of a long-gone past for both of us.

Traditionally, New Yorkers have gone to Radio City Music Hall only at three stages in their lives: 1. when they were children; 2. when they were young and dating; 3. when they had children of their own to take to the annual Christmas or Easter or Fourth of July extravaganza. Patsy, who grew up in New York, was awash with memories of the annual Christmas show which had been the high point of every childhood year.

'First the lights went down and you'd hear the organ. You wouldn't see it, you'd just hear it. Then a purple light would come up over on the side, and you'd see the organ and the organist sliding slowly out of the wall in a purple glow. Then, while the organist played, you had to wait – the wait was absolutely endless because you were so excited

– for the show to begin. Then, while the organist was still playing, you'd look up at the side boxes and they'd be full of Biblical statues. And then, slowly, the statues would move, and you'd see they were people, and they'd come down from the boxes and march slowly up the side aisles and onto the stage. They were marching,' she explained, 'to Bethlehem. And then all the manger animals would file up on stage, marching to Bethlehem, and then a star would appear and lead everybody to the manger for the big tableau.'

Then the hundred and fifty piece orchestra rose slowly up out of the pit and the stage show began.

'First came the acrobats who threw each other around,' said Patsy, 'and then the men with the animal acts who threw the animals around. I always worried for fear one of the dogs would Make, right there on the stage. And then the soloist – it was always some terrible singer – would sing Christmas carols. And then came the ballet. And finally, just as you thought you'd die if they didn't come soon, the Rockettes. And they were wonderful.'

All Radio City Music Hall stage shows followed that format. They were all spectacles, sumptuously costumed and performed against a background of half a ton of resplendent scenery.

'Did you ever see the Fourth of July show, with the electronic fireworks going off at the end?' Patsy asked me. 'The Rockettes wore red-white-and-blue sequin shorts and sequin tap-shoes and sequin Uncle Sam vests, and they all snapped their heads to the left at the same second and when they went *tap*,-ta-ta-*tap*, ta-ta-*tap-tap-tap*, every knee was in an exact line with every other knee. And four hundred men would march down from the boxes in sequin Uncle Sam suits and sequin stove-pipe Uncle Sam hats, singing "You're a Grand Old Flag," and the electric fireworks would go off and make a huge flag for the final tableau.' And she added thoughtfully: 'It was so terrible it was remarkable.'

I'll tell you an old joke that will sum up Radio City Music Hall for you.

It seems a man and his wife went to the Music Hall one Sunday afternoon, arriving toward the end of the film. When it ended, the house lights came up for a few minutes before the stage show and the man rose, murmuring to his wife: 'I'm going to the men's room.'

He located an exit on his floor – orchestra, loge, mezzanine, balcony or second balcony – but he couldn't find a men's room on it. He descended a staircase and looked on the next floor and couldn't find a men's room and descended another staircase. He walked along corridors and pushed open doors, he went along dark passages and up and down steps getting more and more lost and more and more frantic. Just as his need became intolerably urgent, he pushed open a heavy door and found himself on a small street lined with houses, trees and shrubs. There was no one in sight and the man relieved himself in the bushes.

All this had taken time, and it took him additional time to work his way back up to his own floor and locate his own aisle and section. By the time he finally reached his seat, the stage show had ended and the movie had begun. The man slid into his seat, whispering to his wife: 'How was the stage show?'

To which his wife replied: 'You ought to know. You were in it.'

We came out on Sixth Avenue, and maybe because the Music Hall had evoked the past so vividly, we both looked at the avenues with new eyes. The transformation of midtown Sixth Avenue over the past ten or fifteen years has been extraordinary. Back in the fifties, it was one long honky-tonk row of shooting galleries, cheap souvenir shops, third rate second-hand bookstores and dingy cafeterias. Today, from Forty-eighth to Fifty-ninth Street, Sixth Avenue is so opulent a row of office towers set in landscaped plazas that if you put a few flags and trees around, you could almost start calling it The Avenue of the Americas. The best time to see it is early in the evening when you're on your way to a Broadway theatre. At dusk every skyscraper is blazing with light, the plazas are illuminated and walking down the avenue is dazzling.

We had lunch at a Japanese restaurant near the Music Hall; and not till we'd worked our way through both tempura and sukiyaki and the waitress had brought our second pot of tea, did I push across the table to Patsy a typewritten itinerary for Blockbuster Sunday:

St Mark's-in-the-Bouwerie
The Lower East Side (Orchard St)
Chinatown
City Hall
Wall Street-on-a-Sunday
Trinity churchyard.

Patsy didn't bat an eye. She just shot me a sidelong glance and asked:

'Why did you leave it off?'

'Well, I did think about it,' I said, 'because we did go on a very cloudy day, the visibility was only five miles, and I thought I'd wait and see if it's very clear on Sunday.'

'You know we're going back up there,' said Patsy, and added 'WTC' to the bottom of the list.

We poured ourselves more tea and lit cigarettes. Then Patsy staring into her teacup somberly said:

'Do you realize what we owe the Rockefellers?' And she ticked the debt off on her fingers. 'The Cloisters. Riverside Church. Lincoln Center. Rockefeller Center. The UN.'

'Rockefeller University,' I said. 'It's around the corner from me. It's beautiful.' Rockefeller University is a scientific graduate school, it graduates only Ph.D's. 'I read somewhere that its faculty has won nine Nobel prizes in the last five years.'

'From the top of this island to the bottom,' said Patsy soberly, 'and from the East River to the Hudson with Rockefeller Center in the middle, we owe them so much!'

'Harry Truman would tell you that the Rockefeller fortune was built on the blood of Colorado miners,' I said.

'I know, I read Merle Miller's book, too,' said Patsy. 'I know it's blood-money.'

'Still, –' I said.

Patsy nodded.

To the Rockefellers, living and dead, whose blood-money has so greatly enriched the landscape of New York City and the lives of New Yorkers:

Thanks for everything.

Sunday, May 16

Once upon a time, when this city was the Dutch town of New Amsterdam, a new governor arrived from Holland named Peter Stuyvesant. He was a moral man and choleric, and he took a fit at what he found here: one unfinished church, one unfinished school, fifty decaying houses and seventeen taprooms.

Peter Stuyvesant went to work and over the next two decades transformed the town into an orderly and prosperous community of houses, farms and shipyards. He was a bad-tempered man with a dictatorial manner and he stumped around town on his peg-leg quarrelling with everybody. He was also a bigot who wanted to ship all the Quakers to Rhode Island. ('They have all sorts of riff-raff people there,' he explained.) Every now and then, the Staats General sent him peremptory orders to stop harassing minorities.

Stuyvesant built himself a large farm along the East River – a *bouwerie*, as the Dutch called it – where for twenty-four years he lived the good life of an autocratic governor. Then, in 1664, the Duke of York's troops invaded New Amsterdam. Knowing that resistance would get him nothing but a bombed city and slaughtered inhabitants, Stuyvesant surrendered without firing a shot. The Duke of York, not content with re-naming the entire province of New Netherlands 'New York province' after himself, also named the city after himself. New Amsterdam became New York City and Dutch rule came to an end.

Stuyvesant was seventy-two years old by then, and the Staats General in Holland sent him a kind letter saying, in effect:

'You've earned a peaceful retirement. Come on home.'

And Peter Stuyvesant wrote back saying, in effect:

'I am home.'

Whether you called it New Amsterdam or New York, this was his town. What was it to him if (like millions to follow) he had come here from somewhere else? Peter Stuyvesant withdrew to his *bouwerie* and lived out his old age as a private citizen of the city he had governed for twenty-four years. He died peacefully at home, and was buried in a vault in the family church.

Stuyvesant's farm and church are long gone. But a church was later built on the property, in that part of it which is still called the Bowery. And it was at this church – St Mark's-in-the-Bouwerie, at Tenth Street and Second Avenue – that Patsy and I met that Sunday morning, to pay our respects to the first New Yorker.

What we had gone there to see, we found in a side wall of the church: an old stone vault with an inscription which read:

> *In this vault lies buried*
> PETRUS STUYVESANT
> *Captain General and Governor-in-Chief of*
> *New Amsterdam in New Netherlands*
> *now called New York,*
> *and the Dutch West-India Islands*
> *died Feb. 4,* A.D. *1672*
> *Aged 80 years*

'I have suppressed my poor-man's-historian instincts on other tours,' I told Patsy as we left the churchyard, 'but today we're doing Old New York. Here and there I just may remember a fascinating historical note which I will want to share with you.'

'After talking my ears off about Peter Stuyvesant for half an hour, did you think you had to tell me that?' said Patsy.

We walked down along the Bowery and found the sidewalks empty on both sides of the avenue.

'Not a bum in sight,' I said. And Patsy said reasonably.

'I guess like everybody else, Bowery bums sleep late on Sunday.'

We walked down to Houston Street (pronounced Howston instead of Hew-ston, no book I ever read could tell me why) where the Lower East Side officially begins. But we had to walk on down to Orchard Street to see the real Sunday action.

The Orthodox Jews of the Lower East Side shut their shops early on Friday afternoon for the sabbath, and re-open them on Sunday morning. And if you think the street scenes in the movie *Hester Street* depicted a bygone era, go down to Orchard Street on a sunny Sunday morning and correct your impression.

The street was closed to traffic when we got there, and a large banner strung across the street from the tops of tenements proclaimed: ORCHARD STREET MALL. On Orchard Street, the world 'Mall' is about as appropriate as it would be for a street market in downtown Calcutta. We joined a dense mob of people inching along the middle of the street, looking to left and right at the merchandise jamming every inch of sidewalk on both sides of the street.

There were long racks of women's dresses and men's and women's pants, and graduated wooden platforms stuffed with rows of shoes and hats. Sandwiched between the racks and platforms were mountains of T-shirts and ties piled on a piece of blanket spread on the sidewalk. Down the street we passed heavier racks with thick bolts of upholstery fabric, dress wools, and opulent rolls of gold and silver brocade, positively blinding in the sun.

But that was only on the sidewalks in front of the shops. The shop owners obviously felt the need of more display space. Men's shirts on wire hangers hung from awnings and from the fire-escape railings of every tenement. Dresses on hangers hung from flag-poles, handbags hung from hooks driven into the brick walls, and a couple of hundred T-shirts dangled from a clothesline strung along an entire block of third-story tenement windows. In the dizzying welter of merchandise cramming the sidewalks and hanging in midair from every available anchorage, the shops themselves – where uptown New Yorkers buy designer clothes at half price – were almost invisible.

A women was coming towards us, pushing her way expertly through the solid sea of bodies in the centre of the 'Mall', and passing out handbills as she came. We took one. Under the name and address of the store, the handbill advertised:

PARIS IMPORTS

Yves Saint Laurent　　　*Valentino*　　　*Pierre Cardin*
Gucci　　　*Pierre D'Alby*　　　*Ane Klein*
Calvin Klein　　　*French Jeans*

'Tell them,' said Patsy as I wrote all this down, 'the difference between Sunday and Monday. You come down here Sunday to sightsee; you come down Monday-through-Thursday to shop.'

When we came abreast of Fine & Klein, the most famous of the cut-rate clothing stores on Orchard Street, we inched our way over to the sidewalk to look at the Gucci bags and Cardin suits in the window, and I saw what Patsy meant. The store was so jammed with shoppers that an employee stood in the doorway barring entrance to any more customers till some of those inside departed.

This is how you shop down there. Go to a Fifth Avenue store and find the Cacharel suit or Hermès bag you want. Copy down the number on the tag and take the number with you to Orchard Street. Designer clothes are never on display on the sidewalk, and only a few are displayed in the shops themselves. Most of them are kept packed away in boxes. But produce the number of the item you want, and the difference between Fifth Avenue and Orchard Street prices will stagger you.

We passed two stores, close together, which were testimony to the overlapping neighborhoods around us. One was the A-ONE NACHAS KNIT SWEATER SHOP. ('Nachas' is the Yiddish word for 'joy', so if you want an A-1 sweater knit with joy, that's where you'll find it.) The other was a religious artifacts store, its windows crammed with Catholic statues and medallions and an assortment of Christmas creches. The older generation of middle European Jews still clings to the Lower East Side; older Italians still cling to adjacent Little Italy; and below both, new waves of Hong Kong immigrants cling to overcrowded Chinatown. And the extent to which the three neighborhoods spill over into each other is visible on Sunday on Orchard Street. We saw boys wearing *yarmulkas* eating Italian ices, and Jewish and Chinese men deep in conversation. If you're here in September during the biggest of the city's Italian street fairs, the San Gennaro Festival on Mulberry Street, you'll see more Chinese than Italian faces looking down at the fair from tenement windows. And you won't believe it, but on Allen Street there's a Kosher Chinese restaurant where the Chinese waiters wear *yarmulkas*. The truth is that the faces you see down there would stick out like sore thumbs in Rome or the Warsaw Ghetto or Hong Kong; they aren't Italian, Jewish and Chinese faces, they're New York faces.

We walked all the way down Orchard Street to Canal. We had passed famous Lower East Side streets at intersections all the way down. I managed to control myself as we crossed Rivington Street, famous for its huge sidewalk barrels of Kosher pickles. But one block below Rivington, we came to Delancey Street.

'Did I ever tell you about Oliver Delancey, the Outlaw of the Bronx?' I asked Patsy.

'Oh, God,' said Patsy.

'He was a sort of commando raider,' I said. 'The Delancey's were rich Tories, their sons were educated in England and so forth. Well, during the Revolution the Delancey men became officers in the King's Loyal American regiment and fought bravely for the King's cause and they were all due to be knighted after England won the war. So was Jimmy Rivington. He published the Tory newspaper in New York during the British Occupation. The British thought very highly of Jimmy, he was presented to the Prince of Wales when the Prince came to New York. Jimmy Rivington and the Delancey men all expected to be among the first American Knights of the British Empire. Instead of which, they wound up giving their names to the two most famous lower-class immigrant streets in the world.'

'Write that down,' said Patsy automatically.

At Canal Street, we turned west to Mott, one of Chinatown's narrow streets, clotted with restaurants, vegetable markets, curio shops, a Chinese book store, all of them on the ground floors of appallingly ancient, decayed tenements, but with a new modern Chinese Community Centre rising hopefully in the middle of the block.

Since 1963, when American immigration laws were finally amended to include 'orientals,' overcrowding in Chinatown has become more and more severe. A *Times* story identified Confucius Plaza as a publicly-financed housing project, and to walk along Mott Street is to see how desperately it's needed.

It was nearly two o'clock by the time we got there and we were both ravenous; but as far as I'm concerned, there's no better street in New York for handling an appetite. The new Hong Kong immigrants of the sixties brought their Szechuan cuisine with them. They opened restaurants in Chinatown, to which New Yorkers who like hot food – chili pepper hot – become addicted. As the immigrants learned enough English to move uptown, Szechuan restaurants sprang up in all New York neighborhoods; but walking along Mott Street, I happened to see the first Szechuan restaurant I'd ever tried and which I remembered with special pleasure.

'Do you like Szechuan food?' I asked Patsy.

'I like all Chinese food,' said Patsy innocently.

'Well, I haven't been there in a long time,' I said, 'but Mandarin

Inn used to be wonderful. Shall we try it?'

'Why not?' said Patsy. And we crossed the street to Mandarin Inn, where a sign in the hall informed us that Chef Wong demonstrated the preparation of lemon chicken on the second Sunday afternoon of every month. We didn't wait around for the demonstration, but we ordered the lemon chicken, and shrimp with garlic sauce, which were the Specialties of the Day. I ordered a side dish of Szechuan string beans from memory.

'Do you want your shrimp starred?' I asked Patsy as the waiter took our order.

'What do you mean?' she said.

'When a dish is starred or has a red check next to it, it means it's extra hot,' I said. 'Do you like hot spicy food?'

'No,' said Patsy.

'It figured,' I said. So I ordered my shrimp hot, she ordered hers mild. The lemon chicken is always mild, but I forgot to warn Patsy about the string beans. Being deep green, they looked cool. Patsy speared one, dropped it negligently into her mouth, and then began to claw the air. She drank her glass of water, and mine, and a cup of tea before she managed, still gasping, to push the dish of string beans over to my side of the table.

I liked the lemon chicken better than the highly-touted version served at a fashionable uptown restaurant where it's so saturated with sugar you can't taste the lemon.

'In my extremely limited experience,' I said to Patsy, 'every over-priced, super-chic restaurant in New York, where you can't get a table unless they *know* you, turns out to have disappointing food when you finally get there. Whereas every neighborhood in New York has good, unpretentious restaurants where they'll feed you just as well, for half the price and none of the aggravation.'

'Tourists should do what we did at Columbia,' said Patsy. 'Ask somebody going by on the street: "Where's a good place to eat around here?"'

So you do that. Don't stop a man with a briefcase, he's probably a commuter. Wait till a man or woman comes along with groceries, a bike, a baby-coach or a dog and ask him-or-her to recommend a restaurant.

We walked down Mulberry Street after lunch and passed a Chinese

Teahouse and Pastry Shop. I had Sunday brunch in one of those shops once. Trays of hot filled pastry puffs were brought to the table, the pastries on one tray stuffed with shrimp, others with meat and vegetables, with a tray of sweet puffs for dessert.

On Mulberry as on Mott Street, the vegetable stores were open on Sunday, and through the open doorways we could see bok toy, the mustardy lettuce, fresh ginger and black, hundred-day-old duck eggs.

Ahead of us, at the end of Mulberry Street, rose the first towers of Lower Manhattan and we walked on west to City Hall at the upper end of the old city. On a deserted Sunday, you can appreciate the grace of the low white building, its Colonial columns and portico and domed clock tower tranquilly at home among the skyscrapers, thanks to City Hall Park which keeps them at a respectful distance.

'You see that turret window up there on top?' I said, pointing up at the small window under the clock tower.

'What about it?' said Patsy.

'There's a little man who sits up there by himself in an office behind that window,' I said. 'He's been sitting up there for forty years and he's a human encyclopedia of New York City. Anybody in the City Administration who needs a New York fact or date or place-name origin, phones the little man up in that turret. He's been sitting up there through eight or nine administrations with his encyclopedic head, every mayor finds him indispensable and he outlasts them all.'

City Hall Park being the center of a radius of Lower Manhattan streets, we had to decide which exit would take us down to Trinity Church. Patsy studied several YOU ARE HERE maps and then informed me that they were all upside down, but that Broadway should take us down to Wall Street. We crossed an empty, silent intersection and started down Broadway into the financial district.

The absolute quiet and emptiness of Lower Manhattan on a Sunday spreads it out before you like a model city, giving you a chance to see it first in perspective and then, as you walk, in a series of small, clear-cut pictures.

At the corner of Broadway and Liberty, in the shadow of the huge Marine Midland buildings, Patsy clutched my arm and said: 'Look down there!' And I looked down a long curving canyon as dramatic as Wall Street's.

At the next corner, Thames Street, she seized my arm again and ordered: 'Look up!'

On opposite corners of a narrow alley, two buildings rose maybe forty stories above the street, and on what might have been the thirty-fifth floor, a foot-bridge connected the two buildings. Somebody obviously got tired of taking an elevator all the way down, crossing the narrow alley and taking another elevator all the way up, and built a bridge outside two thirty-fifth floor windows to save steps.

We went on down to Wall Street, and there was Trinity Church with the churchyard gate standing open. We found Hamilton's impressive monument, and Gallatin's, and what I consider a fitting monument to Robert Fulton: an enormous, pretentious tomb – but empty. (His remains are buried elsewhere.) And we came upon a gravestone which touched me very much.

The stone must have been recently restored because the legend on it was plain and easy to read from the outside path on which we stood. What touched me, however, was not what was on the stone but what I could read between the lines.

The inscription noted that the deceased had been a 'merchant of New York' until 1783, when he had 'removed to Newfoundland where he established a new home,' and where he had died fifteen years later.

'I promise I won't bore you with any more stories if you'll just listen to this one,' I told Patsy. 'First, read the stone.'

Patsy read it and then asked obligingly:

'Who was he?'

'I don't know. Nobody. Just a merchant,' I said. 'But he was a Tory. 1783 was the year when the British left New York, after seven years of Occupation. They left in November, and most Tories left at the same time. Some of them were afraid of reprisals from the returning patriots, and some of them just didn't want to live under a rebel government; they wanted to stay English. So England offered them free passages to Newfoundland, and they became pilgrims all over again, sailing off to another wilderness – in winter – to start a new life. Well, here's one of them. He "removed to Newfoundland and established a new home there" and died there. Only he must have left instructions in his will for his body to be carried, by ship, all the way back to New York to be buried in Trinity churchyard – because here he is.'

'That's a nice story for a book about New York,' said Patsy judiciously. 'Use that.'

It was after four when we left the churchyard. We had been walking steadily since ten that morning. My shoes hated two of my toes and a bone in my right foot; Patsy's kept mutinously dropping off behind her. But it was a sunny day and in the absence of exhaust fumes, the air was sharply clear. The World Trade Center towers looked closer than they were and we pushed on toward them without bothering to discuss it. If you're gung-ho about New York, and you're that close to that view on a bright, clear day, you're going back up there whether your feet want to or not. But we were very thankful when our feet finally made it to the World Trade Center entrance and we walked into the surrealistic lobby. Then we looked up at the mezzanine.

The line of people waiting to buy tickets ran clear around the mezzanine; everybody in New York had discovered it was a clear day. But the sign on the ticket window said 'View to the Horizon,' and we'd passed the point of no return anyway, so we went all the way around the mezzanine and got on the end of the line, where we stood, inching along, for twenty-five minutes. Then one of the two elevators took us up, and we sat in one window seat after another gawking out and down in blissful silence, the long wait forgotten.

'If it were six instead of five,' said Patsy, 'we'd be able to watch the sunset.'

'Does this building face west?' I asked.

'It faces everywhere,' said Patsy positively. 'It does everything.'

When we'd sat in every window seat, we finally rose to leave. And I don't know why it didn't occur to us that if two elevators took twenty-five minutes to get all of us up there, they would take at least that long to get all of us back down. Standing on line all over again I was getting a backache and I leaned backwards to relieve it. Whereupon Patsy inquired: 'What are you doing?'

'I have a backache,' I said.

'That's not what you do for a backache,' said Patsy. 'Bend forward with your arms stretched out and then bend down till you touch the floor.'

I leaned over and as my fingertips touched the floor, a hand began thumping my head down to meet them.

'Relax your head,' advised Patsy. Which is how I discovered that your head is not like your arms or legs, you can't relax it, or stiffen it, you can't do anything with it. Like Mount Everest, it's just there. And all this time, Patsy's two hands industriously pushed my head down and Patsy's voice commanding authoritatively:

'Relax your head.'

How we looked to the rest of the line it didn't occur to us to consider; we were too busy with what we were doing.

By the time we got back down to the ground floor we were so tired I needed a new definition of the world. Patsy supplied it.

We had a long subway ride still ahead of us, and we had to locate our separate subways through a network of unfinished corridors. Before embarking on this final lap, I fished out my cigarettes and lit one. Patsy usually prefers her own brand but she was just standing, swaying slightly, staring at my pack in a kind of vacant stupor.

'You want a cigarette?' I asked – and took one of mine out of the pack and extended it to her. Patsy stared at it a moment.

'No,' she said finally. 'I wouldn't have the strength to draw on it.'

That's tired.

I didn't hear from Patsy till Wednesday evening.

'I've been paralyzed for three days,' she said when she phoned. 'Both the shoes I wore Sunday have holes in them.'

'Don't complain to me, I've got two corns and a bunion,' I said.

'Well, you told me to save Thursday,' said Patsy, 'but I'm warning you: I'm only up to something very easy and midtown.'

'So am I,' I said – and wondered how to tell her what I had in mind.

'Okay,' said Patsy, 'As long as we don't have to do it this·week, I'll tell you why I called you. There's a black-owned Sightseeing Bus company that does a three-hour tour of Harlem. We have to reserve seats in advance. You want me to call them and book seats for next week?'

'Fine,' I said. 'Any day you can make, I can make.

'Right,' said Patsy – and couldn't resist adding: 'Guess where their first stop is?'

'Where?' I said.

'The Jumel mansion,' said Patsy. 'I told you we'd see everything! Now, what's for tomorrow?'

'We'll only need a couple of hours,' I said cautiously. 'You want to meet me at Bloomingdale's at three?'

'I don't like Bloomingdale's,' said Patsy.

'I went to Zabar's; you can go to Bloomingdale's,' I said. 'Meet me at the Lexington Avenue entrance.'

Considering our mutual fear of heights, I saw no reason to tell her in advance, that I considered it our duty as tourists to get on a cable car suspended over midtown Manhattan, and ride across the East River and back on it.

A few blocks from where I live, there's a pedestrian walk along the river, above the East River Drive. If you're strolling along it, you'll see on the opposite bank a small island, two miles long, running parallel with the East Side from Forty-second Street to Seventy-ninth.

The city bought the island from a man named Blackwell back in 1823 and for years it was known as Blackwell's Island, but in the twentieth century it became better known as Welfare Island because of the free hospitals-for-incurables the city built and maintained there. In the early years of the century the island also had a very jazzy jail. Boss Tweed had 'a magnificent cell' there, according to the brochure, with a picture window to give him a view of the city he'd robbed blind. And Mae West spent ten days there for appearing in a play she wrote called *Sex*.

By the early sixties, when I first became aware of it, Welfare Island was occupied only by two hospitals for the severely handicapped. The hospitals had large, permanent populations and the patients were citizens with voting rights. And since Welfare Island ran parallel with our neighbourhood, it was included in the Assembly district represented by our local Democratic Club. So during every political campaign, our club leaders climbed into a car, with our State Assembly or City Council candidate in the back seat, and drove across the Queensboro Bridge, and then back through part of Queens, to visit the voters on Welfare Island. The trip took fifteen minutes without traffic, thirty minutes with traffic.

This year, the club leaders drove over as usual; but they saw ten times as many voters as ever before and they probably made the trip by car for the last time. Because this year the island has been transformed; it is now Roosevelt Island, a new suburb built to house 2200 families in mini apartment houses. And the island's residents will commute to their New York offices not in fifteen to thirty minutes, but in four. A tramway has been built to carry them back and forth across the East River by cable car, for the price of a subway token. The tram made its first run last Monday.

The cable cars leave from a specially constructed depot above Sixtieth Street and Second Avenue. Which is why I told Patsy to meet me at Bloomingdale's. Bloomingdale's occupies a square block from Fifty-ninth to Sixtieth and from Lexington to Third. But if I'd told Patsy to meet me on the Third Avenue side, she might have got there before I did, she might have looked toward Second and seen the tramway depot – and guessed – and bolted. So we met at the Lexington Avenue entrance to Bloomingdale's.

'Put this in your shoulder bag, but don't forget to read it later, it's funny,' said Patsy, handing me the inevitable clipping.

'Why don't you like Bloomie's?' I asked as we went into the store (where I was going to walk her through to the Third Avenue exit).

'It's too big,' said Patsy. 'I can't find anything.'

'If you just remember that Bloomingdale's was once a cheap department store on Lexington Avenue,' I said, 'that's all you need to know – because it's still, basically speaking, a cheap department store *on Lexington Avenue*. When the Third Avenue El came down and Third Avenue became beautiful and expensive, Bloomingdale's naturally added a beautiful and expensive Third Avenue side. So you take the Lexington Avenue escalator up to the cheap-clothes floors, and the Third Avenue escalator up to the designer-clothes floor. But they have a great furniture department, a great housewares department and a sensational gourmet food ship in the basement, so don't say you don't like it.'

By this time, we had come out on Third Avenue, Patsy following me absent-mindedly. But as we started walking toward Second, she saw the new tramway depot looming overhead at the corner of Second, and stopped cold.

'We're not going up in that ski-lift!' she said.

'We owe it to my readers,' I said.

I kept on walking and she followed me in silence. At the corner of Second Avenue, a flight of stone steps led up to the tramway platform. We reached the foot of the steps and Patsy halted again. She waved an arm toward the cable wire overhead.

'Do you see what you're going to be riding on?' she demanded. 'It's a piece of string!'

'I couldn't do it alone,' I said piously. 'Together, we can do anything.'

She followed me up the stone steps to the platform, where we stood and watched the cable car glide toward us from the island, swaying gently as it crossed the river.

'Will you look how it's shaking?' said Patsy. 'Why do we have to try this thing the first week it's operating? They haven't got it safe yet!'

The car landed, and the people who stepped out of it were smiling, which gave me the courage to push Patsy into it ahead of me. We were joined by a dozen other thrill-seekers with nothing better to do in the middle of a Thursday afternoon.

The cable car, a glass bubble with standard bus seats, runs alongside the Queensboro Bridge, and since we were level with the cars going by on the bridge we had no more sense of height than we'd have had in an ordinary El train. What we did have, as the car stood poised over midtown Manhattan at the edge of the river and then started slowly on its way, was a goggle-eyed view of present-day transportation.

Below us, on land, was the usual Second Avenue traffic jam of buses, trucks and cars. On the water were a couple of barges, a commuters' motorboat and a Circle Line Sightseeing boat taking tourists on the time-honoured trip around Manhattan island. Above us, planes flew in the distance, and as we crossed the river, a helicopter went by on its way to one of the airports.

And Patsy, who had been shaking when she stepped into it, was darting back and forth from one side of the car to the other, barking: 'Look down there! Look over here! Look out that way!'

The tramcar landed at the new suburb, unfinished and sparsely inhabited as yet, though the rental offices were busy. We walked nearly the length of it, admiring the small six and seven-story apartment houses, the new streets and park, the new school and swimming pool, the very old church and the old Blackwell house on its way to becoming a community centre.

'It's pretty now, like a toy city,' I said to Patsy. 'But you can visualize the fast-food stores and parking lot and they've already got space set aside for the suburban shopping centre. Riding a cable car over the East river is something tourists might want to try. But once they get here, all they'll see is one more standardized suburb.'

(Two days later, riding a cable car over the East River turned out to be something half of New York wanted to try. On the tram's first weekend, twenty thousand New Yorkers converged on it, bringing their children and a picnic lunch, prepared for a day's outing on Roosevelt Island, which had no picnic facilities. The families picnicked all over it and, when the trash baskets overflowed, littered all over it. The island also had no public toilets, and the results of that were so horrendous that the beleaguered islanders threatened to close down the tramway if the weekend invasion continued. It didn't. Within two weeks, the novelty had worn off and the tram trip to Roosevelt Island joined the list of sightseeing tours New Yorkers are definitely going to take some day, like the trip to the Statue of Liberty.

That afternoon when I got home I dug Patsy's clipping out of my shoulder bag. It was from the *Times* and featured a photograph of Trinity churchyard and the intelligence that the graveyard had become a favourite lunchtime meeting place for young pot-smokers. I phoned Patsy.

'I forgot to tell you,' she said. 'We're booked for the Harlem tour at ten A.M. Monday. Penny Sightseeing Bus, 303 West Forty-second, write it down.'

I wrote it down, and said:

'I read that clipping. Do you really think a story about pot-smoking in Trinity's graveyard belongs in a book for tourists?'

'It's a modern sidelight. Put it in,' said Patsy. 'Now listen. I've been thinking about that story you told me. About the Tory who left New York after the Revolution and fled to Buffalo.'

'NEWFOUNDLAND,' I said. Buffalo. I was losing all my respect for Harvard.

'Well, wherever it was,' said Patsy. 'What exactly did the stone say?'

I went to get my notes and came back and reported:

'I didn't take his name. What I took verbatim was that he was a 'merchant of New York who removed to Newfoundland in 1783 and established a new home there,' and I must have looked at the birth and death dates because I made a note that he died up there fifteen years later.'

'Was it a gravestone,' asked Patsy, 'or a plaque?'

'A gravestone, I think,' I said.

'I think so, too, but you'll have to make sure,' said Patsy. 'Because it occurred to me: if it was a plaque, then he's buried in Newfoundland and somebody just put up the plaque in his memory.'

'You've just ruined a beautiful story,' I said. 'But the lettering was very clear, I could read it easily from the outside path, so it might have been a plaque.'

'Is it worth going back down to check it?' Patsy asked. 'Or do you just want to phone them?'

'We have to go back down anyway,' I said. 'We still haven't toured the Stock Exchange.'

'Oh, right,' said Patsy. 'And I want to check up on that bank; I want to see if they've put up a new wall plaque. All right, just put the Tory's gravestone on your list or we'll forget it.'

As things turned out, we were to be in no danger of forgetting it. Ever.

This day started with a mystery, and Patsy and I aren't sure it didn't end with one.

We'd been having unnaturally hot weather and a month earlier than usual, New York City was air-conditioned to death. To give you an example – and a warning: two friends of mine landed in hospitals with pneumonia, in July, from the icy, air-conditioned offices they worked in. I get frozen out of restaurants and movie theatres all summer; and since the buses to Jersey resorts always delivered me to the beach with a sore throat and a sinus cough, I began to worry about the Harlem sightseeing bus. On Saturday, therefore, I phoned the Penny Bus Company. A man answered the phone.

'I'm booked for your Monday morning tour,' I said, 'and I wondered whether your bus is heavily air-conditioned and whether we'll need to bring sweaters.'

And he said:

'You must be Mrs Gibbs.'

My mouth fell open.

'I'm coming with Mrs Gibbs,' I said.

'Oh, that's right,' he said. 'There are two of you. We do have one air-conditioned bus, but the air-conditioning doesn't work very well so it's never very cold.'

I thanked him and we hung up; and I called Patsy. I told her that the man who answered the phone had said immediately: 'You must be Mrs Gibbs' and I went on: 'We must be the only passengers on the bus. Will you mind that?'

'No, it means we can ask a lot of questions,' said Patsy.

We met in front of the bus office and went upstairs to the ticket office. There was a man behind the desk and he smiled and said good morning, and Patsy said:

'We have seats reserved on the ten o'clock bus.'

And he said:

'You're Mrs Gibbs.'

But when we paid for our tickets, he got out a list of names and checked off ours at the bottom of a long list.

'The other passengers have all gone downstairs to the bus stop,' he said. 'You'd better go right down; the bus'll be along any minute.'

As we went downstairs, I said to Patsy:

'Maybe he knows we're the only whites on the bus.'

We got down to the bus entrance and found the other passengers assembled on the sidewalk. There were thirty-five of them. All thirty-five were white.

'It's a Group,' Patsy murmured. 'We're the only ones not in the Group.'

But we examined our fellow-passengers furtively and, except for a couple here and a threesome there, they were obviously strangers to each other.

The bus arrived, the door opened, and as we filed into the bus, the driver, who was also white, beamed at us and greeted us individually with 'Good morning,' and 'Hello, how are you?'

We found seats and settled ourselves and I got out my notebook. Then the tour guide came aboard. The tour guide was a handsome, middle-aged man and the only black on the bus. As the bus pulled away and headed uptown, the guide said, in a resonant baritone voice:

'I want to welcome you, and to ask you to tell me whenever I'm going too fast for you. Mrs Penny, the owner of the bus company, tells me you all speak English, but wherever we stop, there will be information sheets available in your own language. According to my list, you're all from Germany, France or Australia, but sometimes the list is incomplete, so if you need information sheets in some other language, just tell me.'

The man I talked to on the phone had said, 'You're Mrs Gibbs,' as soon as he heard my American accent. Patsy and I were the only Americans on the bus.

The guide told us he had been in show business for twenty years and that conducting sightseeing tours was something he did in his spare time.

'I do this because I enjoy it,' he said. 'I like Harlem and I enjoy showing it to people.'

(The bus wasn't air-conditioned and as I sat happily by an open window, Patsy, perspiring freely, muttered in my ear: 'Make a note: No smoking, no john and no air-conditioning,' and declined my offer to trade seats with her. 'I don't want that hot air blowing on me,' she said.)

The bus was rolling along Central Park West and the guide, who had been pointing out the sights along the way, suddenly paralyzed us by pointing to the building Patsy lives in.

That is one of the city's finest old apartment houses,' he announced, and added: 'Steve Lawrence and Edie Gorme live there.'

'They moved out,' Patsy hissed at me. 'Should I tell him?'

'Have you got any celebrities to substitute?' I asked her.

'Margaret Mead?' suggested Patsy. 'Abe Burrows? Helen Gurley Brown?'

'Fine,' I said. 'We'll tell him later.'

The bus drove on up to 116th Street where the guide pointed upward to a back of beyond view of the spires of St John's Cathedral and part of the Columbia quadrangle, the buildings so far above us on a cliff we had to crane our necks to see them.

'Do you see where we were?' Patsy squeaked. 'On that parapet? We had to be crazy!'

We were in Harlem now, driving through a neighborhood of sharp contrasts. On our left were huge modern housing projects with ground-floor playgrounds and landscaped walks; on our right, directly opposite the projects, rows of indescribably decayed and crumbling five-story brownstone tenements. But as we rolled on upward, past the graceful stone entrance gate to New York City College and then past the Grange, Alexander Hamilton's home, we were on a wide avenue driving through an attractive, middle-class Harlem neighborhood where old shade trees on front lawns framed bay-windowed Victorian houses. We passed a modern Episcopal church building which the guide told us had been built by its black parishioners in 1970, after the old church building had burnt down, and which had won prizes for its architect.

I was taking frantic notes on all this when Patsy turned to me abruptly and demanded:

'Why?'

'Why what?' I said.

'Why are we the only Americans on the bus?'

'I don't know,' I said. 'Maybe Americans don't know about the tour. I didn't.'

'Then how did the foreigners find out about it?' said Patsy. 'They can't all have read the fine print in the Convention & Visitors' guide the way I did. I was looking through it to see if we'd missed anything or I'd never have known about it either.'

The bus drew up outside the Morris-Jumel house and as we piled out, I said to Patsy:

'When the guide isn't too busy, I'll ask him.'

One of the curators met us at the door and she obviously knew the Penny operation well because she stood ready with mimeographed information sheets in German and French, and four in English for us and two young men from Australia.

The house was built before the Revolution by Roger Morris, a Tory who abandoned it to emigrate to England. During the war it served as headquarters first for Washington, then for the British and finally for the Hessians; and the military documents and letters on display around the walls dealt mostly with the British-Hessian Occupation. Years later, the house was bought by a Frenchman named Jumel, whose chief claim to fame was that his widow was married to Aaron Burr for four months; and a few Burr portraits and letters were also on display, along with a great many Jumel possessions, none of them particularly interesting.

Patsy and I found the house and its contents dull; what the German and French tourists thought, we didn't know. When you're in a Revolutionary War museum and the only comments you hear around you are in French and German, you feel a little weird. So it was a relief when one of the Australians pointed to the date on a military despatch and said to his companion: 'That was the year Australia was first settled!'

Patsy and I went outside for a cigarette and a look at the view: the Jumel house is on a hill above the Harlem River. As we looked across the river to the woods drifting northward along the opposite bank, I said:

'That wood over there once belonged to a very sociable Dutch burgher named Jonas Bronch. He came to New Netherlands and bought a stretch of farmland over there and he built a big farm and a big farmhouse for his family. But they got bored living up there by themselves, and Jonas started inviting New Amsterdam families out to his place for a week or two. So you'd be walking along Wall Street or the docks, and you'd see a family piling their children and their clothes-boxes into a boat and you'd ask them where they were going.

And they'd say: "We've been invited up to the mainland, to visit the Broncks" or "We're going up to see the Broncks." I don't know who changed the *ck* to an *x*.'

The guide came out with the rest of the tourists and led us all around the corner to a narrow street, a cul-de-sac two blocks long that was probably once a mews attached to the Jumel house. On both sides of the street were trim lines of small, upright houses with front steps that ran parallel with the sidewalk, rising to a landing where they turned a right angle to the front door. But you could only see the steps by walking around a barrier. In front of each house, a tall, left-handed triangle of brightly painted wood hid the steps and the landing from view. One barrier was dark green, one bright yellow, most were white. The line of houses with their brightly-painted shields seemed to have dropped into twentieth century New York from another world.

'This street is Sylvan Terrace,' the guide told us. 'The houses are very expensive; only wealthy black families can afford them.' And as he led the way back to the bus, he told the foreigners:

'There was a time when black New Yorkers had to live in Harlem because they were excluded from housing everywhere else. Now that they can live in other neighborhoods, when wealthy black families buy houses in Sylvan Terrace, it's because Harlem is where they want to live.'

We drove along Edgecomb Avenue, an attractive residential street. Then we turned down Eighth Avenue and were abruptly on a depressed, dirty main street lined with shabby tenement storefronts. But as the bus approached 139th Street, the driver pointed to the block of it opening off Eighth Avenue.

'This block,' he said, 'and the next one – 138th Street – are special. I want you to look at them.'

We looked down 139th Street and saw a line of tall, handsome brownstones on a street that was scrupulously clean.

'These two blocks are very famous,' said the guide. 'They're called "Strivers' Row." The houses were built by Stanford White, back at the turn of the century. The name "Strivers Row" may have come from a West Indian named Striver who lived there. But the people of Harlem love their myths; and the Harlem folk tale is that the name comes from the fact that Strivers' Row is where all the poor people of Harlem are striving to get. For years, Strivers' Row had the only fine housing open to black people. The houses are still fine and they're still expensive. And like Sylvan Terrace, the Strivers' Row houses are owned by people who don't have to live in Harlem but want to.'

At 135th Street and Seventh Avenue, the foreigners heard the name of Harlem's favourite son for the first time. At that corner, Seventh Avenue becomes Adam Clayton Powell Boulevard ('though they don't acknowledge the name-change downtown,' the guide added dryly). Powell was elected to Congress in 1945 and steadily re-elected until his death in 1972. But he was also a preacher, and the bus made its second stop at the Abyssinian Baptist church which Powell made famous. At the height of his ministry, church membership stood at 18,000. Today it may still be the largest church congregation in the country with 12,000 members.

We were welcomed to the church by an aide to the minister who gave us a brief history of it, pointed out the church's chief ornaments and then took us into the Powell room, which might once have been a large social hall and is now a Powell museum. The photographs, plaques and testimonials, including one from the Late Emperor Haile Selassie of Abyssinia (now Ethiopia), form a visual biography of Powell. He was a handsome man and the photographs of him are strikingly alive. More than that, they point up the singular fact of his life. Powell was expelled from Congress for precisely the same kind of political corruption for which a white Senator had his wrist slapped by the same Congress in the same year. And the life of prejudice and hatred he endured, in and out of Congress, he could have avoided. Adam Clayton Powell could have passed for white and chose not to.

I was sorry we saw the inside of no other church. And when we drove past a Muslim mosque, I'd have liked knowing whether it was the one from which Malcolm X first proclaimed to the people of Harlem that black was beautiful; but his name was never mentioned by the guide.

The tour made its final stop at a horribly dilapidated building on 135th Street which houses the Schomburg Collection, the largest collection of black history and art in the country, if not the world. But another Penny bus was parked in the only legal space available in front of it so our tour bus had to bypass the collection. We learned later that we'd have seen very little of it even if we'd gone in. Most of the valuable art objects and manuscripts are packed away in crates, waiting for the new Schomburg museum building which was to have been built this year. The architect's plans were complete and the site selected, when the city's financial collapse put an end to the Schomburg's hopes of a decent home.

The bus rolled on down to 125th Street, Harlem's main shopping street (the guide told us that one of its two black-owned banks was founded by Johnny Mathis) and then on down through the terrible slums which were the only Harlem we'd ever read about: the burnt-out buildings and uncleared piles of rubble that look like a bombed-out city, the inhabited tenements as desolate and unfit for human habitation as the abandoned buildings crumbling away beside them. It was a relief at 116th Street, to turn east to Lexington Avenue, to the gaudy bedlam of the main shopping street of Spanish Harlem.

'It looks a little like Orchard Street,' said Patsy as we peered out the window at the racks of dresses and cardboard packing cases overflowing with wigs and sweaters that filled the sidewalks. What was definitely not Orchard Street was the atmosphere: the Spanish signs above stores the Latin music blaring from radios up and down the block and the staccato, stentorian Puerto Rican voices raised in the Puerto Rican English known as 'Spanglish.'

The bus turned down Fifth on its way back to Forty-second Street and the driver invited passengers to say where they'd like to be let off along the way. The two Australians wanted to get off at Seventy-ninth Street to visit the Natural History Museum, unaware that it was clear across the park on the West Side.

'They'll never find it,' said Patsy. 'I'm going to get off with them, I'll walk them across the park, I'd walk home that way anyway.'

'Ask them how they found out about the tour,' I said. All four of us got off at Seventy-ninth, Patsy and the Australians went west through the park, I walked down through it to Seventy-second and then home. On my home, I bought a *New York Post*. I read the *Post* over lunch and then I phoned Patsy, knowing she'd have got home by then.

'What did you find out from the Australians?' I asked her.

'They're architecture students,' she said enthusiastically. 'They're over here on a six-month tour of the country, the Australian government's helping them. They've covered a thousand miles of this country in three months, they told me all about New Orleans and St Louis!'

'What did you find out about the Harlem tour? How did they know about it?' I prodded.

'Oh,' said Patsy. 'I forgot to ask.'

'Never mind,' I said. 'I have to call the tour guide anyway and give him the new celebrities in your building. Now then. Have you read the *Post*? Did you see what's opening to the public for the first time on May 29?'

'What?' asked Patsy.

'Ellis Island,' I said.

'Oh, God,' said Patsy. 'My grandparents came to this country through Ellis Island. When can we go?'

'Monday?' I suggested.

'Monday's memorial Day! We'll be away,' said Patsy.

'Let's give it a week for the first crowds to thin out anyway,' I said. 'How's Friday, June 4? We'll get an early start and do the Stock Exchange, and stop at Trinity to check out that gravestone, and have lunch at Delmonico's and finish up at Ellis Island.'

'It sounds like another blockbuster day,' said Patsy.

'It should be,' I said. 'It's our last.'

'Oh,' said Patsy, sounding subdued, and we hung up.

The next morning I phoned the Penny Sightseeing Bus Company and got the name and telephone number of our guide and phoned him. I gave him Patsy's new list of tenants ('Margaret Mead?' he said. 'Oh, my! Thank you very much.') and then I said: 'Will you tell me something? How did all the foreign tourists know about your tour?'

'Mrs Penny has had fantastic publicity in European papers,' he said. 'Back in 1967, the AP ran a story on the tour and it was picked up by some European newspapers. And people over there who read about it took the tour when they came here, and then went home and wrote to their home-town newspaper: "You were right, it's a great tour" and that got her more publicity. And it just keeps mushrooming.'

'Didn't the AP story run in American newspapers?' I asked.

'Oh yes,' he said. 'And the *New York Times* ran a story on us; the press has been very good to us.'

'Then Americans do know about it,' I said. And he said 'Oh yes.'

I thanked him and hung up, still mystified. Two weeks later, when Patsy's son came home from college, he and a friend took the Penny tour, and they, too, were the only two Americans on a bus crowded with foreigners.

'I think I understand it,' I said to Patsy when she relayed this information to me. 'Foreigners are curious about our racial troubles so a tour of Harlem attracts them. White Americans don't like thinking about our racial troubles so they avoid the tour.'

'And black Americans?' Patsy inquired. 'They come to New York as tourists, too. Why don't they take the tour?'

Mystery unsolved.

Saturday, May 29

From Memorial Day weekend in May to Labor Day weekend in September New Yorkers divide into two groups: 1, those who always leave town on weekends, and 2, those who never leave town on weekends. Those of us in Group 2 have the standard negative reasons for staying home: we hate traveling on crowded highways and trains, and if we work all week and count on weekends to do our housekeeping chores, we hate coming home tired on a Sunday night to a dirty apartment, and overflowing laundry bag and an empty refrigerator.

But there's a positive reason that's equally potent. New York has a special charm for us on a summer weekend, when the town empties out, when the trucks and commuters and commuters cars are gone. The air is cleaner, the city is quieter, and the peaceful, empty avenues seem especially wide and beautiful. When we've had enough of the peace and quiet, we head for Central Park where the action is.

On weekdays, the park itself is the town's only quiet, peaceful oasis. The playgrounds will be busy, and you'll pass a few baby-coach brigades, dog-walkers and teenage ball games; but there are vast, green empty stretches and I love it that way. On summer weekends, the park is jammed and jumping and I love it that way.

So on Saturday of this first holiday weekend, I got up early to get my cleaning and marketing done by early afternoon and then headed for the park. Alone. On weekday afternoons, I go with my true love, a worried-looking, doe-eyed German shepherd named Duke, who lives on the sixteenth floor with parents who are out at work all day and a brother who's in college. The park is more fun with a dog, and these days safer. I have never personally seen anyone or anything menacing in Central Park in all the years I've been going there, with or without a dog, you understand, but the newspapers' lurid accounts of muggings have made me cautious. If the newspapers printed – which they never do – equally lurid descriptions of car-crash victims, you'd learn to be cautious about your killer car. As it is, you probably know that cars kill and maim six hundred times as many people as muggers do, but you go on driving your car. I go on loving Central Park.

Today I went alone, partly because on a holiday weekend the park is too crowded for Duke. He's the longest German Shepherd you ever saw, and if he chased a stick across a park lawn on a holiday weekend he'd wreck ten picnics. But mostly my mind was on this book, and on the secret of Central Park which only New Yorkers know about, and I went over there looking for signs of that secret.

There was the usual holiday jam at the Seventy-second Street entrance: crowds around the ice cream and pretzel stands and a tangle of bikes and baby-strollers, as cyclists and parents tried to work their way through the crowd and into the park. Just inside the entrance on my left, Nancy's playground was crowded with holiday fathers. Its bright red and yellow poles are faded and weatherbeaten now.

Nancy's playground (which doesn't have her name on it) is one of the small, pre-school playgrounds you'll find at four- and five-block intervals throughout the park. One young mother used to call hers 'The Snake Pit' because she was stuck in it all day every day, summer heat or winter snow, till her toddler graduated to one of the school-age playgrounds and could go without her. Well, about ten years ago, my friend Nancy was stuck in the Seventy-Second Street playground with her two-year-old son. It was the usual antique playground with iron swings and a sandbox, and Nancy decided it ought to be modernized.

Nancy became Chairwoman of a Mothers' Committee to raise funds for the project. She ran a big movie benefit and a fund-raising cocktail party, and finally the committee had enough money to hire a designer and finance the construction of new playground equipment. And one fine spring day the new playground opened, with bright red and yellow poles and a tree house and a turret house and stone picnic benches and tables alongside the miniature wading pool.

But during the winter, Nancy had gotten pregnant again, and she and Ed needed a larger apartment. By spring, when the new playground opened, they'd moved up to the Eighties over near the East River and Nancy was taking her two sons to Carl Schurz park instead. And every time she rode downtown on a Fifth Avenue bus and saw the bright new playground from the bus window, she felt like Moses riding past the Promised Land.

On my right, across the road from Nancy's playground, a broad lawn slopes down to the Model Sailboat Pond, with the Model

Boathouse (a gift of the Kerbs family) beside it. Press your nose against the boathouse door and when your eyes have got used to the dark interior, you can see all the elaborate boats in dry-dock: Columbus's fleet, pirate ships, whaling vessels, all fully rigged, and Spanish galleons complete down to the galley slaves at the oars. The hobbyists who built them hold a regatta on a Sunday in June, and if you're here on the right Sunday it's something to see.

At the far end of the Pond is the Alice in Wonderland Statuary (a gift of the Delacorte family) depicting the Mad Tea Party in bronze. A gigantic Alice presides over the tea table where the Dormouse, Cheshire Cat and March Hare are dominated by the Mad Hatter, or at least by the height of his mad hat. Older children climb to the top of Alice's head and sit on it, younger ones climb to the top of the Mad Hatter's hat, and toddlers crawl or stagger in and out among the giant mushrooms under the tea table.

(Alice in Wonderland is equalled in popularity only by the Children's Zoo down at Sixty Fifth in the park, the gift 'To the Children of New York' of the late Governor and Mrs Herbert Lehman. The Zoo buildings – including Noah's Ark and Old McDonald's Farm – are brightly colored and have entrance gates no higher than a five-year-old. You can see them from a Fifth Avenue bus window.)

On the western rim of the Sailboat Pond opposite the Model Boathouse, is Hans Christian Andersen. The great bronze figure sits at ease, leaning forward slightly, a book open on his left knee. His nose is worn shiny by the thousands of children's hands that have used it as a lever by which to hoist themselves up to sit piggy-back around Hans Christian's neck.

But to see him properly, you have to visit Hans Christian with a child who has just learned to read, and who will climb up on Andersen's right knee and read aloud to you, from the open book on his left, the story of the Ugly Duckling. The duckling himself sits at Andersen's feet, listening with permanent bronze attention. This statue isn't as popular with children as Alice. But if you're a parent or grandparent watching a child read from Andersen's book, or a group of children sitting on the ground at his feet listening to the Story Lady from the New York Public Library read one of his fairy tales, you'll find the expression on Andersen's face very moving as he looks down at the children.

(At the back of the statue, an inscription in the stone explains that the statue was a gift to the children of New York from the children of Denmark.)

When Duke is with me, we walk north from the Sailboat Pond toward Dog Hill, and we usually pass the Clown on our way. Nobody seems to know who he is. All anybody knows is that on weekday afternoons he'll turn up in the park in a clown's motley and makeup, to sing and tell stories to the children who collect around him. I see him usually near Alice-in-Wonderland; friends of mine have seen him at other stations. Rumor has it he's a Wall Street stockbroker. But one Sunday when Duke and I were on our way to Dog Hill with our friends Richard and Chester-the-Sheepdog, we passed the Clown and I said:

'I've never seen him here before on a Sunday.'

And Richard said:

'I though he was taller. Are you sure this is the same Clown?'

The foot of Dog Hill is at Seventy-sixth Street and the hill slopes gradually upward to Seventy-ninth, rolling backward in a broad sweep as it rises. We claim it's the largest canine social hall in the world. On a sunny weekend afternoon, there'll be forty or fifty dogs charging around, two or three of whom always appoint themselves a welcoming committee and streak all the way down to the foot of the hill to greet every new arrival. It's the dream of my life to make enough money (which I won't) or leave enough money when I die (which I might) to donate a dog drinking fountain to the Hill. If there's room on it for an inscription, it'll read:

> *To the dogs of New York City*
> *From an Admirer.*

This town has got the friendliest, most sociable dogs you'll ever meet.

From Dog Hill, Duke and I usually push west to the Ramble, a small wood with winding paths and streams, and on over to the Rowboat Lake where he goes swimming. Then we may walk up along the western bank and above it to see how Shakespeare's garden is coming along.

A month ago, the once-beautiful garden was a wasteland of dead flower beds and weeds, the decaying footbridge crumbling into the empty moat. The city has had no money for gardeners or workmen for several years. But during the past month, anonymous volunteers have been working in the garden, early every morning and on weekends. They've cleared out the debris, and weeded and replanted and watered, and spread leaf-cover over the worst-damaged plots, and the garden isn't what it was but it's beginning to grow again.

The garden is set on a high hill overlooking the Shakespeare theatre, and Duke and I generally circle the theatre coming back over to the East side. Officially, it's the Delacorte Theatre. But I suspect the Delacortes would agree that it ought to be called the Joe Papp Theatre instead.

Joe Papp began putting on free productions of Shakespeare, in a clearing in the park back in 1954. Robert Moses was Czar of the parks in those days and he demanded that Papp charge admission and use the money to pay the city for damage to the grass. Papp went to court, to sue for the right to present Shakespeare free of charge. He won the suit. Moses asked the city to appropriate funds for a proper theatre, to save the surrounding lawns, and the Delacortes – and thousands of anonymous New Yorkers – contributed the rest of the money. The theatre opened in 1961 and seats three thousand people at free Shakespeare productions every summer, nightly-except-Monday.

Coming back east from the theatre a couple of months ago, Duke and I passed a grove of newly-planted pine trees at the far end of the lawn behind the Metropolitan Museum. The trees were planted by a man whose name I wish I remembered. I read about him in the *Times* a few days afterwards. A *Times* reporter saw the man planting trees and asked him why he was doing it, and the man said he'd just happened to notice a bare stretch of ground at that end of the lawn and he thought a grove of evergreens would be nice there.

Since Duke wasn't with me today, I didn't walk north from Seventy-second, I went a little south and west instead, to Central Park Mall. There's a bandshell at the entrance to it. The Naumberg Symphony Orchestra gives free concerts there on summer evenings – and on holiday afternoons, which I didn't know till I got there today. There was an all-Mozart concert in progress when I went by, and the benches which seat a thousand people were almost completely filled. There are band concerts there, too. And I don't like band music but I'll have to go to the June 10 band concert, out of apartment-house loyalty. There's a Russian refugee couple in my building named Litkei. Mrs Litkei is a retired ballerina; her husband is a musician. And this morning, they put handbills under all the doors in our building (and all over the neighborhood on street-light poles and lobby tables) which read in part:

In the Name of All Foreign-Born Americans
in Grateful Appreciation to the United States of America
Erwin Litkei
proudly presents
The 26th U.S. Army Band . . .

How can you not go to that?

Beyond the Bandshell, the Mall itself runs through the park for several blocks. Today's warm weather had brought out the food vendors – and I don't mean the usual pretzel, Italian ice and hot-dog vendors. Along with the shish-kebab stands and Italian sausage stands presided over by enterprising families, two young men were broiling chicken and corn on the cob over a charcoal fire, a middle-aged couple was cooking tacos and four young people sat behind a long table with two signs, one advising SMILE! BE HAPPY! and a smaller one advertising Magic Foods to Turn You On! The magic foods were apples, bananas, peaches, watermelon slices and coconuts. At one table, two girls were selling their homemade date-nut and pumpkin breads. Knowing they had potential customers in my building, I asked:

'Are you here every weekend?'

'I don't know,' one of them answered uncertainly. 'This is our first day.'

Entertainers were performing to small crowds on the lawns beside the Mall. Two college students were doing rope tricks, a Puerto Rican band was playing Latin music and at the far end, three students were playing a Haydn trio. A collection plate at their feet bore a sign explaining that classical music lessons cost money.

From the Mall I went west to the Sheep Meadow, where the Philharmonic and the Metropolitan Opera give performances on summer evenings, one Philharmonic concert drawing 250,000 people. The Sheep Meadow has an elastic seating capacity. There aren't any seats. You sit on the grass and keep inching over to make room for one more. (The concert and opera performances are paid for by private citizens and corporations, both usually anonymous.)

The size of the park – it's twice the size of Monaco – is a great boon on summer evenings. Down at the Wollman Skating Rink (gift of the Wollman family) the Schaefer Music Festival features rock-and-roll concerts (sponsored by the Schaefer Beer company). And loud as they are, the rock concerts are so far away that they never interfere with Mahler or Puccini holding forth on the Sheep Meadow – which in turn can't be heard by the actors or audience at the Shakespeare Theatre – which doesn't interfere with the sounds of the free Jazz Festival or Harlem Dance Theatre performance going on up on the Harlem Mall.

Circling the Sheep Meadow and coming back east, I noticed the new green trash baskets. There are several hundred of them in the park now. The Central Park Community Task Force keeps adding batches of them with money raised by the Central Park Community Fund. Both organizations are composed of New Yorkers whose names wouldn't mean anything to you. They're trying to do for the park what the city can no longer afford to do. But there's a much older organization of volunteers called the Friends of Central Park. Which brings us to Estelle, a fellow-member of the Democratic club where Patsy and I first met and the guiding spirit behind the Friends of Central Park.

For years, Estelle has been the chief thorn-in-the-side of every city official, parks commissioner and private enterprise threatening her park. She has stood on picket lines outside the Metropolitan Museum of Art through one losing battle after another. And she fought harder than anyone else in the heart-breaking losing battle against the Metropolitan Transportation Authority, which is now engaged in ripping up whole acres of the park clear through from East Sixty-fourth to West Sixtieth, to build a commuter's subway. Through Central Park. It's because of the yawning craters and the old trees uprooted and destroyed to make room not only for a subway but for an MTA office building in the park, that I have described nothing in the park below Sixty-fifth Street. When you drive down Fifth Avenue, you'll see the ugly great construction wall, the crude building and a glimpse of the havoc being wrought by the subway construction. And I can write 'You'll see' with grim confidence – though I don't know when this book will be published or when you're coming to town. The office building, the wall, the subway construction and the ravaged park land will still be there. Count on it.

We thought Estelle would never recover from that blow, but she did. Fighting such juggernauts as the Metropolitan and the MTA, she loses more battles than she wins, but she keeps bouncing back. She keeps on organizing picket lines and mass protests, raising money for a Tree Restoration Fund and demanding action from every new parks commissioner.

In recognition on which, there's to be a birthday party in Estelle's honour on July 21. Patsy's in charge of it. More than a hundred of Estelle's friends have been invited to a Bring-Your-Own-Picnic Supper at the Central Park Lake boathouse which is where Estelle wants it. Before the party, she'll receive an official Citation from the Mayor, to be presented to her by the Commissioner of Parks (if she's speaking to him). The party is in celebration of a milestone birthday of one of the most devoted of those unsung friends of Central Park who are the secret of its glory.

On July 21, Estelle will be ninety.

Friday, June 4

Since this was our last day, Patsy came over East and we took the Lexington Avenue IRT down to Wall Street together. We came up on the sidewalk in front of Trinity Church and I said:

'Let's get the inscription off that Tory's gravestone first. It'll only take a minute. The stone's at the edge of the cemetery; I read it from an outside path.'

'I know,' said Patsy. 'It's on the Gallatin side.' (The graveyard has two sections; Hamilton is buried in one, Gallatin in the other.)

We opened the gate and entered the churchyard, and stopped and stared with pleasure. The cemetery had been transformed by new plantings: flowering bushes where none had been before, even new trees where none had been before, and everywhere on the ground thick patches of green leaf cover.

'They've dressed it up for the Bicentennial!' I said.

We started along the outside path of the Gallatin side and Patsy, ahead of me, stopped at the spot where she remembered I'd read the inscription. There was no stone there. What *was* there, was a large patch of green leaf cover backed by a flowering bush.

Some facts in this world you can accept. Now and then you're faced with a face you can't accept.

'It must be further along,' I said.

We moved along the outside path slowly reading every stone. We circled the entire path. My Tory merchant wasn't there.

'He's on the Hamilton side,' I said. And we went over to the Hamilton side and walked slowly along the outside path reading every stone. My Tory wasn't there.

We entered the cemetery grounds and picked our way among the inner paths where we hadn't set foot before. We did every path, inch by inch, kneeling to read every stone, in a silence that got more and more pregnant. We did every path in both sections of the cemetery and it was a long time before we finally straightened and stared at each other.

'All these new bushes and leaves,' said Patsy tentatively.

'Exactly,' I said. 'They've covered that poor slob's stone with green leaves!'

'Let's go ask somebody,' said Patsy.

We went into the church, but nobody was around at that early hour. There was, however, a rack of books and pamphlets inside the doorway, including a book labelled *History of Trinity Churchyard*. We carried it to a nearby bench and sat down to examine it.

Since we didn't know my Tory's name or birth and death dates we couldn't find him. But reading a few pages, we did come upon mention of a deceased parishioner whose remains had been moved from the west section of the cemetery to the south, or maybe it was from the west to the north. And the book also contained a reminder that while Robert Fulton's opulent crypt was in Trinity churchyard, Robert Fulton wasn't.

We returned the book to its rack and left the church and walked through the churchyard in silence. but as we passed the spot where we were certain the plaque-or-stone had been, Patsy stopped. She stared down at the leaves and the flowering bush, and shook her head in disbelief.

'It's remarkable,' she said in an awed tone. 'In this town, you not only get pushed around all your life, you get pushed around after you're dead!'

'I'm getting to the bottom of this,' I said. 'Tomorrow morning I'm phoning Trinity Church.'

(The next morning I looked up Trinity Church in the Manhattan phone book. I stared at the listing for several minutes. Then I pulled myself together and phoned Patsy. 'Go look up Trinity Church in the phone book,' I said. 'I'll wait.' And we gawked at it together for five minutes before we hung up.

I defy you to find another city in which a church parish takes up half a column in the phone book, with a total of forty-seven separate phone numbers. Forty-six are for the Rector, Associate Rector, Deputy Outreach & Planning, Parish Administration, Parish Resources, Parochial ministries, also Accounting, Administration, Budget, Buildings, Camp & Conferences, Cemetery Ofc., Chapels, Clerk, Communications, Food, Maintenance, Personnel, Purchasing, Real Estate and Schools. The forty-seventh is for All Other Business, of which it's a little hard to think of any. Not wanting to be transferred from Cemetery Ofc. to Administration to Outreach, I abandoned the phone and wrote a letter to the rector, asking politely whether my

Tory had been moved elsewhere or just covered with leaves.

I received a charming reply but not until the rector had worn himself out trying to locate my merchant's name and stone-or-plaque for me. Without success. Letters flew back and forth between us, and finally he wrote to say that while Trinity had, in former times, moved gravestones from section to section when it wasn't sure where they rightly belonged, this practice had been discontinued a generation ago, and my Tory was therefore probably under the leaves and the rector himself hoped to search for the gentleman on the first winter day when the leaves were gone.)

We left Trinity, and Patsy headed across the street to check the side wall of the Irving Trust. There was no new plaque, only the pale square of stone where the old one had been. Patsy went into the bank to inquire, innocently, about the missing plaque. I reached her side just as the bank official was saying regretfully: 'Vandals stole it, I'm afraid.'

'It was only a plaque, it had no historical value,' I said as if I'd never said it before. 'Couldn't the bank afford to have a new one made?'

And he said, with as much huffy reproof as if he'd never said it before: 'I'm sure the bank is doing that.'

As we left the bank Patsy, glancing from the blank spot on the bank wall to Trinity churchyard across the street, said morosely:

'One thing about the Stock Exchange: it'll *be* there.'

The Wall Street entrance to the New York Stock Exchange is for members and employees only. Tourists go around the corner to 20 Broad Street and up to the third or 'Visitors'' Floor.

We stepped out of the elevator and a receptionist waved us toward the Visitors' Gallery, a long hall to the right of the reception desk. A plate glass window runs the length of the hall and we went up to the window and found ourselves looking directly down into the Floor of the Exchange two floors below. Other visitors were lined up alongside us and a guide was explaining the functions of everything we saw below us: the 'Big Board,' with its listing of stocks traded, the electronic ticker which has replaced ticker tape, the trading stations and the men and women whose blue, maroon or grey jackets identified them as brokers or assistants or runners. A few customers stood behind the entranceway to the Exchange, their eyes on the electronic ticker panel.

'You know what brokers call this?' a man standing next to me said to his companion, pointing down to the Floor. 'Ulcer Alley.'

From the gallery, the guide led us down the opposite hall, and after seeing a few exhibits there we filed into a small theatre to see a cartoon film entitled: *One-Man Band Goes to Wall Street*. The cartoon story of how a small company grows large enough to be listed on the Big Board was entertaining; but its high-school textbook explanation won't give you any practical grasp of how the stock market works. The difference between the film's theory and Ulcer Alley's practice was underscored by the contrast between the gay insouciance of the cartoon and the grim, unsmiling faces on the Exchange Floor. As I remarked to Patsy when we left: 'It's a nice place to visit but I wouldn't want to live there.'

Delmonico's restaurant (not to be confused with the restaurant in the Hotel Delmonico on Park Avenue) is at the corner of Beaver and South William Streets and we were going there for our final celebration lunch because an article in New York Magazine suggested it might be a tourist attraction. It is.

One of Patsy's clippings said that the original Delmonico's had gone bankrupt and closed in 1917. But walking into the present restaurant, we found that hard to believe. Where Fraunces Tavern has been 'restored' with self-conscious charm, Delmonico's seems never to have changed at all; it looks exactly as it must have looked a hundred years ago. To walk through the vestibule into the grandiose saloon with its heavy mahogany bar, and then push through the swinging doors into the restaurant, is to walk back into the 1870s. From the patterned brocade wallpaper and heavy iron sconces to the ornate chandeliers with their load of small green lampshades, everything seems to be just as it always was. If you remember *Life With Father*, you find yourself glancing at the door, half-expecting to see Father Day shepherding the family and Cousin Cora in to his accustomed table.

My friend Richard has a cookbook entitled *The Epicurean*, compiled by the Delmonico chef and published in 1920, which I covet and can't get him to part with; and the cookbook requires 1180 pages to hold the laborious recipes and gargantuan menus which made Delmonico famous, in the gluttonous Edwardian days when it was the scene of ten-course testimonial dinners to President Grant, the Grand Duke Alexis of Russia, Charles Dickens and Ferdinand de Lesseps.

The modern menu has shrunk to fit modern stomachs, though the food is still good (and still expensive). But it's less the food than the evocation of a bygone era that makes lunch at Delmonico worth the price.

When we came out, we could see Battery Park a few blocks below us, and we walked down to the park ticket booth where, on our first sightseeing day, we had bought tickets for the ferry to the Statue of Liberty.

'We've come full circle,' said Patsy.

The Ellis Island ticket booth was next to the Liberty Island booth and we bought tickets and waited with other tourists to board the ferry. A guide rode to the island on the ferry with us and warned us, on the way, that twenty-odd years of disuse had left the island's buildings badly eroded by water and weather. The wooden beams above the main hall, he said, had so rotted away that fences had to be thrown up to prevent injury to tourists from falling beams, before the island could be opened to the public. (The National Park Service, which oversees Ellis Islands, has had its budget severely cut by Congress.)

As the ferry drew alongside the dock, we saw the hulk of the original ferry, the *Ellis Island*, still at anchor. The *Ellis Island* had met the immigrants as their ships docked in New York harbour, and ferried them to Ellis Island for medical and legal processing before they were allowed to set foot in the New World. Those who failed the medical and legal examinations never would set foot in it.

We were taken to the Main Hall, a vast room where the immigrants were separated into national groups, and tagged, before they were sent on to the examination rooms. Opening off the room we saw ancient lavatories – and heard an elderly man behind us say: 'That's it! That's where we washed!'

We saw the dormitory rooms where the immigrants slept, and the medical examination rooms where those found to have tuberculosis or trachoma, or any other incurable or contagious disease, were denied entry. When the breadwinner of a family had bad lungs or a faulty heart, the whole family might be rejected since they might become public charges without him. More terrible still was the plight of a healthy family in which a single child was found to have TB. The family had to decide whether to give up its chance at a new life in America and return to Europe, or send the child back to the Old World alone.

The legal examination consisted of questions: 'Can you read and write? Have you got a job here? Who offered you the job? Who paid for your passage?'

These last two questions were designed to weed out the 'undesirables': prostitutes, spies, revolutionaries and strike-breakers. Strike-breakers were the most numerous. The island's peak years were 1892 to 1929, when labour was organizing its first major strikes for decent wages and working conditions. The great steel companies and railroads went to lengths to import cheap immigrant labour with which to break the strike. (See the Frick Collection, Carnegie Hall, Rockefeller University...)

Rejected immigrants were isolated in a special building on the island to await the ships that had brought them to America and were now required to pick them up and return them to Europe. But most of the immigrants had nothing to go back to. They'd sold everything – house, land, farm tools, possessions – to raise passage-money for the trip. There's a tower above the main building on Ellis Island. And during the night when no guards were on watch, rejected immigrants climbed to the top of the tower and jumped to their deaths. Five thousand bodies of immigrants were burnt in mass cremations on the island, since there was no money for burial. How many more immigrants were drowned and their bodies never recovered, nobody will ever know.

Such stories were bearable to us because we were told that the overwhelming majority of immigrants – 98 per cent of them – were accepted. After days of harrowing uncertainty, they were given legal and medical clearance, were put aboard the *Ellis Island* once more, were ferried past the Statue of Liberty into New York harbour where they stepped ashore, home free.

As we were leaving, I looked back at the great, empty Main Hall, more dilapidated but probably no more grim and forbidding now than when the immigrants were herded into it, tense and frightened, to await the all-important examinations. Standing there with Patsy Gibbs at my side – granddaughter of Ellis Island immigrants, whose children will be second-generation Harvard graduates – it seemed to me that every New York sight we had seen, from one end of the island to the other, was insignificant compared with the gaunt and crumbling wreck of Ellis Island.

It was after five when we finally stepped ashore at Battery Park and walked once more, as we had on our first day, up to the broad intersection leading into the city. As we waited for a green light, the canyons and towers of Lower Manhattan stretched ahead of us; and every street and skyline grouping was familiar.

'We own this city now,' said Patsy. 'Do you feel that way?'

'I've been defensive about it for so long,' I said. 'Every TV newsman tells me the city is dying, every newspaper story harps on crime and bankruptcy – and then you see a headline reading FORD TO NEW YORK: DROP DEAD. It gets to you, without your realizing it. I'll never be defensive about it again. It's a marvelous city.'

Patsy was standing rooted to the sidewalk, her mouth open, her eyes wide with shock.

'Defensive!' she repeated in a scandalized voice. 'Are you crazy! This is the most fabulous city on earth!'

And we walked on peacefully through the narrow streets toward the subway we could take together as far as Grand Central.

'I don't see how this can be our last trip,' said Patsy. 'There have to be places we didn't see!'

'A few,' I said. 'Four hundred art galleries. Forty museums. Two hundred-and-something landmark houses. SoHo. Astor Place. We never got down to see Washington Market at five in the morning. We never took the helicopter trip from Thirty-fourth Street up over Central Park. But I've got a deadline on this book, and all I've written so far is a thick book of notes and a prologue.'

We went down the subway steps and put our tokens in the turnstile. The platform was crowded – it was the five o'clock rush hour – and we stood off to one side by ourselves. I looked at Patsy's face and wondered if mine looked the same.

'You know,' I said, 'we can come down here again. It's probably slipped your mind but we live here! We can do the whole tour over again, any time we want to!'

But we knew we never would. We'd been on a holiday and the holiday was over. I was on my way back to my typewriter; Patsy was

on her way back to her family. In a few days, we'd have settled back
into the routines of our separate lives.

The subway train roared into the station, splitting eardrums as
usual. As it screeched to a halt, Patsy turned to me and shouted:

'It was the best two months I ever had!'

'Me, too!' I shouted back.

The doors opened and we squeezed into a car jammed to the doors
with rush-hour riders. But the densely packed bodies somehow
shifted, willing, as always, to make room for two more tired New
Yorkers on their way home.

Q's Legacy

1

How It All Started

Q and I first met on a summer morning when I was eighteen, at the main branch of the Philadelphia Public Library where I'd gone in search of a teacher; and I took him home with me despite certain doubts about his fitness for the post.

This was during the Depression, at the end of my only year at college. Knowing my parents couldn't afford to send me to college, I'd gone to a special academic high school that taught students to compete for college scholarships. In my second year (when I hit Geometry) I knew I wasn't bright enough to win one of them. I excelled in English and I got good grades in History and languages (I tried Latin, Greek and French in successive years). But I barely passed Geometry, Algebra and Chemistry, and if the teacher hadn't liked me I'd have flunked Physics. And college scholarships went to students with a record of 'general excellence' in high school.

Still, there was one scholarship to Temple University my teachers thought I could win. Temple was looking for liberal arts students to enroll in an experimental teacher-training programme called 'The X Group.' Since liberal arts were my best subjects, I took the X Group scholarship exam and – in one of my best subjects – failed so spectacularly I stunned the entire Board of Examiners into sending for me afterwards out of morbid curiosity. The subject was History.

Our high school History exams had never included maps, so my teacher never knew I couldn't read them. But a friend warned me that the X Group History exam included 'a Map question,' and I set out to cram for it. Since we'd studied both American and European history, I decided the Map question would probably deal with both continents. I went to the library and brought home two history books, one with a map of Europe, the other with a map of the forty-eight states. Then I sat down to memorize both of them.

Both maps were oblong. Every country on the map of Europe was in a separate color. So was every state in the Union. I started with the map of Europe and after a few evenings of intense concentration I tested myself. Being very nearsighted, I couldn't read print without my glasses, so I took them off and – unable to see the printed names on the map without them – I triumphantly identified the pink blob down in the left-hand corner as Spain, the purple mass up on the right as Russia and so forth. I knew Europe cold.

Memorizing the forty-eight states was much harder. As I settled at a desk for the history exam, I hoped the Map question would deal with the upper layer of the middle states instead of the lower layer.

The History exam was in two parts, each worth fifty points for a perfect score of a hundred. Part I was a list of questions requiring written answers and when I finished, I knew I'd come close to a perfect fifty on it.

Part II was a large folded sheet of white paper, which, when I opened it, turned out to be a map. It was round, it was black-and-white and it included the entire world. There were no printed place names on it. Under the map was a long list of place names in alphabetical order – Abyssinia to Zanzibar. At the top of the map was a single instruction:

'Insert each place name correctly on the map.'

Forget the middle states; on that map I couldn't find Europe. But you don't flunk worse for wrong answers than for no answers and I thought if I inserted all the place names somewhere, by luck and the law of averages I might get a few of them right. As far as I know, I didn't. What stunned the Board of Examiners into sending for me was that after scoring a perfect fifty on the first half of the exam, I'd labelled the Pacific Ocean 'Africa.'

To sum up: I excelled in English. This won me a one-year scholarship to the X-Group, where (by postponing Calculus and Physics till some later year) I got top grades. But when the year ended, the Dean told me regretfully my scholarship couldn't be extended for another year. Because of the deepening Depression, all Temple's scholarship money would have to go to senior students who couldn't graduate without it.

This was a great blow to my parents, but a secret relief to me. In my year at Temple I'd learned nothing about English literature or the art of writing, which was all I wanted to learn. In the fall I would be free to find my own teacher.

That June I got a job in a bookshop, substituting for the regular assistant who was going to Maine with her parents for the summer. And when she told me business in the bookshop was very slow in summer and I'd have long empty hours there, I decided my education wouldn't have to wait till fall. I was to start work in the bookshop on a July Monday, and on the Saturday before, I took the subway downtown to the imposing main branch of the library. I went into the vast circulation room and asked the lady behind the desk where I'd find books on English literature, especially college textbooks. She sent me to a double aisle of bookshelves marked 800 and told me which subdivisions to look under.

Standing there, staring at the long shelves crammed with books, I felt myself relax and I was suddenly at peace. I knew who I was and what I was doing there, and I had all day to find what I was looking for.

The books were arranged alphabetically by author and I started with the A's, taking down one volume and then another, reading the author's credentials – 'Chairman, English Department, Vassar College'; 'Professor of English at Yale University' – and then the chapter headings and the first few paragraphs of a chapter.

I worked my way through the M's without finding what I wanted. What I wanted was the Best – written in language I could understand. I hadn't defined 'the Best' but I was discovering what it wasn't. Most of the textbooks confined themselves to nineteenth and twentieth-century writers, omitting what I'd been taught were the greatest works of English literature: Shakespeare, Milton and the Bible. And all of them were written in learned, academic language that was over my head.

I went on through the N's, O's and P's, fighting a suspicion that what I wanted didn't exist.

There was only one book under Q.

ON THE ART OF WRITING
by
Sir Arthur Quiller-Couch, M.A.
King Edward VII Professor of English Literature
in the University of Cambridge

The dust-jacket biography told me the author was a graduate of Trinity College, Oxford, and that the book was one of several volumes of lectures delivered to his students at Jesus College, Cambridge, where he still taught. It added that he was also the author of popular novels which were signed simply 'Q', the nickname by which he was known to his students.

If you wanted instruction in how to read and write English, Oxford-and-Cambridge was definitely the Best. I ran my eye down the list of chapter headings:

'On the Practice of Writing'
'On the Capital Difficulty of Verse'
'On the Capital Difficulty of Prose'

I could understand them.

Chapter V was headed: 'Interlude: On Jargon.' Since I didn't know what 'Jargon' was, I turned to the chapter and began to read, and came to a pair of sentences set off in the middle of the page:

'He was conveyed to his place of
residence in an intoxicated condition.'
'He was carried home drunk.'

Q said that the first sentence was Jargon and the second was good English prose.

I thought it was a misprint; the printer must have got the two sentences backward. I read a little further and came to a quote from a Prime Minister in the House of Commons:

'The answer to the question is in the negative.'

'That means No,' said Q. 'Can you discover it, to mean anything more? – except that the speaker is a pompous person, which was no part of the information required.'

So it wasn't a misprint.

I was very shocked. I liked long fancy words; I thought they were literary. I didn't want to write 'He was carried home drunk' all my life; it was lower class. But I read a little more and came to a phrase I'd seen in dozens of textbooks as a chapter heading: 'Transition Period' – 'which means,' said Q, 'we haven't much to say, just about here.'

I stood staring at the page with two glaringly wrong sentences set off in the middle of it and considered Q's pros and cons. He spoke a language I could understand, and he had a sense of humour, which all by itself set him apart from the rest of the professors I'd been reading all morning. And he was Oxford-and-Cambridge. I decided I could study with him without necessarily agreeing with everything he said. I took home *On the Art of Writing* and one other book of his lectures.

Both were four-week books and at the end of four weeks I trudged back to the library to renew both of them, in what was turning out to be a very wearing summer. In the first chapter of *On The Art of Writing* he threw so many marvellous quotes at me –from Walton's *Angler*, Newman's *Idea of a Universiy* and Milton's *Paradise Lost* – that I rushed back to the library and brought home all three, determined to read them all before going on to Q's second lecture. Which would have been perfectly possible if I hadn't included *Paradise Lost*. In *Paradise Lost* I ran into Satan, Lucifer, the Infernal Serpent and a Fiend, all of whom seemed to be lurking around the Garden of Eden and none of whom my teachers at Rodeph Shalom Sunday School had ever mentioned to me. I consulted my Confirmation Bible, but I couldn't find Milton's fearsome personages in Genesis. I concluded that Lucifer and the Fiend weren't Jewish and I would have to look in the New Testament for them, and since this was an entirely new book to me, Q had to wait while I read that one, too. But I'd saved enough out of my ten-dollar weekly paycheck by then to buy both books of lectures, freeing me to take my time over them, with plans for taking two more out of the library in the fall.

In September, the bookshop job ended, and when all my friends were going back to college I was happily mapping out a daily course of study with Q: two hours of Q, two hours of Milton, two hours of

Shakespeare, one hour of English essays (dessert). I began reading industriously all day long, unaware that my Depression-ridden parents were anxiously waiting for me to go out and find another job.

My Uncle Al was living with us at the time. (He'd been my rich Uncle Al till the stock-market crash wiped him out. Now he lived with us as a paying boarder.) My Uncle Al realized that I wasn't trained for the ordinary jobs open to young women. But his former bookkeeper, a Mr Green, had opened a business school where girls were taught 'office skills,' and Mr Green, out of friendship for my uncle, offered to accept me in the school's ninety-day secretarial course at a reduced rate. My parents were so grateful for this opportunity I couldn't tell them I wasn't. In November (weeping secretly over it in my room the night before), I had to drop out of Q's classes to study shorthand and typing at Mr Green's school.

I was a real joy at that business school. Mrs Green taught our shorthand class and I wasn't there a week before I was obliged to correct her grammar. She dictated a sentence that began: 'I cannot help but think' – and I raised my hand and told her the phrase was ungrammatical.

'You can say "I cannot but think" or you can say "I cannot help thinking,"' I explained kindly. 'But you can't say "I cannot help but." It's wrong.'

She was a small, worried-looking middle-aged woman with the Depression and us to contend with, and she was too chronically tired to be angry. She just looked confused and mildly resentful and she sent one of the girls for Mr Smoter to settle the matter. Mr Smoter taught Business English. He was also young and good-looking and I had a crush on him. Mr Smoter came and was duly consulted about 'I cannot help but think.'

'Well, it's not good grammar,' he admitted reluctantly, with the eyes of the class glued on him. 'It's a double negative.'

This coup brought me to the attention of the school leader, an animated black-haired kid named Rita, whose prestige stemmed from the fact that her barber father had once shaved Al Smith, a losing presidential candidate. Rita headed the school's ruling clique and after my triumph over Mrs Green, she invited me to go along with the clique to the drugstore where they gathered for sodas after school.

Rita and her friends were quick-witted and intelligent; they had no trouble with shorthand or typing, but they spoke a dese-dem-dose English and they sweated to construct simple business letters for Mr Smoter's class. They were vastly impressed by a classmate who could actually correct a teacher's grammar, and as soon as they learned I hankered after Mr Smoter, they went to work devising ploys to get him for me. The best was Rita's. She got up in Business English class and suggested that after every Friday's English test, Mr Smoter award a kiss to whoever got the best score. She made him stick to this award for the rest of the ninety days. Which was one reason why I had such a good time in that school I was almost sorry when the course ended.

Through the next two years and a succession of office jobs, I went on reading Q, and out of my earnings eventually managed to buy all five volumes of his lectures. And broke as we were, when my mother saw a new volume of them displayed in Wanamaker's book department, she bought it for me.

At the beginning of the third year, my Cambridge education hit a snag. As suddenly as if I'd been struck by lightning, I was stagestruck. I joined a Little Theatre group as an actress and I began to write plays in the evening instead of studying with Q. At the end of the thirties I won a national playwriting contest sponsored by the Theatre Guild. The prize money was to support me for a year while I studied in a seminar for young playwrights to be conducted at the Guild. So I moved to New York and my books, and Q, moved with me.

The Theatre Guild was Broadway's most distinguished producing organization, so committed to producing plays for their artistic merit rather than their commercial appeal that Broadway columnists dubbed it 'The Thitter Geeld.' But the year of the seminar, the Guild's luck seemed to have run out. It produced five straight flops.

Terry Helburn, one of the two Guild producers, made me her protégée, and two years later she gave me a job writing publicity stories in the Guild press department – and the Guild was still producing five flops a year. I loved the job and I loved Terry – five feet tall with fluffy, blue-rinsed white hair and a habit of referring to New York's eight dignified drama critics as 'the Boys.' ('I don't know what the Boys want,' she'd say without rancour, reading the reviews of each successive flop.) I even liked Lawrence Langner, her co-producer, with his neat brown clothes and neat brown mustache and his incessant inter-office memos on Economy. ('Please save the envelope containing this memo. It can be re-used for inter-office memos. We are all wasting too much stationery.' 'As only three people use the Press Department bathroom, the Empire Linen Rental Service will limit your supply hereafter to three towels per week.')

My job was to write feature stories about the stars of Guild shows, which Joe, the Guild press agent, could place in New York's eight daily newspapers. If the star had a big name (we had Katharine Hepburn in one flop), Joe took her to lunch at Sardi's and I tagged along; he asked the questions and I took stenographic notes of the answers. When the 'star' was unknown – like the young ingenue Celeste Holm in another of our flops – I interviewed her by myself in the Press Department over drugstore coffee. But in my third year there, the Theatre Guild astonished Broadway by producing a musical. It was called *Oklahoma!* and it broke the Theatre Guild's losing streak by being a smash hit. This time when Celeste Holm turned up in the cast, she and I had a high old time over lunch at Sardi's.

The Guild had an unfortunate habit of closing down for three months every June and moving to its summer theatre in Westport, Connecticut, where it got along without most of its New York staff, including me. I had to find my own summer theatre job every June and since it barely paid my summer living expenses, my New York home was a cheap hotel room that I could vacate in June and move back into in September. The room was too small for bookshelves, and anyway I was too broke to buy them. The books I'd brought from home were kept on the closet floor, with the closet shelf reserved for Q.

I'd begun sneaking back into his classes in the evening and guiltily wallowing in Walton and George Herbert and Leigh Hunt when I was supposed to be studying Ibsen, Chekhov and Stanislavski. I got all the books from the public library and – desolately – returned them just as I was learning to love them.

But a year after *Oklahoma!* opened I left the Guild and began to earn a living of sorts working part-time and at home reading scripts – plays and novels – submitted to the New York Story Department of Paramount Pictures. Since it was steady all-year-round work, I was able to sign a lease on what the English call a 'bed-sitter': a furnished living-room with a studio couch for sleeping, and the use of a communiy bath and kitchen up the hall.

It was a big room flooded with sunlight, and I found I could read Paramount's galleys or playscripts in the evening, type my reader's report after breakfast and have the whole day free for writing my bad plays. (They specialized in plotless charm.) I also found that after three years in an office, working at home was like being let out of prison.

In May, a friend gave me her old orange-crate bookshelves and my happiness was complete. I painted them bright blue (to go with the slipcover on my easy chair) and then made a list of the books I wanted to buy.

A few mornings later I was turning the pages of the morning *Times* on my way to the theatre page when I was stopped by a two-column headline above an unfamiliar face, on the Obituary page:

Quiller-Couch, Anthologist
Dies at 80

The obituary writer seemed to regard Q's editing of *The Oxford Book of English Verse* as his principal achievement, and I added it to my book list. Then I sat and studied the controlled, weather-beaten face I'd never seen. I felt suddenly lost with Q gone. Till I looked at the books of his lectures ranged on the bookshelf and thought: 'He's not gone, you nut, you have him in the house!' I cut out the obituary and put it carefully between the pages of *On The Art of Writing*. (It's still there, in dried yellow fragments. I just pieced them together so I could quote the headline for you.)

Then I set out to buy the books he'd taught me to love. Most of them were out of print – or might as well have been. There was one bookshop on Madison Avenue, called Chaucer Head, which displayed gold-embossed, leather-bound classics in the window, and I used to stop and stare at them like a dog at a butcher-shop window. Chaucer Head probably had most of the books I wanted, but the plush interior looked so forbiddingly expensive I never had the nerve to set foot in the place. (If Shakespeare will pardon me, it's poverty does make cowards of us all.) The fine Fifth Avenue bookstores – Brentano's and Scribner's – also had English classics, only in fine leather-bound editions I couldn't afford. The modern neighbourhood bookstores didn't have them at all. But somebody told me there was a row of secondhand bargain-basement bookstores down on East

17th Street and at the best of them, Barnes & Noble, I found what I wanted. More or less.

Barnes & Noble bought and resold discarded school and college textbooks. In 'cloth' bindings. Quotation marks because they felt like cardboard. A few I bought were reasonably clean. Some were horrors. My Catullus, for instance, had an ink-stained cover and on every page, phrases and paragraphs encircled in decorative graffiti and margins filled with classroom notes and translations. All in ink. Not ballpoint ink. *Ink*. I used to spend weary evenings trying to erase the worst of the mess without rubbing holes in the cheap paper.

Never mind. Bad as they were, the books didn't have to be taken back to the library just as I was beginning to understand them. By 1948, my shelves were full and I was considering adding another orange crate, when all of us in the bed-sitter building got eviction notices. The building was to be gutted and remodelled.

A friend took my books in – I didn't own much else – and with a suitcase in one hand and my typewriter in the other, I set out, in the teeth of a postwar housing shortage, to hunt for a place to live. After eighteen months of wandering – of two-week and two-month sublets for a total of eleven addresses and phone numbers and mail that took months to catch up with me – I finally found a dark little converted apartment in a house in a quiet row on East 95th Street. A friend built me long bookshelves from wooden slats and crates he found in the building's cellar, I painted them (and everything else in sight) with shiny white enamel, and on a September day in '49 I finally moved into a clean, bright, makeshift apartment that was all mine. Two days later my books came home. As I put them up on their shiny shelves, I told them I was finally going to see that they were properly clothed in decent editions.

A few nights later I was reading the bookstore ads in the Out-of-print Books column of the *Saturday Review of Literature*. There was a whole column of out-of-print bookstores in New York I hadn't known about (having spent my time with friends more interested in Broadway and Hollywood than in English classics). I got a pencil and was circling the names of those that seemed most likely to have the books I wanted, when my eye fell on an ad lower down in the column:

Marks & Co., Antiquarian Booksellers
84, Charing Cross Road
London WC 2

London had held a special glamour for me from the time when I was
eight or nine and my parents began taking me to the theatre. London
was *The Barretts of Wimpole Street* and *Berkeley Square* and *Pygmalion*. It
was also Private Lives and Design for Living because whether Noel
Coward's characters were disporting themselves in Paris or on the
Riviera, you knew they lived in Mayfair.

Then Q brought English literature into my life and my passion for
London grew. Sam Pepys's London might be gone, but Leigh Hunt's
was still there. I wanted to take the walks he took at night. I wanted
to stand on Westminster Bridge and look at the view, because
Wordsworth said Earth had not anything to show more fair. But it was
all day-dreaming. Between my hand-to-mouth income and my fear
of travel, I never really expected to see London. Staring at that ad, I
thought it would be a lovely consolation prize to hold in my hands
books that actually came from there. Marks & Co. might be another
Chaucer Head, but while I was afraid to walk into such a bookshop
I wasn't afraid to write a letter to one. I wrote to Marks & Co.,
requesting three books and warning the shop that I couldn't pay more
than five dollars for each of them.

Someone at Marks & Co. – the letter was signed with the initials
FPD – wrote back that two of the books I wanted were in stock and
were being sent to me, for much less than five dollars each. And when
they came in the mail I couldn't believe them. They were more
appealing to me than the volumes in Chaucer Head's window – old,
mellow leather-bound books with thick cream-coloured pages, but
not so opulently fine as to make me feel guilty if I underlined a phrase
here (in pencil) or made a margin note there when I felt like it. They
didn't have the look of rare or fine books, they looked like the friends
I needed them to be. For a while I just stood, turning the pages of
each, and I knew I'd never look anywhere else for books.

I was between plays that fall. If you're a writer with nothing in the
typewriter and time on your hands, you write something – anything
– just to keep from going crazy. I began writing long, goofy letters to
Marks & Co., addressing them first to FPD and then, when I finally

wormed his name out of him, to Frank Doel, who handled all my book orders. Then one of the girls in the shop began slipping personal notes in with the books she mailed to me. By which time I'd learned about England's food rationing. I began sending food parcels to the shop at Christmas and Easter, and all the people who worked in the shop wrote to thank me, and so did Frank Doel's wife, Nora, who told me about their two daughters, Sheila and Mary. So by 1952, when I broke into television as a writer of dramatic scripts, my correspondence with Marks & Co. was a part of my life. And the beautiful books kept coming.

As the fifties wore on, and I wrote more and better-paid TV scripts, I began to regard a trip to London as a distinct future possibility and I kept threatening the shop with a visit. The only dream that took precedence over a trip to London was of one day living in a real apartment in a real apartment house. And eight years after the first one, a second eviction notice arrived in my mailbox. But this time I had a solid bank account and the prospect of earning more and more money writing for television.

On a spring morning, I went around to Second Avenue where, on the corner of 72nd Street, a new apartment house was under construction. It would be months before the building was finished, but there was a rental office on the ground floor and sitting in that rental office with the building plans spread out before me, I signed a three-year lease on an apartment that wasn't there yet. But the floor plan indicated a large living-room with a small alcove opening off it, a bathroom adjoining the alcove and a complete kitchen just off the foyer inside the front door.

In the six months before the building was finished, I blew my entire bank account on the first real furniture I ever owned. Only the best would do, especially for the alcove where I'd be working all day: a teak desk, an English walnut telephone table and walnut-stained bookshelves with small cabinet drawers below them, to run the length of the long back wall. I bought living-room furniture and wall-to-wall carpeting, and grey wool custom-made drapes to cover the long picture window and keep out the glare of street lights.

Herbie, the carpet-layer, unpacked all the furniture for me and helped me put it all in place. When he left, I went into the kitchen, with its gleaming new white refrigerator and sink and cabinets, and carefully stripped the brown paper off the shining new stove. Then I took a bath in my first real tile bathroom. I spent the evening sitting first in the deep armchair, then in the modern Swedish rocker, to feast my eyes on the living-room. Then I curled up on the carpet in the middle of the room and stared at the rows of books looking so proud on their first real bookshelves on the alcove wall. And when I took a last long look around the room before crawling into bed that night, I said aloud:

'It's a palace.'

(After all these years it's still a palace to me. I clean it every Saturday, to wake up in a Sunday-clean house, and I still sometimes come home late on a Saturday night in winter, close the door behind me and lean against it, to stare at the freshly polished furniture, warm brown against the grey carpet and drapes, and think: 'Isn't it beautiful?')

But now that I was a proper householder I found more expenses cropping up: a vacuum cleaner: complete sets of china and silverware that didn't come from Woolworth's: handsome new towels befitting my handsome three-by-five bathroom. So it was a couple of years before I could start saving for the trip to London. I set my sights on the summer of 1960.

In the late winter of 1959, the TV show I was writing for went off the air. In the spring no new assignments were offered me. In the summer of 1960, I woke up and realized that the entire television production industry had pulled up stakes and moved to Hollywood. The era of live TV had ended. From then on, dramatic television shows would be filmed like movies. Most of my fellow TV writers had already followed their careers to California. But Hollywood isn't a place, it's a way of life. And it wasn't for me.

I spent the summer searching the *Times* Help Wanted columns for jobs open to writers. There were jobs listed for ad agency copywriters, medical writers, writers with degrees in the sciences, writers with experience on magazines or in publishing offices. I was secretly relieved not to qualify for any of them. Better to starve at home than wither and die in an office prison. But I had to fight a sense of panic. I couldn't see how I was to earn a living for the rest of my life.

Early in the following winter my agent called to ask if I had any old plays or TV scripts she might sell to West German television. She told me what they were looking for and I got a few TV scripts down from the closet shelf and the only two plays that hadn't gone down the incinerator. I'd kept both for sentimental reasons.

One was about life at the Theatre Guild and the backstage story of *Oklahoma!* Looking at it, I remembered what one producer had said when he rejected it.

'This isn't a play,' he told me. 'It might make a good magazine article.'

'That's prose,' I thought, staring at it. 'I can't write prose.' And an old line dropped into my head:

'To the writer of good honest prose, these notions are about as useful as the wind in the next street.

Where had I read that? Oh, Q. He was talking about German literary criticism, if I remembered right. I probably didn't. I hadn't read Q in years. And then I think my mouth fell open. Q! How many years had I sweated through his lectures on how to write prose? How many models of English prose had he sent me to that I'd loved for years, including Hunt and Lamb and Hazlitt and what were all their essays but magazine articles reprinted later in books? And I thought I could hear Q remarking that possibly I couldn't write prose, but with the rent coming due every month it might be advisable to try.

It took me two weeks to convert the Theatre Guild play to a magazine article and when I finished it I mailed it to *Harper's Magazine*. Then I reread the second play and I spent another two weeks converting that one into a magazine article. With beginner's luck, I sold the first to *Harper's* and the second to *The New Yorker*. So of course I spent the rest of the winter and spring writing thirteen more magazine articles I couldn't sell anywhere. I was very broke by June when the Harper's article finally appeared. A few days later a letter arrived in the mail from Harper & Row, Publishers.

Dear Miss Hanff:
  'This is just to tell you how much I enjoyed your story about the Theatre Guild in this month's Harper's.
  'Do you have a book in mind?

Sincerely
Genevieve Young'

I wrote to Miss Young, explaining that I was a TV writer, and didn't have a book in mind. But when she got the letter, she phoned and said why didn't we have lunch anyway? and we set a date for Friday of the following week. Maybe by that time, she said, one of us would have thought of a book for me to write.

I spent that week in a sweat that had nothing to do with the summer heat. In spite of the hundreds of bad books I'd suffered through as a professional reader, I was in awe of people who wrote them. But now that the suggestion had been made, I itched to try writing one – and found there was no kind of book whatsoever I was equipped to write. I didn't like novels. (I subscribe to Randall Jarrell's definition of a novel as 'a prose narrative that has something wrong with it.') I had no qualifications for writing history or biography. And having neither literary reputation nor Palace connections, I was in no position to write the kind of book I most loved to read: memoirs, diaries, letters. I flogged my brain to try and think of anything I could suggest to Genevieve Young. Nothing came.

I dressed very carefully for the lunch, to give myself a veneer of confidence. Hong Kong dresses were still fashionable, and I'd bought a brown linen one at Saks the summer before, which still looked chic. It was a beautiful day and I wanted to walk down to *Harper's*, but I didn't. I wore the white high-heeled pumps that hurt, and took a Madison Avenue bus. The bus was nearly empty, but I stood all the way to 33rd Street so as not to crease the linen. I got off the bus in front of *Harper's*, took the elevator up to the editorial floor and gave my name to the receptionist. And when she phoned it in and told me Miss Young would be right out, I draped myself negligently on a chair arm (to avoid stomach creases in the dress) and waited.

My only consolation, when she came out, was that even she knew the name 'Genevieve' was too fussy for her. The first thing she said – after 'Hi' – was 'Call me Gene.' She was a head taller than I was, she had jet-black hair and a beautiful face, she was regally poised, she was Chinese – and the beige silk Hong Kong dress she wore had been made for her. In Hong Kong. ('My sister lives there.') Its slit skirt in no way impeded her long-legged stride toward the elevator, and as I stepped in beside her she towered over me, which the Chinese are not supposed to do. We went next door to a hotel dining-room where she strode to her regular table. I pattered along behind her, feeling small, round-shouldered and inferior.

We settled opposite each other and ordered lunch. As the waiter departed, Gene hopped a little in her chair and said:

'I've got a great idea for your book! Why don't you write a funny book about everything that's happened to you since you first came to New York to crash the theatre?'

Warmth flooded through me and I was glad she was tall and beautiful and had genuine Hong Kong dresses and enough assurance for both of us.

'I could write that,' I said.

I spent the next six months writing the story of my life for Gene (and $1,500), and since the construction was all wrong I had to spend another six months rewriting it. The book, called *Underfoot in Show Business*, crept out during a New York newspaper strike, got mildly approving reviews in other cities, took a few years to sell its 5,000 copies and then (the only thing it ever had in common with the books I loved) went out of print. And I embarked on a decade-long battle to keep the rent paid.

I wrote training films for the Women's Army Corps, I wrote articles on American history for a children's encyclopaedia, I wrote a couple of children's bedtime stories. Month after month I worried about the rent and had bad dreams, at night, of a third and final eviction notice; but by some miracle I managed to keep the rent paid and the palace roof over my head without borrowing money.

Every few months Gene Young phoned. Gene is telepathic and her phone calls always came when I was out of work. I'd say hello and Gene would say, without even the preamble of hello:

'What are you doing? Are you eating? I worry about you.' Or: 'I'm just checking up on you, are you writing anything?'

Between assignments I went doggedly on trying to write magazine articles. (I am extremely bull-headed. It took twenty years of trying before I acknowledged I couldn't write a producible play. Magazine articles were this decade's plays.) Whenever I wrote one, Gene read it and told me what magazine editor to send it to ('Use my name'). When it came back, as it always did, she said: 'Meet me for lunch.'

She thought of another book for me to write and got me another $1,500 in advance. When I finished the book it was dull and pointless and we both knew it had to go down the incinerator. And I couldn't return *Harper's* $1,500, having flung it all away recklessly on food and rent.

Then, in the mid-sixties, I began to get fairly steady work writing short American history books for children. Each book paid a thousand dollars – no royalties – and each took me two to three months to research and write; and since this was a very good way to starve to death, I went back to reading scripts for a film studio, this time United Artists.

Now among the children's history book assignments was one about the founding of the Virginia and Massachusetts colonies. Both had bored me when I was a child. All I remembered of the New England settlement was Longfellow's *Courtship of Miles Standish* and how Miles Standish's emissary, John Alden, proposed to Priscilla in Standish's name and was told to 'Speak for yourself, John.' I was even more bored by the Virginia myth of Pocahontas laying her head on the block to save Captain John Smith from being beheaded by the Indians (who didn't behead their victims and wouldn't have had the slightest idea what a 'block' was). To an eight- or ten-year-old, all the early settlers seemed to have come up out of the sea, from nowhere.

I went to the library and brought home a load of history books. Chapter I of the first book I opened was a wooden account of investors in London putting up money for the first expedition to 'Virginia' – the name Englishmen in 1620 gave to the entire North American continent. I spent an evening copying out dreary lists of ships' supplies and the names of shipowners and investors. One investor's name, George Carteret, rang a faint bell, and I tried to remember where I'd heard it before. Then I gave it up and went to bed. I was drifting off to sleep when a line of print, literally, appeared inside my eyelids:

'Dined with Sir G. Carteret.'

I sat bolt upright and shouted into the darkness:

'Pepys!'

I got out of bed, turned on the lights and got down Pepys from the bookshelf. I knew the diary began thirty-five years after the first settlements and though I sat huddled in a down quilt reading every mention of Sir G. Carteret listed in the index, I couldn't find out whether he was the investor or the investor's son. It didn't matter. Suddenly the world the investors lived in was real to me; it was the end of Shakespeare's world and the beginning of John Donne's. It was moving inexorably toward Milton's and Cromwell's Puritan world, which took root in Massachusetts. A few days later I went berserk with excitement to read that one of my book's heroes, Roger Williams, the Father of American Religious liberty, had been the protégé of the great jurist Sir Edward Coke, 'in whose house he was ever treated as a son,' according to Coke's daughter. What did I need with Priscilla and her 'Speak-for-yourself-John?' I had a young heretic named Roger Williams fleeing persecution at the hands of the Star Chamber, whose most rabid heretic-hunter was his foster father, Sir Edward Coke.

If all this history is boring you to tears, you're not alone. I was spending my evenings at the time working in political campaigns at the local Democratic Club, and I couldn't wait to share all this exciting history with everybody at the club. Well, even the club lawyers listened glassy-eyed with boredom. But a few days later, Gene Young made one of her periodic phone calls.

'What are you doing, are you eating?'

'I'm writing an American history book for children,' I said.

'You are?' said Gene, with such interest I thought she'd misunder-stood me.

'It's for kids!' I repeated. 'Aged eight to ten.'

'I want to take you to lunch,' said Gene. 'How about Friday? Pick me up at the office at one.'

I picked her up and we went to lunch. As soon as we'd ordered, Gene said:

'Tell me about the history book.'

'It's about the early settlers of Virginia and Massachusetts,' I said. 'Pocahontas-and-all-that, but I've discovered –'

And Gene interrupted with lordly assurance:

'Oh, I know all about Pocahontas. Somebody else was in love with her and she said, "Speak for yourself, Miles Standish."'

When I recovered, I stared at her beautiful face and asked:

'Where did you go to school?'

And Gene said:

'I went to kindergarten in Shanghai, first grade in London, to second and third grades in Paris and fourth grade in Manila.'

She told me her father had been a diplomat for Nationalist China. She was born in Geneva – which is why they named her Genevieve – in the thirties. ('My father was a delegate to the Second Opium

Conference.') 'Pearl Harbour happened when I was in the fifth grade in Manila,' she went on. 'The Japanese invaded the Philippines right afterwards. They interned all the Chinese diplomats, including my father. We didn't find out for sure until the war ended, but they executed them all.'

Gene and her mother and two sisters were confined in a house with the women of other diplomatic families.

'The mothers organized a school for us. The local teachers taught us the history of the Philippines, an old man – the only Chinese male the Japanese hadn't killed – tried to teach us Chinese, and the servants taught us all the dirty words in Tagalog.'

At the end of the war, Gene's mother brought her daughters to the United States on her diplomatic passport. Gene was enrolled in a fashionable boarding school – where her Philippine education put her at a peculiar disadvantage.

'On my first day at Abbot Academy, the headmistress told me I would have to "set an example" because I was the only Asian in the school,' Gene said drily. 'How could I tell her I'd never learned the Pledge of Allegiance to the flag? We didn't recite it very often anyway, and when we did the whole school recited it together and I just mumbled through it and came in strong on "With liberty and justice for all".'

'Do you know it now?' I asked.

'Where would I learn it?' she demanded. 'I mumbled through it for four years at Wellesley, too.'

I said that not knowing it didn't exactly blight her life. Gene said flatly:

'It could! I've applied for American citizenship. At the end of my probationary period, they give me a citizenship test. I don't know what the questions will be.'

She showed me her Green Card, certifying her a legal alien, and she showed me the list of requirements for making it through the five-year probationary period. Her Green Card could be revoked if she

(a) broke the law by so much as a traffic violation.
(b) belonged to a 'subversive' organization.
(c) committed adultery.

There were ten or twelve other requirements, all of them prohibit-
ing acts Gene would be perfectly free to commit once she became a
citizen.

For the next few months we met regularly. I was writing books for
two children's history series and I poured all my research into Gene's
tensely interested ears. In the spring of 1968, she phoned to report that
she'd been given a date for her immigration hearing. It would include
an interview, a literacy test and a citizenship test.

'Friends of mine have already taken it,' she said, 'and they told me
the citizenship test is confined to one question. It can be about
anything – the Constitution, the Supreme Court, anything.' Then she
said: 'I have to take two character witnesses with me to the hearing.
Will you be one of them?'

'Of course I'll be one of them. I'm your coach!' I said.

On the appointed morning, I met Gene and her worried-looking
second witness, Dolores, at a subway station for the trip to the
courthouse in Brooklyn. I wore my best suit, Dolores wore her best
dress. Gene, who had given up Hong Kong dresses for monotone
sweaters-and-pants, wore a grey cashmere sweater, matching grey wool
pants and a wide suede belt that was just a shade darker. With her glossy
black hair piled high, she was a walking definition of the word 'svelte.'
Dolores, who was a *Harper's* copy editor, was small and bespectacled like
me, and behind her glasses her eyes were wide with apprehension. She
was convinced that one wrong word from her during the hearing would
get Gene instantly deported to Communist China.

All the way to Brooklyn we shouted questions at Gene over the
screech of the subway.

'BILL OF RIGHTS?' shouted Dolores.

'FIRST TEN AMENDMENTS. I KNOW THEM!' said Gene.

'ELECTORAL COLLEGE?' I shouted. And Gene shouted back:
'WHAT ABOUT IT?'

We arrived at the courthouse, hoarse and tense, and took seats in a
large room full of Hungarian refugees and exiled Croatians, Ukrainians
and Armenians. All of them looked tired, grey-faced and shabby – and
not one of them seemed as frightened of the coming ordeal as we
were.

Gene's number was called and the three of us filed into a small
cubbyhole to one side of the main room. A young immigration officer

sat behind a desk. A court clerk lined us up in front of the desk and we all raised our right hands like three over-age Girl Scouts and solemnly swore to tell the truth. Then the clerk departed and the three of us were left facing the immigration officer. After a morning of downtrodden immigrants from Mittel-Europa, he was eyeing the tall, chic Chinese and her two small decorous protectors with fascinated disbelief.

He told Gene and me to wait outside while he questioned Dolores, and we went back to the main room and sat. After ten minutes Dolores came out (very pale) and told me to go in. I went into the private office, and the young immigration officer asked me how long I'd known Gene and how much I knew about her. I gave her a glowing character reference and then he dismissed me and told me to send Gene in. Gene went in alone for her citizenship test. And Dolores and I sat and waited.

When Gene came out she looked strained, but she didn't report on the test till the three of us were out in the hall.

'I don't know whether I passed or not,' she said. 'First he pushed a pencil and paper at me and said: "Write *The cat ran down the street*." I'd forgotten about the literacy test. And I was so rattled I said: "The what did what?" And he said: "You're a *Harper's* editor and a Wellesley graduate and you can't spell cat?"'

The citizenship test question was: What is a pocket veto?

'I knew what it was, but he questioned me about the history of it and when a president uses it, and I'm not sure I knew enough to pass.'

We were huddled in the hall, anxiously trading information about pocket vetoes, when the young immigration officer came out of his cubbyhole and headed for the elevator. Then he stopped, hesitated, turned and walked slowly back to us – and for half a minute I stopped breathing.

'If you're going to lunch,' he said, 'Sam Wu's is the best Chinese restaurant in Brooklyn.' And he told us how to find it.

In June, Gene was notified that she had been granted citizenship and was to go back to the courthouse for her swearing-in. She phoned me when she got home and I said:

'Congratulations. How was it?'

'I wasted a lot of worry. It was okay,' said Gene. 'There were two hundred of us and the judge who administered it had us all recite the

Pledge of Allegiance together. So I just mumbled through it and came in strong on "With liberty and justice for all".' And she added: 'He was a nice old thing; he was having so much trouble with his new dental plate he wouldn't have noticed my lips didn't move.'

I wrote another book for her that year. I left it at her office and she phoned the next day and said bluntly:

'I read it. It doesn't work.'

I sat down and read it myself and saw Gene was right. The book went down the incinerator. I was still reading scripts for United Artists, but even with an occasional children's book I was earning so little that I managed to hang on to my apartment and stay out of debt only by buying nothing I didn't absolutely need. And I didn't absolutely need to own more books.

Then, in September of '69, I got an assignment to write a full-length book for teenagers on the young reformers of the sixties. With money coming in I decided to splurge on a set of Jane Austen for my best friend, whose birthday was coming at the end of October; and for the first time in two years I wrote to Frank Doel. ('Still alive, are we?' I began. And Frank wrote back: 'Yes, we are all very much alive and kicking . . .')

He had no Austen to sell me, which turned out to be a blessing because the teenagers' book took much longer than I'd expected and by December, when I began the final draft of the book. I was very low in funds. I thought I'd better phone the editors of the two children's history series and get an assignment for February.

Both greeted me warmly on the phone, not having heard from me in six months. And in my memory, both broke the same news to me in the same words:

'Oh, we're not publishing the history series anymore. These kids won't read history; they say it's not relevant.'

That evening I tried to take stock of myself and my future, but there seemed no stock to take. I was a failed playwright, a TV writer whose experience in live TV was useless in an age of film and a writer of children's history books nobody was publishing anymore. I was nowhere. I was nothing.

In January, revisions of the sixties book staved off the blank future for a few more weeks. Early one morning I left the house to spend the day going from library to library in search of transcripts of Southern civil rights trials. It was nearly six when I finally walked into the lobby and stopped in the mail room to pick up my mail. I had an armload of books and I went through the mail that lay on top of them as I rode up in the elevator. Among the pile of bills and throw-aways was the familiar thin blue envelope from Marks & Co.

There was something wrong with it. Frank Doel always typed the name and address single-spaced and always spelled out my first name. On this envelope the typing was double-spaced and the letter was addressed to 'Miss H. Hanff'. I thought:

'He's left the shop.'

I was tired and depressed and the wrong-looking letter threatened to depress me further. I put it on the table and decided it would wait till after dinner. I made myself a rare and extravagant martini and worked a *Guardian Weekly* crossword puzzle as I drank it. And the letter waited.

I cooked dinner and went on working the crossword puzzle as I ate. Then I poured a cup of coffee and lit a cigarette. Feeling more cheerful ('If he's left the shop, you can always write to him and Nora at home, you have their address'), I reached for the blue airmail letter.

8th January, 1969.

'Dear Miss,

'I have just come across the letter you wrote to Mr Doel on the 30th of September last, and it is with great regret that I have to tell you that he passed away on Sunday the 22nd of December, the funeral took place on Wednesday, the 1st of January.

'The death has been a very great shock to Mr Cohen, especially coming so soon after the death of Mr Marks.'

2

'They've Shot Goldberg'

At any time, the news of Frank's death would have been a grief to me, and the one death too many among those I'd loved without ever meeting them. (I'd been working in the presidential campaign of Robert Kennedy when he was murdered, two months after the murder of Martin Luther King.) Coming when it did, the news was devastating. It seemed to me that with the double loss of Frank Doel and Mr Marks, the last anchor in my life – my bookshop – was being taken from me. I began to cry and I couldn't stop. I don't know at what point in my crying I began to mutter over and over:

'I have to write it.'

Then I stopped crying abruptly and went cold inside. I could only write it if I still had Frank's letters.

I'd begun saving them twenty years earlier because a tax accountant wanted a record of what I spent on books. When he discovered I spent too little for a sizable tax deduction he lost interest, but I'd got into the habit of saving them by that time and I went on doing it. The thin blue airmail letters with a rubber band around them took up no space, lying nearly flat under manuscripts in a back corner of one of the six small cabinet drawers under my bookshelves. But year after year when I cleaned out the cabinets, I'd come on them and wonder why I was saving them. Sitting there that evening, I vividly remembered that when I'd reorganized the cabinets a few weeks earlier I'd stood by the waste basket hefting the letters, debating whether to keep them or throw them out. I couldn't remember which I'd done. And I was afraid to find out.

I carried the dinner tray to the kitchen and washed the dishes. I mopped the kitchen floor, emptied the garbage, wiped the dinner table. Then I poured another cup of coffee. The letters had become terribly important; they had to be there. Finally, I made myself get up and walk to the cabinet by the window where I'd always kept them. I opened the drawer and reached in the back corner. They weren't there. I pulled out the drawer and hunted through the papers in it, but the letters were gone.

I looked in the second cabinet and then, with mounting irrational panic, through the next three. I came to the sixth and last drawer – a catch-all attic of a cabinet – and in my anxiety yanked it clear out of the wall unit. And there, in a back corner, was the familiar flat blue packet. I sat down on the floor and cried with relief. (Part of my mind was demanding 'What's the matter with you? Why is it so important?')

I carried the letters to the table and opened them – and snapshots of young families spilled out of them. Some were from Nora Doel, some were from one of the girls who worked in the shop, all of them were ten or fifteen years in the past. I found two letters from an old lady named Mrs Boulton who lived next door to the Doels. They'd persuaded her to sell one of her hand-embroidered luncheon cloths to the bookshop staff to send me, one Christmas. ('I don't usually part with any of my work,' she'd written when she got my letter telling her how beautiful it was.) I found snapshots of Frank standing proudly beside his new secondhand car. I was laughing by this time. I poured another cup of coffee and settled down to read the letters.

By the time I went to bed I was positively happy. I was going to relive the lovely episode Marks & Co. had been in my life by making a short story of the correspondence. *The New Yorker* sometimes published short stories in the form of letters and if I constructed the story properly they just might buy it.

But when I finished the story in March, it ran to sixty-seven pages, more than three times the length of the only story I'd ever sold to *The New Yorker*, and I didn't know where else to send it.

When in doubt, send it to Gene.

The story had no title so I put a sheet of paper in the typewriter and typed the address of the bookshop – 84, Charing Cross Road –

as a stopgap title. The title would make no sense at all to Americans, but magazine editors always change authors' titles to suit themselves so it didn't matter. I put the story in an envelope and mailed it to Gene with a one-line note:

'What do I do with this?'

A few days later the phone rang and when I said hello, a familiar, forthright voice said:

'I loved it, I cried. Why do you always send me things I can't publish?'

'It's too long for *The New Yorker*,' I said. 'I thought you could tell me where to send it.'

I heard Gene sigh.

'Let me think about it,' she said. A week or two went by before she called me back.

'Our sales manager is an antiquarian book dealer on the side,' she said. 'So I gave him your manuscript to read. And he said to me: "I love it. But if you're thinking of publishing it, I have to tell you it's not gonna sell." So then I went to the top and gave it to Cass Canfield, the chairman of our board. And he said: "It's charming. But it's terribly slight. And it's letters. You know letters don't sell."'

'Well, who told you it was a book?' I said impatiently. 'It's sixty-seven pages! I just thought you might know some literary quarterly I could send it to. It's too long for the only magazines I read.'

'That's the trouble with it,' said Gene. 'It's too short for a book and too long for a magazine article. It doesn't fit anywhere.'

She returned it to me and it lay on my desk for a couple of weeks. It was still there one night when Maia Gregory phoned. Maia was the United Artists story editor for whom I read a few novels a week. She lived in the building next door to mine and she phoned that night and said, as usual:

'Come on over; I have work for you.'

I hung up and started for the door. Then I had a thought. I went back to the desk, picked up the manuscript and took it with me; and when Maia handed me the galleys of a novel to read, I handed her the manuscript and said:

'Do me a favour. Whenever you get time, will you read this thing and put an X against every letter I can cut? I want to send it to a magazine and it's much too long.'

'Oh, goody, I have something to read in bed,' said Maia.

I went home and read the galleys, and after breakfast the next morning got to work on my reader's report. I was halfway through it when Maia phoned.

'I know one publisher who just might be crazy enough to publish this,' she said. 'I'm having lunch with him. Can I give it to him?'

'Sure,' I said. We hung up and I went back to my reader's report. Two weeks went by. Then the phone rang one morning and a pleasant baritone at the other end said:

'Miss Hanff? This is Dick Grossman' – and waited, obviously expecting the name to mean something to me. It didn't, and he added: 'Your publisher.'

'I don't have a publisher named Dick Grossman,' I said blankly. And he said:

'You do now. We're going to publish "84, Charing Cross Road".'

'In what?' I asked.

'As a book,' said Dick Grossman. And I said: 'You're crazy!'

A few days later I went down to Grossman Publishers for a story conference. Dick Grossman operated a small publishing house out of an old, spacious stone house on East 19th Street, with high ceilings and a fireplace in every room. He published slim, offbeat volumes – Ben Shahn, a new translation of Catullus, James Lipton's *An Exaltation of Larks*. (Dick left the publishing business a year or two later and it was a genuine loss; there were and are few like him.) Dick's editor wanted to read any of Frank's letters I'd omitted and when he read them he wanted all of them included, together with answers from me, and eventually the book ran to ninety pages, which was a little more respectable. (In my excitement I forgot to tell him that a London street address would mean nothing to American readers and that we needed a new title. For the rest of my life I was going to be told by neighbours and fellow dinner guests how much they'd enjoyed my book '64 Charring Road' or '47 Crossroads.')

Dick Grossman wanted to bring out the book in the fall of 1970 (it was too late for his fall '69 list), and in the catalogue he sent out early in July, the book was listed for September publication. That catalogue was responsible for the last blue envelope that would ever come in the mail from Marks & Co.

'Dear Miss Hanff,

'We have just learned that your book "84, Charing Cross Road", is listed in Grossman's catalogue of publications for August.

'You will be sorry to learn that owing to a redevelopment scheme, these premises are due for demolition in the near future. So after fifty years in the Charing Cross Road, we will be closing down at the end of this year.

'As well as being a tribute to the firm, your book will, in a way, be its obituary.'

Fortunately, I was too busy that summer to mourn the bookshop. I was president of the Democratic Club and we were heavily involved in the gubernatorial campaign of former Supreme Court Justice Arthur Goldberg. It was the first campaign I'd worked in since Bobby Kennedy's death, and through the summer and on into September I was preoccupied with it.

On a Friday morning in September, therefore, while everybody else was reading the morning *Times* over breakfast, I was studying a list of election districts that still needed workers – unaware that the morning *Times* carried a two-column review of *84, Charing Cross Road*, which began: 'This is a charmer.' I was pencilling in names of potential E.D. captains, when, at a little before eight, the phone rang. At that hour it could only be a club member reporting some new crisis. Sure enough, when I said Hello, Bill, one of the club regulars, was at the other end. How was I to know he was looking at a book review?

'Hi,' he said.   I said: 'What's the matter?'

'Have you seen the *Times*?'

'No,' I said. 'What's happened?'

'Are you sitting down?' asked Bill.

And with 1968 rushing back to me, I thought: 'My God, they've shot Goldberg!'

Only Chicken Little would believe what happened to me from then on. First, reviews began coming in from all over the country, so glowing I couldn't believe them. Then it was bought for reprint by the *Reader's Digest*, and the *Digest* check – $8,000, which I also couldn't believe – put me back on my financial feet for the first time in ten years.

The book appealed to only a small percentage of readers so its sales were what publishers politely call 'modest.' But what its readers lacked in numbers they made up for in fanaticism. It wasn't till a couple of years later that I first read in a trade paper that 84 was known to the publishing trade as 'a Cult book,' but from the beginning that's what it was.

If you write a Cult book – and your current address is printed at the top of the last dozen pages of it – and your phone number is listed in the Manhattan phone book, the Cult loses no time getting in touch with you.

Every morning when I went down for the mail, the little steel cubbyhole mailbox was so stuffed with fan letters I had to pry them out in sections. Some began: 'Dear Helene. I hope you don't mind my calling you that. I feel as if I know you.' Some of them moved me to tears. And one began simply:

'Dear Miss Hanff:
    'Would you consider marrying a fifteen-year-old boy with terminal acne?'

I answered every letter and saved them all carefully in a shoebox – which became two shoe boxes and then three, all bursting out of shape as more and more letters were crammed into them. Once, in a temporary fit of common sense, I considered throwing each letter away as I answered it, but the thought shocked me. It seemed so coldly ungrateful and God knew I wasn't.

It was a pity I couldn't keep the phone calls in a shoebox. The first few were ordinary enough. Readers in New York or in some Jersey or Connecticut suburb finished the book, reached for the phone and got my number from the operator, finding it quicker and more satisfying to talk to me than to write to me.

The first flatly incredible call came on a hot September Saturday. I was on a ladder cleaning the kitchen cabinets, clad chiefly in sweat, when the phone rang. I sprinted down the ladder, streaked across the living room, picked up the phone and – so as not to offend whichever friend was at the other end – said, very fast:

'I'm housecleaning the kitchen, I'll call you back, who is it?' And a man at the other end said imploringly:

'Oh please don't hang up! It's taken us three hours to get through to you. We're calling from Prince George, British Columbia. '

He and his wife had planned a weekend holiday to celebrate the birth of their son, but at the last minute the holiday had been cancelled.

'We couldn't go away so we read your book instead. And it cheered us so much we thought we'd treat ourselves to a phone call.'

'Why couldn't you go away?' I asked. And he said:

'We're snowed in.'

A woman phoned one evening from Lubbock, Texas, and said:

'We can talk as long as you're willing. The phone call is my husband's fortieth birthday present to me. He knew it was the one thing I wanted.'

A woman phoned one morning from Alaska and apologized for the 'intrusion.'

'This must be costing you a fortune!' I said. 'Why didn't you write to me instead?'

'I'm married to an Eskimo and we live three hundred miles from the nearest town,' she said. 'I didn't want to wait till spring when the roads clear and we can get into town to the post office.'

A man called from San Francisco one Sunday afternoon – and from then on he phoned regularly, once a month, to ask how I was and what I was writing. And there was the inevitable fly-in-the-ointment. Jay Schmidt.

Jay Schmidt phoned at dinner time one night and said he was calling from Texas, he was eighty-four, he had lung cancer but he felt fine – it was in remission – and he loved my book. He felt like talking and it was quite a while before I could get him to hang up so I could finish cooking dinner.

From then on, he called regularly once a week, always at dinner time. 'Jay, I've got company coming in ten minutes and I'm not dressed,' I'd say hurriedly. Or: 'Jay, I'm halfway out the door, I'm going to a concert.'

And each time, Jay would say:

'You haven't got five minutes to talk to an old man who's dying of lung cancer?'

He kept it up for two years. Then the phone calls stopped and I wished him Godspeed.

And there was the bitter winter night when the ringing phone got me out of bed at three in the morning and a young Hollywood composer said proudly:

'I've been up since six this morning but I made myself keep awake until midnight, so as not to call you before nine P.M. your time. I didn't want to interrupt your dinner.'

I explained to him he'd got the time difference backward, and I stood freezing by the open window for twenty minutes while he apologized abjectly and profusely for getting me out of bed, and told me how much *84* meant to him.

After the phone calls came the invitations. From total strangers.

'My friends and I are great admirers of your book and most anxious to meet you. I should like to give a luncheon for you at the Century Club on any Tuesday in November. Will you let me know which date is most convenient?'

'My husband and I are great fans of your book, so are three couples who live near us. I'd love to give a small dinner party for you on any Friday evening you name.'

How do you write back and say that, like everybody else, you're too shy to walk into a roomful of strangers and make conversation with them while they stare at you?

A couple in Minnesota and another in Florida wrote months in advance to give me the date of their projected one-week trip to New York and to ask which day of the week I'd be free for lunch or dinner. I dreaded spending a long dinner hour with strangers who might find me a crushing disappointment, but how do you write back in November that you're all booked up for the second week in February? I was totally unprepared for all this and I didn't know how to handle it.

There was an avalanche of Christmas cards from fans that first year. And a few days before Christmas a package arrived from Marks & Co. I opened it and found inside a first edition of *Daddy-Long-Legs* inscribed to me by Joan Todd, Frank Doel's secretary. When I turned the page I saw a second inscription. It was laboriously hand-printed in pencil on a torn scrap of paper taped to the page. It was written by the Marks & Co. shipping clerk. It read:

'This was the last parcel I packed up before the firm closed down. Pat.'

Shortly after the new year began, Dick Grossman phoned.

'André Deutsch wants to bring out *84* in London,' he said. 'He's one of England's best and most discriminating publishers. You couldn't ask for a better.'

A few weeks later my agent phoned to say a contract had arrived from André Deutsch, setting publication date for June 1971 and offering two hundred pounds in advance of royalties. Without any forethought I heard myself say:

'Tell him to keep the money over there for me. I'm going over in June.'

All these years later – now that Frank was dead and the bookshop closed – I was finally going to London.

Shortly before I was to leave, a retired actress gave a dinner party for me and over dinner she suggested I keep a diary while I was in London.

'So much will be happening to you,' she said. 'You think you'll remember it all but you won't.'

Much as I loved reading diaries I'd never believed in keeping one: it was too much like talking to yourself. But that spring there was a fad in New York for something called 'the Nothing Book' – a clothbound book of empty pages – and the day before I left for London, a friend gave me one 'so you can keep a diary in London.'

I took a morning plane, landed at Heathrow at ten P.M. – and by midnight, so much had already happened to me that I sat on the edge of the bed and recorded the evening's events in the Nothing book. From then on, through five hectic, wide-eyed weeks in London, I made myself do this every night, no matter how late I got in or how tired I was. When I came home I typed the scrawled diary entries and put the bundle of typewritten sheets in a cabinet drawer, relieved to know I had a record of the trip to take out and read some day.

The London reviews were as glowing as the American ones, and I took a set to Gene Young one day when we met for lunch.

'You don't know what it does to me,' I said, 'that after being nursed along by you for ten years, I finally write a book that gets rave reviews in two countries – and it's published by somebody else.'

'What it does to YOU!' said Gene with feeling. And I went home vowing to write a new book for her. For months I ransacked my mind for one. Nothing turned up.

A fresh ton of letters arrived from England and Australia. A few were from Londoners who had bought books from Marks & Co. One woman wrote that she had passed the shop one morning during the Battle of Britain, to find its windows had been blown out by the bombing the night before.

'The sidewalk was covered with shattered glass, but passers-by had stopped and were picking books out of the gutter and putting them carefully back in the broken window.'

There were letters from readers who had been children during the war and remembered 'the arrival of the marvellous food parcels from America.'

The fan mail kept coming all that winter and spring, much of it from England. On a June evening, remembering the previous June and wishing I were back in London, I got out the typewritten diary and settled in the armchair to read it and relive the trip.

'Whenever I write a letter to somebody, I mail it without reading it over,' a fellow TV writer once told me. 'I know if I read it over I'll start rewriting it.'

I hadn't read a paragraph of that diary before I had to get a pencil and rewrite a sentence to clarify it. Three hours later, when I went to bed, I'd only read through the first two days' entries – and both were so heavily marked up I knew I'd have to retype them in the morning if I ever hoped to read them again.

As I ate breakfast the next morning, it occurred to me that if I rewrote the diary and cut it. I might be able to sell it to a travel magazine. At nine o'clock I put paper in the typewriter and got to work. And at ten o'clock my telepathic friend phoned.

Gene had been busy moving from the suburbs to the city and from *Harper's* to Lippincott and I hadn't talked to her in several months. When I picked up the phone and said hello, she said:

'I just thought I'd find out what you're doing.'

'An hour ago I started rewriting the diary I kept in London,' I said. 'I thought maybe –'

'You're writing another book!' said Gene. 'This one's mine!'

I looked at the paper in the typewriter. I was on page 4 and I hadn't even got as far as the first entry, I was just writing an introduction. Okay, I was writing another book.

During the next several months Gene phoned every few weeks for a progress report. Late on a Friday afternoon in November, I took the last page out of the typewriter and without stopping to stack the pages, dialled her number. When she came to the phone I said:

'Wanna buy a book?'

'You finished it!' said Gene. 'Bring it down.'

'I have to proofread it; I'll bring it down Monday,' I said.

'I'll proofread it. Bring it down now.'

'I have to shower and change and it's after four. I couldn't get down there by five anyway!' I said.

'Get down when you can. I'll wait,' said Gene.

I got to Lippincott's at five-thirty and there was nobody there but Gene. We Xeroxed the manuscript and then we went to Schrafft's to celebrate. Schrafft's – a chain of tearoomy restaurants noted for its gooey desserts – was the only place where I could have my martini and Gene could have her hot butterscotch sundae with toasted almonds.

On Friday night, Gene read the manuscript and on Saturday, she phoned to tell me she loved it.

On Monday, Lippincott's editor-in-chief read it and on Tuesday, Gene phoned to say triumphantly that the editor-in-chief liked it and Lippincott was going to publish it.

On Wednesday, the author read it. With increasing horror. On Wednesday afternoon, I phoned Gene.

'This thing is awful!' I said. 'Garrulous Gertie comes home from London and has to tell everybody about her trip. Who the hell cares about my trip?'

'Everybody who read *84, Charing Cross Road*,' said Gene promptly. And it hit me with full force that my beloved Cult was going to rush out and buy this mess and I would die of shame.

In December, I made the few changes Gene wanted and a hundred hair-splitting changes of my own in an attempt to improve it. When the galleys came in January, I read them and discovered I hadn't improved anything.

'Lippincott's going to lose its shirt on this thing,' I told Gene when I returned the galleys.

'Why are you worrying about Lippincott? They've got more money than you have,' Gene pointed out reasonably. Then she said:

'It's going to be a rush job, we have an April publication date. You'll have to find me a new title in the next week or two.'

'What's the matter with "London Diary"?' I asked.

'It's a little less than compelling,' said Gene in a withering tone. 'I can't go to a sales conference with anything as dull as that!'

We'd mailed a copy of the manuscript to André Deutsch and my agent phoned to say he liked it and was going to publish it. I called Gene and told her and she said:

'I'll see him next week; I'm going to London on business. I'll tell him a new title's on the way. You'd better have one by the time I come home.'

Gene had gone abroad a few years earlier, and had regaled me later with a description of what she'd gone through, watching airport Immigration officials – in Amsterdam, in Rome, in Paris – pore over her Nationalist Chinese passport, turning it four ways, hoping to get it right-side-up, and finding they couldn't read a word of it in any direction. ('I couldn't help them,' she'd explained apologetically. 'I couldn't read it either.')

She was still away when the page-proofs of the book arrived in February, but when I went down to her office to return them a few days later, she was back behind her desk.

'How was the trip?' I asked.

'Great,' said Gene. 'I had a wonderful time in London.'

'What was the high point?' I asked.

She looked at me and hesitated. Then she said:

'You won't believe it, but the high point came after I landed at JFK. It was mobbed and I was annoyed, I was tired and I had to stand on a long line at the Immigration desk. We inched along and finally I got to the desk and put my new passport on it, and the man behind the desk looked at it and stamped it. Then he pushed it back to me and said: "Welcome home." And I had tears in my eyes.'

The alien with the Chinese passport was finally an ordinary American citizen coming home.

Which was as it should be, since the inside of Gene Young's head is about as Chinese as General Motors. She phoned me one evening and announced triumphantly:

'I've got the title for you!'

'What is it?' I asked.

'*Son of 84, Charing Cross Road*,' said Gene.

I told her I'd see us both dead first. We finally settled on *The Duchess of Bloomsbury Street* (another long, wordy title nobody would ever get straight). But when the cover design arrived it featured a Lion and a Unicorn holding up a copy of *84, Charing Cross Road*. I phoned her the next morning.

'Did you really think I'd approve this cover?' I demanded. 'You don't have approval. I sent it as a courtesy,' said General Motors. 'Are you going to be home all afternoon? I'm sending a man up for your fan mail. We're getting out a special mailing to all your fans.'

That afternoon the man from Lippincott carted off five shoeboxes full of fan mail. And that night or the next, I dreamed I was opening sad and accusing letters about the new book, from ex-fans who had trusted me.

In March, advance copies of the book were sent to 'the trade' – reviewers, publishers, bookstore owners. I was tired of worrying about it by then, and wishing I had something new to write, when a letter came in the mail from Holt, Rinehart & Winston, Publishers. I'd never written anything for Holt, Rinehart, but they published school textbooks and I thought maybe they knew I'd written children's history books and were offering me work. I opened the letter and glanced down at the signature: 'Tom Wallace, Editor-in-Chief. Then I read the first sentence – and my legs were suddenly so weak I had to sit down.

'Dear Miss Hanff
    You've done it again . . .'

He'd read an advance copy of *The Duchess of Bloomsbury Street*.

A few days later a letter came from the owner of a bookshop in a New York suburb.

'Dear Miss Hanff:
    You've done it again.'

And it seemed to me that the Lord must be feeling guilty about what He'd put me through in the sixties and was seeing to it that I could do nothing wrong in the seventies.

The reviews were 'mixed'. I give you the last lines of two of them:

'This book is an act of love. I loved it.'
 – Neil Millar; *Christian Science Monitor*

'The book should never have been published.'
 – John Barkham; *San Francisco Chronicle*

(John Barkham was the dean of American reviewers, but he bounced right off Gene. 'He's in the minority,' she said. 'The book's selling very well.')

Then the deluge of fan mail began pouring in from both countries. To my unspeakable relief, the Cult had not only survived My Trip but enjoyed it.

I'll never know a Christmas as wild as that one. Along with the blizzard of cards came gifts, including more books than I had room for.

There were books sent to me by their unknown authors, there were seventeen books about London and England, a few about Australia (from Australian fans) and from a woman in Switzerland the complete works of Washington Irving in two-inch miniatures. There was a beautiful set of Jane Austen from a woman in Australia who wrote that she was getting old, she knew her children would sell her books when she died and she wanted her Austen in the hands of someone who would appreciate it. (At the time, *Pride and Prejudice* was the only Austen I owned; I'd read the others and hadn't liked any of them much. But if the donor is reading this, I want her to know that just last week I finished rereading all of the others in turn, not for the first time, and blessed her all over again for putting Jane's books so firmly on my shelves.)

And there was the truly awesome volume from a couple who owned an antique shop in upstate New York and who wrote that the book was worthless as an antique. It was a 1651 edition of John Donne's poems. I put it up on the shelf in a plastic sandwich bag because I was afraid to touch it. (It's still in the sandwich bag and I'm still afraid to touch it.)

Along with the books came the edibles and the unclassifiables. The edibles included pecans from Georgia, cheese from Wisconsin, homemade preserves from three young matrons in Oregon and an enormous box of grapefruit sent to me from Florida by a man who lived in Michigan. (He was only wintering in Florida and I had to phone the Florida fruitseller and get the man's Michigan address so I could write and thank him.)

The unclassifiables included a plate with the raised head of Shakespeare on it; a Hanff family tree painted in oils; a yard of Nottingham lace; a miniature koala and a miniature Eskimo doll for my Christmas tree and a pair of skittles. (If you've read about 'beer and skittles' and wondered what skittles were, mine are small varnished sticks about six inches long, smooth and rounded with decorative knobs at each end. They could be the banister posts of a doll's-house staircase.

Considering all of which, you'd think I'd have been grateful enough not to complain about the one fly in the Christmas ointment. I complained incessantly about it. It began late in November when I came home one afternoon and the doorman said:

'There's a package for you.'

The package clearly contained a book and I carried it upstairs with pleased anticipation. Then I opened it. It contained two books. Written by me. And a letter from a man in Boston:

'The enclosed books are part of my Christmas gift to my mother in Canada, to whom a personal inscription from you would mean so much. I enclose her name and address. And will you include a covering note to say the books are from her son Tad? (She doesn't call me Thomas.)'

From then on, a similar package arrived in the mail room every day. One package contained two 84's and two Duchesses.

'The enclosed sets of your books are Christmas gifts. One set is to be autographed to my fiancé in Alabama, whose name and address I enclose, and the other is for my sister, Grace, and can be returned to me at the above address in Chicago.'

'Enclosed please find your two books. They are for my son and daughter-in-law in Tel Aviv. Will you be kind enough to autograph them and then add Happy Hanukah from Mother? I enclose the postage.'

Some enclosed the postage; some suggested I bill them for it. Nobody sent a stamped, self-addressed bookmailer. I had to run down to the stationery store for them, autograph the books, address and staple the bookmailers, lug them to the post office and stand in a Christmas line.

'Just mail them back where they came from!' an irate friend advised me.

But you can't do that to people – and I'd have had to stand in line at the post office just as long to return them.

My reward came a few days before Christmas with the arrival of the one gift I still prize above all others.

To understand the saga of that gift, you need to know that in the two and a half years since *84* had been published, I'd answered hundreds of fan letters and that while a few fans' names stuck in my memory, most of them didn't. You also need to know that I answer every letter off-the-top-of-my-head, commenting on what each letter-writer has written to me. Occasionally, I remember what I wrote in answer to a particular letter. Mostly I don't.

Well, six months before this particular Christmas, on a morning in July, I got a postcard from a New York couple who were vacationing in London. They wrote that they were fans of *84* and had gone around to Charing Cross Road to see the empty bookshop, which was still standing. And they added:

'We met your friend Dan Kelly from Omaha. He says to tell you he's getting the sign for you.'

I didn't have a friend named Dan Kelly in Omaha, and I didn't know what sign he was talking about. Having no New York address for the writers of the postcard, I threw it away and forgot about it. Till a November evening when my phone rang and a pleasant male voice said:

'Hi! It's Dan Kelly in Omaha.'

That brought the postcard to mind and I said – extra-cordially to cover my ignorance:

'Oh, how *are* you?'

'Fine,' he said. 'I've got the sign for you.'

I couldn't bluff my way through that one.

'What sign?' I asked.

'You mean you don't remember?' he said – and I could hear his face fall. 'I wrote to you a year ago and told you I'd been to London and I'd stood across the street from your bookshop, watching the Marks & Co. sign swing in the breeze and thinking: "I should steal that for Helene." And you wrote back: "Why didn't you?"'

On his return trip to London the next summer, he had gone to the

London City Council and got permission to remove the sign; he'd found a London firm to crate it and ship it to his home in Nebraska; he was coming to New York on business in December and would deliver it to me personally in time for Christmas.

Three friends were on hand when Dan Kelly arrived with the unopened crate. I sat cross-legged on the carpet and pried the nails out, one by one. When the lid was finally removed, I lifted out of the crate two thin sheets of glass. Between them, on black cloth backing, large silver letters spelled out the legend:

```
BOOKS  ≡

        ≡  MARKS
        & CO.  ≡

              ≡  BOOKS
```

Few moments in my life have equalled that one. The three friends carted off the sign to have it framed for me and on Christmas Eve helped me hang it on the short alcove wall, at a right angle to the long wall of bookshelves holding all the books that came from there.

A few nights later, I was sitting over coffee after dinner, feasting my eyes on the sign. Flush with the base of it, on the bottom bookshelf, was a small row of books. They hadn't come from Marks & Co. Their cheap cloth covers were badly faded and I never read the books anymore. But year after year, when I'd tried to throw them out, they'd stubbornly refused to depart. I stared at the faded covers that hid the underlinings, the brackets, the margin notes with which one earnest, inadequate student had disfigured the seven volumes of Cambridge lectures by Sir Arthur Quiller-Couch. The time had come to add up what I owed to Q.

I owed him whatever literary education I had – and enough training in the craft of writing to have kept myself alive by it through the sixties. I owed him my shelves full of books – and my choice of Marks & Co. over the column of New York bookstores. Wherefore I owed him *84, Charing Cross Road* and *The Duchess of Bloomsbury*

Street – and the hundreds if not thousands of friends both books had brought me in the mail and over the phone.

It was an awesome legacy for a Cambridge don to have conferred on a lowly pupil he never knew existed three thousand miles away.

I didn't know all of it was only the legacy-so-far. The rest of it was waiting to be delivered to me piecemeal, over the next several years, in London.

3

Drowning on Television

On a January day in 1975, a cable arrived in my agent's office and she called to read it to me.

KEEN TO ACQUIRE 84 CHARING CROSS ROAD FOR BBC TELEVISION

MARK SHIVAS

Mark Shivas, she told me, was one of the BBC's best young producers. Being a fan of BBC television, I was very flattered. I phoned the news to all my friends and it was my friend Susan who said brightly:

'You'll see your whole life pass before you and you won't even have to drown.'

In February, Hugh Whitemore's script arrived. I'd wondered how on earth he was going to turn a book of letters into television dialogue. He hadn't tried to. You might say he scorned to try. He'd let the letters themselves take the place of dialogue by doing the whole script in a television technique known as 'voice-over.'

'Voice-over' meant that the audience would hear a letter read by a disembodied voice while the owner of the voice performed pantomime action on the screen. To do an hour-long TV show this way from beginning to end required the kind of audacity known as 'chutzpah'.

514

A week later I got the news that Anne Jackson had been signed to play me, and Frank Finlay, a London stage star, would be playing Frank Doel. Then a letter arrived from Mark Shivas to say rehearsals would begin early in April and the show would be taped on April 25, 26, and 27. Was I coming over for it?

I had no work in the typewriter. I can only write about what happens to me and nothing much had happened to me lately. But it occurred to me that sitting in a TV studio watching an actress pretend to be me definitely classified as something-happening-to-me that I could write about afterward. I typed a few pages that were something between a memo and an outline and sent it to the *Reader's Digest*. And the *Digest* – a Lord Bountiful among magazines – agreed to stake me to a ten-day trip to London for the last week of rehearsals and the three days of taping, provided I was willing to travel economy-syle.

'We presume she doesn't have to stay at the Dorchester?' was the way the *Digest* editor put it to my agent. Who answered promptly: 'No, no. Cheap-cheap.'

'Cheap-cheap.' was the slogan of BOAC's Show Tours that season. The next day I went down to the BOAC office on Fifth Avenue and bought a Show Tour ticket. The package included a hotel room on Russell Square – and where would I rather wake up on an April morning?

Then one night I saw Anne Jackson and her husband, Eli Wallach, on a TV talk show. They were obviously warm, friendly people and the thought of what I was planning to do to one of them appalled me. Maxine, the bosom friend of my youth, was an actress and I tried to imagine the look on her dramatic face if she had to rehearse the part of a real woman and found the real woman sitting in the rehearsal room staring at her while she did it. I worried about this for a few days. Then the BBC phone calls started coming and I forgot about Anne Jackson.

I'd always marveled at the absolute authenticity of BBC productions. I was to spend the next few weeks in New York and London finding out how they achieved it, and my education began with those phone calls.

The first call came early one morning. I said hello and a woman at the other end shouted over a bad connection that she was calling from London, her name was Beryl and she was assistant to Mark

Cullingham, the director of *84, Charing Cross Road*.

'We'd so much appreciate it if you'd take the following books down to the BBC office in Rockefeller Center to be mailed to us, to be used in the production,' she said. 'Have you a pencil?'

And she named eight of my oldest and most cherished books. She might as well have said, 'We'd so much like you to mail us eight of your fingers.'

Fortunately, I had an excuse.

'You couldn't possibly use them on camera,' I said. 'They've been on open bookshelves by a window for twenty years – and between air pollution and steam heat, they're all wrecks! The covers are cracked, some of the bindings have edges so ragged you'd think mice had chewed them.'

'Not to worry!' Beryl shouted firmly across three thousand miles of ocean static. 'If you can take them down tomorrow in time for the four o'clock mail pouch we'd-be-so-grateful.'

Anybody but a congenital worm would have said 'No!' But I stood at the phone meekly writing down the address of the BBC office and agreeing to deliver the books in the morning.

I got them down from the shelves and looked at them and my heart failed. The green leather cover of my *Elizabethan Poets* – a present from all my friends in the bookshop – was faded and cracked at the edges, but at least the cover was still firmly attached. The cover of Newman's *Idea of a University*, with its dusty gold seal, was so loose I didn't think it would survive the trip. But the next morning I took them all down to the BBC office and handed them over to a stranger with all the confidence of a mother handing over her sickly infant to be shipped across the ocean without her.

A few days later Beryl phoned again.

'Do you still have the table cloth sent you by the bookshop for Christmas in 1953?' she inquired.

I don't know what I answered to that one but it was something noncommittal: 'I'm not sure,' or 'I'll have to look.' Whatever it was, Beryl translated as Yes.

'Well, *would* you take it down to the BBC office to be mailed to us?' she said briskly. 'We'll take very good care of it.'

The cloth, which had been embroidered by old Mrs Boulton, Frank Doel's neighbour, was round. Since I'd bought an oblong dinner table when I moved into my palace, I'd finally given the cloth to my friends Kay and Brian Huson – less because they had a round Colonial table than because Brian, an Englishman, had known all about my correspondence with Marks & Co. In the days when I worried because I could afford to send only one parcel for the entire shop, it was Brian who had assured me that the Charing Cross Road bookshops were 'all quite small.'

I had a hunch the cloth was still in their house in Rowayton, Connecticut. Unfortunately, Kay and Brian weren't. They were in Beirut, where Brian was working for an American bank. Their two sons would be no help since both were at Brian's old school in England. On the chance that there were tenants in the house I phoned the Connecticut number.

A woman answered and said Yes, she and her husband were the Husons' tenants but she'd never met them. Her husband, a British civil servant, had met Brian in Beirut and rented the house from him there. Understandably, she wasn't about to rummage through Kay's linens for me, but she said she'd discuss the problem with her husband and call me back.

She phoned the next morning to say that her husband had talked to the Husons in Beirut (they sent their love) and she'd found the cloth and was mailing it to me. It arrived and I took it down to the BBC. And Beryl made her third and last call.

'Do you have photographs of your old flat and your present flat?' she asked. I said I had no photos of either and Beryl said:

'Well, *would* you have some taken of your present flat and mail them to us? The designer is most anxious to have them.'

So that evening an obliging gent who lived on the sixteenth floor came down to my eighth-floor apartment carrying his Christmas camera with the long lens, and photographed every inch of the living-room and alcove. A few days later, a set of glossy colour prints went off by airmail to London.

Late in March, Anne Jackson phoned.

'I'm leaving for London next week to start rehearsals for *84, Charing Cross Road*,' she said. 'Can I come around and meet you before I go?'

Feeling very English, we made a date for her to come to tea at four the following Friday. ('*Just* tea,' she said firmly. 'I'm dieting.') At exactly four on Friday my doorbell rang and I opened the door to her. Annie – which I was told to call her before she'd been here two minutes – was startlingly beautiful. She had perfect cameo features, a flawless milky complexion and a thick mass of burnished red hair. Having been plain and mousy all my life, I thought: 'What a face to be playing me!' But we were the same height, we both wore sweaters, pants and flat-heeled shoes, and Annie got so carried away by this she announced:

'We look alike!'

'Don't I wish it,' I said.

She walked in and headed straight for the bookshelves, which won my heart. Few visitors do that.

Over tea, we discovered we both came from Pennsylvania, we both had half-blind left eyes and we shared a couple of other ten-cent characteristics I've forgotten but which seemed of heavy significance at the time. By the third cup of tea we were such old friends I said:

'Please tell me honestly' – which is what you say when you want to force a kind soul to lie – 'If I come over for the last week of rehearsal, will it bother you to have me there?'

'Of course not!' said Annie gallantly. 'You have to come!'

She told me she'd be staying at Brian Aherne's house in Maida Vale.

'They're living in Switzerland and they've lent me the house for a month. But I'm taking my sister, Bea, along for company, and during the last week Eli and our son Peter will be there. So I can't offer to put you up. But I want you to come to Maida Vale every evening you have nothing to do. I don't want you sitting alone in a hotel room.'

She gave me Brian Aherne's address and wrote the name of my hotel in her pocket address book. Then she got out a tape recorder and had me read a few of the *84* letters into it so she could study my voice. When she left I felt as if I'd known her for years.

Two long newsy letters came from Brian Aherne's house in the next two weeks. Annie reported that every member of the cast had gone alone into a soundproof room to record his or her letters on tape; that Frank Finlay was a wonderful actor to work with: and that Mark Shivas was a love. A third week crawled by, and I was finally on my way back to London.

It was too early for the roses in Russell Square, but when I walked into the hotel room, there was a water glass full of pink garden roses on the dresser. Propped against the glass was a note:

'Picked this morning and covered with greenfly. Welcome!'

Mark Shivas

Alongside it were two messages. One said that a BBC car would call for me at nine the next morning to drive me to the BBC Rehearsal Block in North Acton. The other said that Miss Anne Jackson expected me for dinner the following evening.

At nine the next morning the desk phoned to say the BBC car was waiting, and I went down to the lobby. The desk clerk pointed out a slight young man waiting by the door and when I reached him he said:

'Miss Hanff? I'm your driver.'

'Isn't it a beautiful day?' I said. The driver hesitated a moment. Then he said:

'I'm also your producer. Mark Shivas' – and stuck out a hand.

Everything about Shivas was unassuming, including the battered green jalopy he helped me into. I told him it wasn't the limousine I'd planned to become accustomed to and he said No, it was a colorful, democratic car that liked Americans. The jalopy coughed its way out on to a highway and I asked:

'How far is it to North Acton?'

'Forty-five minutes,' said Shivas. 'Less, of course, in a fine car like mine.'

We talked about London neighborhoods – he told me he lived down in the East End, across the river – and then I said:

'All my life I've wanted to meet a producer so I could ask him this. What exactly does a producer do?'

'A producer,' said Shivas, 'finds a book he likes, and picks the best adapter for it – and the best director – and the best cast – and the best set designer. Then he sits back and lets everybody else do the work.'

'But you oversee rehearsals,' I said.

'Oh, no,' said Mark. 'I never go to rehearsals. I keep out of the way till the taping starts.'

Translation:

He lived in the East End, at the other end of town from Russell

Square in Bloomsbury. He had no reason to be at that morning's rehearsal and wouldn't stay for it. He had driven through London's morning rush-hour traffic to get me, and was now driving all the way out to North Acton – where he would turn around and drive back to his London office – just so I wouldn't have to make the trip with an impersonal BBC driver on my first day and wouldn't have to introduce myself when I got there.

I asked what shows he'd produced and he said his first show was *The Six Wives of Henry VIII*. It was several years in the past and I said:

'You don't look old enough to have produced that.'

And he told me he'd been the youngest producer the BBC had ever hired when they trusted him with it. (He's produced a string of prize-winning TV shows since then, including my favourite *Glittering Prizes*, and it's typical of Mark Shivas that all his productions are famous while he stays unobtrusively in the background.)

The BBC Rehearsal Block is a seven-story building that's permanently unfurnished. There's a cafeteria on the top floor but the other floors have only large, empty rehearsal rooms. When a cast is rehearsing in one of them, a few pieces of prop furniture are installed. They're removed when rehearsals end.

The cast of *84* was rehearsing when we walked in. But Annie, sitting at an old typewriter table at the far end of the room, saw me and rose, and she and I loped toward each other, met in the middle of the room and embraced, murmuring reassuring nothings to each other. That stopped rehearsal for a few minutes and Mark introduced me to the rest of the cast and to Mark Cullingham, the director. Then he left for London, I retired to one of the folding chairs along a side wall and rehearsal resumed.

At one end of the room was the makeshift bookshop set: two desks, a few straight chairs and an old bookshelf. At the other end, Annie presided over a studio couch, a typewriter table and an ancient kitchen stove. There were books on the typewriter table but they weren't mine. The books in the bookshop set weren't mine either. The cast was rehearsing with prop books and I wondered where mine were. Then I forgot them and concentrated on the rehearsal.

Somebody turned on a tape recorder, I heard Annie's voice begin a letter to Frank Doel – and Annie began to perform the pantomime action of dressing to go out. Her action had to be timed to the split second so that, after buttoning a blouse, putting on a sweater, picking up a handbag and a manuscript, she went out the door at the precise instant when her taped voice ended the letter. Frank Finlay and the others in the bookshop set had to time their action just as precisely, but their scenes had bits of dialogue, which gave them a respite now and then. Annie worked alone and got no respite at all.

During the lunch break, Frank Finlay told me he was taking Nora Doel and her daughters to supper after his performance that night. He was starring in a West End play, acting every night and rehearsing in *84* all day, and he was giving Nora, Sheila and Mary tickets to the show and taking them to supper afterward because that was the only free time he had, to ask them questions about Frank Doel.

When rehearsal ended, Mark Cullingham introduced me to the set designer, who showed me the model of the bookshop set and asked me about the layout of my 95th Street apartment. By the time I got back to Russell Square it was too late to walk around Bloomsbury. There was barely time to dress for dinner at Annie's.

If you're old enough to have seen Brian Aherne on stage in *The Barretts of Wimpole Street* or in a whole string of Hollywood comedies back in the thirties and forties, you'll know why it seemed very glamorous to me to be on my way to his house. It was one of a row of grandly Victorian houses on the street where the Regent's Park canal ends. The canal boat passengers were stepping ashore a few yards up the street as I got out of a cab.

I went up the broad front steps and rang the doorbell and Annie came to the door. She dragged me along a hall and then down a steep flight of steps to the kitchen – and opened the oven door with a flourish, to show me what she'd done for me. In the oven, alongside a sizzling roast, was a Yorkshire pudding she'd made from the recipe in *84* which she'd been rehearsing in pantomime for two weeks.

Beautiful as the house was, I could understand why the Ahernes didn't live in it. Victorian London houses were built for 'Upstairs, Downstairs' families with pleny of servants, and the servants were of no concern at all to the architect. So when dinner was ready, Annie and her sister, Bea, had to carry heavy dinner platters of roast beef, Yorkshire pudding and vegetables up two steep flights of steps to the dining-room. (I was only trusted with the bread tray and coffee pot.)

We adjourned for coffee to a dramatically beautiful drawing-room.

The walls were covered in deep brown velvet, set off by a great white stone fireplace and gleaming white woodwork; and the matching brown velvet sofa where we curled up with our coffee faced a long window wall of nubby white silk drapes.

It was the first of several relaxed and chatty evenings I spent there and those evenings gave Annie and me a grin months later when we discovered we'd both been working during them. Annie'd been studying me for the next day's rehearsal; I'd been studying her for the *Digest* article.

(How much she'd learned about me in those evenings I didn't discover till a year later. Watching her at rehearsals, I was aware of one characteristic she'd caught. Like all very nearsighted people, I'm awkward and clumsy. Annie had seen this in my attempts to help her in Brian Aheme's kitchen: what I didn't spill I dropped. In her pantomime, she not only caught this clumsiness and made it funny, she somehow made it appealing. But a year later, when *84* was shown on PBS, a friend told me: 'Her gestures were so like yours it was spooky!' And another friend phoned from California to say: 'I know you recorded the letters yourself. I recognized your voice.')

I met Nora and Sheila Doel one night for dinner, and they were full of their evening with Frank Finlay.

'He questioned us for two hours, Helen,' said Nora. (She never did learn to call me Helene.) 'He wanted to know about Frank's gestures and his mannerisms and what clothes he liked. He made Sheila get up and show him how Frank walked, and she walked back and forth for him and he watched her. Then he got up and tried it – and he walked so like my Frank I couldn't look.'

Rehearsals ended on a Thursday; on Friday, the production was to move to the BBC Television Centre at Shepherd's Bush for the three days of taping. On Thursday afternoon, when the last run-through ended, Mark Cullingham took my arm and escorted me cere-moniously to the long table at the back of the room where the set models had stood. There, set out in two neat rows, were my books. I stared at them and I couldn't speak. They had been transformed.

What I was staring at in light-headed disbelief was a row of leather covers that had for years had ragged, chewed-looking edges. The original covers were still there, but they were miraculously whole again. Which was only part of the transformation. The once-faded green leather binding of my *Elizabethan Poets* was clear emerald, its gold-tipped pages gleamed, its chewed edges were gone. The cover of my Newman was firmly attached, its deep brown pigskin glowed with a patina it had never had in my lifetime, and the long-faded gold seal shone against it. On all the books, old stains were gone, imbedded dust was gone, the covers were fresh and bright again.

'We called Buckingham Palace and got the name of the Queen's bookbinder, and he restored them for us', I heard Mark Cullingham say. 'The leather's heated till it's pliable and then it's stretched downward and the ragged edges are cut off.' He went on talking about the special solution for cleaning the gold and I still couldn't speak. I don't know how long it was before I managed to thank somebody.

The schedule for the BBC's three-day taping of *84* would have caused riots in any other industry: 10 A.M. to 10 P.M., Friday, Saturday and Sunday. At 9 A.M. on Friday, Mark Shivas called for me in the jalopy and we drove out to Shepherd's Bush. And it's too bad the BBC TV Production Centre isn't open to tourists. The building is astonishing and, as far as I know, unique.

It's a grey-and-green stone oval, several stories high, with no windows and only one door. Inside the door, whether you turn left or right, if you keep walking long enough you'll eventually come around to the door again. But you don't go left or right, you walk straight ahead, across the lobby and through a pair of swinging doors. As Mark pushed them open he said blandly:

'The show's being taped in Studio 6 of the Green Assembly.'

Then he pointed upward, at the ceiling.

Strung along wires under the ceiling were three crisscrossing strings of small lights, like Christmas tree lights, one set red, one green, one blue, each set branching off in a separate direction. We followed the green lights, but as we went along corridors and down steps and through more corridors and up steps, the green lights crisscrossed the red lights at one turn, and the blue ones at another, so constantly that a stranger could get hopelessly lost. The building is a maze.

We came to a large green neon sign reading Studio 1 and walked past four more signs till we came to Studio 6. There, Mark pointed my way down the Dressing Rooms corridor. Then he left me and I followed more green lights and signs, past Dressing Rooms 18, 19 and

20, and came to Dressing Room 21, where Kate Binchy, the pretty Irish actress who was playing Nora Doel, wanted me to see her 1950s wardrobe and the silver-framed wedding photograph she and Frank Finlay had posed for, to be used in the Doels' living-room set. Ten minutes after I got there, Chris, the floor-manager (equivalent to a theatre stage-manager), came for me and took me out to the studio floor.

'I want you to see your bookshop,' he said.

The studio floor was a vast clearing in an encircling forest of wires and cables that rose from floor to ceiling, completely hiding the walls. Spaced across the floor were the three sets to be used in that day's taping: my former apartment, the Doels' living-room and the one large set which would be in use on all three days: the bookshop. It was walled off from our view as we approached it.

'The two Marks and the set designer,' Chris told me as we walked, 'went to all the secondhand bookshops in London to talk to people who had once worked at Marks & Co. They quizzed them about where every desk and door and staircase had been. Then the designer went home and drew a sketch of the shop and took it back to them for correction till he'd got every detail right. So,' he finished, 'what you'll see is an exact replica of your bookshop, reduced to scale.'

And he walked me around to the bookshop's glass front door and opened it for me and I walked into my bookshop. It was shabby and comfortable, with old desks and lamps and a solid old staircase. The bookshelves were exactly as my friend Maxine had described them to me in a letter – heavy oak that had turned grey with 'must and dust and age.' I gravitated to the shelves and found them crammed with books. Not the usual stage 'prop' books – dilapidated junk-shop volumes collected at random to fill up the shelves. The books on these shelves were those of a genuine antiquarian bookshop, many with fine bindings, some just old, with the musty smell of buried treasure.

'They were all lent to us by London booksellers, ' Chris said. 'They feel a proprietary interest in the show.'

He left me and I started to browse among the books. I was still at it when Mark came for me at ten, and led the way up a ladder to the glass-enclosed control booth.

Most of the booth was taken up by a half-moon table brightly lit by five studio lamps, one at each of the stations identified by placards:

Producer, Director, Assistant to the Director, Vision Mixer, Lighting Director. The two Marks found an extra chair and made room between them at the table for me and my notebook and pencils.

When I looked straight ahead, I saw five monitors suspended in a black void. When I leaned over and looked down, I saw the studio floor so far below that the sets looked like three doll houses flung far apart across a wooden plain, surrounded by a towering wire jungle.

Chris, in charge of floor operations, was already getting instructions over his walkie-talkie from Mark Cullingham, who spoke into a table mike. It was Mark Cullingham's stream of instructions, to be relayed by Chris to members of the cast, that told me why it took three twelve-hour days to tape a one-hour TV show.

Television has no equivalent of a stage dress rehearsal. In the theatre, dress rehearsals take place on the stage of the theatre where the play is to open. They may go on for a week or more, all day long and sometimes far into the night.

But the cast and crew of a TV show have the use of a studio only on the three days of taping, which means that every scene has to be dress-rehearsed on the studio-floor on the day it's to be taped. And since visual effects are of first importance to the camera, every scene has to be dress-rehearsed over and over until every visual detail is perfect. So Mark Cullingham's instructions to Chris were a steady stream of hair-splitting corrections:

'Has that door been moved or is John not on his marks?'

'Ask Frank to tip his head a bit more to the right . . . Yes, and can he lower his hand with the letter in it so we see his face? . . . No, that's too low . . . That's good. All right, once more, please.'

And since the director oversees every detail with godlike authority, any small deviation from rehearsed movements is sacrilege.

'Annie's gone completely mad! She looked at her watch! She's never done that before! . . . All right, once more, please.'

'Once more, please' was a mechanical refrain, like a dentist's 'Open wide, please,' as every scene was rehearsed and rehearsed five or six times – though each scene contained only one or two letters and ran only a couple of minutes. Not until Mark Cullingham had pinpointed and corrected every microscopic visual flaw did he say into the mike:

'All right, let's go for a recording.'

And Chris's youthful voice would rise to an authoritative bellow:

'All right! Vairry q-u-a-a-t, please! This is a recording! VAIRRY VAIRRY Q-U-A-A-T!'

And the scene was videotaped. Then dress rehearsals began on the next two-minute scene.

I spent the morning thinking that if I were Annie or Frank Finlay it would drive me crazy to be constantly nagged about the angle of my head or the position of my hand when I was trying to concentrate on acting. But when we adjourned to the top-floor cafeteria for lunch, I mentioned this to Annie and she looked faintly surprised and said, Oh, no, that was no problem. And Kate Binchy, overhearing this, explained it in a single sentence:

'All the interior work's been done.'

Through three weeks of rehearsal, the cast's and the director's only concern had been with what each character was thinking and feeling. So by the day the taping began, Annie and Frank and the rest of the cast had their interpretations locked inside their heads where the incessant visual instructions couldn't touch them.

I was so fascinated by the technical details of the videotaping and so busy getting it all down in my notebook I was only vaguely aware that the words being spoken were from the letters in *84, Charing Cross Road*. We were having dinner on the cafeteria's outdoor porch when somebody asked me:

'How does it feel to see yourself on television?'

I wasn't seeing myself on television. I was seeing Annie Jackson, moving around in an English bed-sitter that bore no resemblance whatsoever to my old converted apartment.

That was on Friday. On Saturday – I suppose because I'd got used to the videotaping process by then and could ignore it – something inside me began to change. As gradually as stepping from very shallow water into slightly deeper water, I began to see the bookshop set, not as a set, but as my bookshop. Frank Finlay, looking more and more like the snapshots of Frank Doel Nora had sent me, spoke the letters in a voice, and with inflections, so exactly as I'd imagined Frank Doel to sound when I'd read his letters that the two Franks became one. And when Frank picked up a book that was unmistakably mine and handed it to one of the girls to mail to me, the illusion was overpowering: Frank Doel was still alive, the other friends I'd made in the bookshop still worked there, the shop itself was still thriving at 84, Charing Cross Road.

Late that afternoon, as I was watching the bookshop staff open one of the Christmas parcels, remembering Brian Huson's 'the bookshops are all quite small,' a messenger tiptoed into the control booth and laid a slip of paper in my lap with a single sentence on it:

'Mr Brian Huson will pick you up for dinner at six in the lobby.'

The explanation was as matter-of-fact as the very British Mr Huson himself. (English doesn't describe him; he's British, like the Empire.)

'I'm staying at my club. I flew in from Beirut yesterday on business,' he said as we drove to a nearby restaurant. 'After dinner last night I was in the lounge looking through a copy of *Radio Times* and I came on a story about *84, Charing Cross Road* being filmed this weekend. So this morning I phoned the BBC and they said Yes, you were here and you had an hour's dinner break at six.'

We lingered over dinner so I was late getting back to the control booth. As I slid into my seat at the half-moon table and looked out at the central monitor, I saw old Mrs Boulton working on the Husons' luncheon cloth.

At ten P.M. when the taping ended and we drove back to London, I was vaguely depressed. I told myself I was tired; it had been a long two days of note-taking.

But that night I dreamed of the bookshop. I'd never dreamed about it before but I'd never had a concrete picture of it in my mind before. Now I saw it vividly. I saw Frank and the girls and Bill Humphries and Mr Marks, the owner. They were all busy dusting the bookshelves and straightening the books, and Frank was putting a tumbler of pink garden roses on his desk – all because I was finally coming to London and they were getting ready to welcome me. Then it was a sunny morning, I was stepping out of a car on to the sidewalk of Charing Cross Road and walking up to the bookshop door. But the shop was closed. Its empty windows were dirty and the letters over the glass door were chipped and peeling. I tried the door and it swung open and I walked into a cold, bare room with dismantled bookshelves lying on the floor, and an empty staircase running up to rooms I knew were desolate and abandoned as the one I stood in.

The dream woke me. And lying there in the darkness at two or three in the morning, I tried not to hear the lines that were like a dirge in my head:

'"Tell them I came, and no one answered,
   That I kept my word," he said . . .'

I fell asleep eventually. I woke Sunday morning to bright sunshine and
it was easy to put the bad dream out of my mind and enjoy the day's
taping.

Since it was my last night, I had dinner with my only close friends
in London, Leo and Ena Marks, son and daughter-in-law of Marks &
Co. We'd seen so little of each other in the ten days I'd been there
that we sat a long time over dinner and I was an hour late getting back
to the control booth. If I'd gone back earlier, I'd have watched half a
dozen rehearsals of the scene in progress, which would have lessened
the impact. As it was, I slid into my seat just as Chris was calling for
quiet. A moment later I saw, coming up on the screen in front of me,
my own apartment. I saw my slatted coffee-table and beyond it, the
grey drapes at the picture window. I was vaguely aware that the desk
wasn't mine and that the bookshelves were on the wrong wall. Then
Annie walked into the room. She had mail in her hand. She opened
a letter and stood reading it – while the impersonal voice of a
secretary told her Frank Doel was dead. I sat remembering the
January night when I'd come home from the library to find that
wrong-looking letter waiting for me. And when Annie, in a moving
gesture, swept up a load of books in her arms, my throat tightened and
I looked away from the monitor for a minute. When I looked back,
Annie was curled up on the floor, sorting books. My books.

I was looking at my own apartment and at books that were
unmistakably mine, but I wasn't there. Somebody else was going
through my books. Suddenly, it was a visible fact to me that Frank
Doel wasn't the only one who had died. I must have died, too – or
how could someone else be sitting on the floor a few feet from my
coffee-table, pawing through my most cherished books as if they were
hers? When she picked up *Elizabethan Poets*, the green cover itself
seemed to cry out to me for rescue. I wanted to shout:

'Put that down, it's mine! It was a present from the shop – from
Frank and everybody!'

I didn't shout. Like the dead heroine of *Our Town* watching the
living move about in her childhood home, I knew my shout wouldn't
be heard. But she had been seeing the past. I was looking at the future

and I was powerless to prevent it. I didn't know I was crying, till Beryl reached across Mark Cullingham to press my hand firmly and whisper: 'Are you all right?' (meaning Pull yourself together). And I sobbed testily:

'Of course I'm not all right! Anybody can see I'm a complete mess!' And Shivas laughed and put an arm around me, and I swam up from the dark waters and back to the land of the living.

A year later the show was bought by PBS and I finally got to see it. There was a special preview showing at Channel 13, for me 'and seventy-five close friends' – meaning my six close friends and the entire Democratic Club – and I was nervously wondering whether I was going to start weeping again, at the sight of the bookshop I'd waited too long to visit or the preview of my own Passing. But I didn't weep. I watched the screening with unalloyed pleasure. On the night of the broadcast I watched it a second time on my best friend's colour TV set with even more pleasure. I loved it from beginning to end and I could have watched it a dozen more times if I'd been let.

You only drown once.

4

Fan Fare

In 1975 there were no longer any shoeboxes of fan mail on my closet shelf: they'd been gone for over a year. What happened was that after *The Duchess* came out in both countries I'd acquired several more shoeboxes full of mail till the stack of them reached nearly to the hanging light bulb. One night, as I opened the closet door and pulled the light cord, the bulb burned out in a momentary flash of blue flame – an inch or two from the shoeboxes. The closet is just inside the front door; the only other exit in case of fire is out the eighth-floor window.

I replaced the light bulb. But when I went to bed that night I couldn't fall asleep. I kept seeing those shoeboxes jammed with dried paper an inch or two from the little blue flame. Finally I got out of bed, carried the armload of shoeboxes down the hall and sadly dropped down the incinerator a couple of thousand beautiful testimonials to my talent and character. From then on I threw away every fan letter as soon as I answered it – except for one special handful.

Each year a few letters came in from English readers who wanted to show me the literary sights in their home towns. These letters I stashed in the England Corner – a back corner of the breakfront where I kept my passport, London address book and the maps of London and England we all know I couldn't read. Now and then on a winter evening, I'd take them out and reread them, and throw away those too old to make use of if I ever did get to England for a literary sightseeing tour. I remember one, for instance, from an Oxford don, offering to show me Newman's rooms at Oriel. 'But don't wait too long,' he warned. 'I'm eighty-four.' Rereading it three years later, in the summer of '77, I threw it away; I'd waited too long. For a grim economic reason.

Between 1974 and 1977, I managed the considerable feat of writing three successive books which had to go down the incinerator. A fourth, written on commission – a tourist guide to New York called *Apple of My Eye* – was published, but the money I got for it just paid my living expenses while I researched and wrote it. I wasn't earning enough in royalties to afford another trip to England, and in the fall of '77, in a fit of housecleaning and pessimism, I threw away the clutch of fan letters still in the England Corner. But that winter, a few more dribbled in.

'Dear Miss Hanff,

'... If you come to Winchester, we'd love to show you Izaak Walton's memorial and Jane Austen's grave in Winchester Cathedral. And afterwards, we'd drive you the short distance to Chawton to see Jane's house.

'I must warn you, we are a retired couple and very dull.

Jean Gomme'

'Dear Miss Hanff,

I am a friend of the caretaker of John Henry Newman's house at Littlemore. If you come again to Oxford, I could arrange to have you taken through the house ...'

'Dear Miss Hanff

'I am one of those umbrella-waving tourist guides you avoided when you toured London. I'm so sorry you never got to the Tower of London while you were here.

'If you ever come again, I'd love to give you a personally guided tour of the Tower, and show you some things you missed at Westminster Abbey.

'I promise not to bring the umbrella no matter how hard it's raining.

Judy Summers'

There was a letter from a girl named Doris, who worked in a Brighton bookshop and wanted to show me the Pavilion 'if you can come on a Sunday.'

Then one morning my phone rang and a light, rather husky English voice that could have been male or female said:

'Miss Hanff? I've just finished reading *Apple of My Eye* and I loved it. I love New York, I come over every year.'

'Where are you staying?' I asked.

'Oh, I'm not there now,' said the voice. 'I'm calling from London.'

'What part of London?' I asked. There was a pause.

'Well, actually,' said the voice, 'I'm calling from Harrow School infirmary. I have the flu.'

I said I didn't think his parents would appreciate the long-distance phone call and he said:

'Oh, my mother won't mind, she calls New York all the time, she loves it, too.'

He asked what other books I'd written. I gave him the titles and wished him a speedy recovery, and we hung up. A week later, the letter arrived:

'Dear Miss Hanff,

'I am the fifteen-year-old Harrow schoolboy who phoned you last week. I have just read *The Duchess of Bloomsbury Street* and I enjoyed it very much but I have one criticism.

'You spent three full pages on Eton, and you never even mentioned Harrow. Why don't you come back to London next summer? You could stay with my mother and me at our house in Kensington and my mother would drive us to Harrow and I would give you the Grand Tour.

Peter Astaire'

Then in March the bone-crusher arrived.

'Dear Miss Hanff,

'I am the widow of Frederic Brittain, biographer of Sir Arthur Quiller-Couch . . .

'If you ever come to Cambridge I'll give you tea in Q's room and biscuits from his tobacco jar.

Muriel Brittain'

I got down my copy of the Brittain biography and saw that it had been published in 1948. I wondered how old Muriel Brittain was.

'*Don't wait too long.*'

I got out my maps and saw (or decided) that all the places fans wanted me to visit were within a day's round trip of London. I could manage the plane fare, but a Show Tour package would give me too little time, and the cost of a hotel room and three restaurant meals a day would break the bank entirely. I stewed about this for a week or two. Then one fine April morning André Deutsch came to breakfast.

André is a London publisher with a special fondness for American authors. He's the English publisher of John Updike, John Kenneth Galbraith, Peter Benchley and Marilyn French, just to name those I can remember offhand. And every year he comes to New York to buy new books for his list and see all his American authors, including me. The phone will ring one morning and a Continental voice will announce:

'Helene? Darling, it's André, I just got in from London. Can you give me breakfast on Tuesday? At eight o'clock?'

Or he forgets to phone and comes anyway. I assume he makes up a tentative schedule on the plane coming over because one year, on a hot July morning, I was in the kitchen getting breakfast in my bra and bikini panties when the buzzer sounded and the doorman said into the intercom:

'Gentleman on the way up.'

It was 7:50 by the kitchen clock and I said:

'What-do-you-mean, a gentleman on the way up at this hour! Who is he?'

The doorman asked the caller's name and reported:

'Mr Deutsch.'

I hadn't known he was in town. I tore into the living-room – which hadn't been dusted lately – and barely made it inside a T-shirt and slacks when André walked in. He kissed me and I said:

'You might have let me know you were coming!'

And André said reasonably:

'I must have, darling. It's down in my book.' And he showed me his pocket engagement book where it said under Tuesday, '8 A.M. Breakfast with Helene.'

I love him, so it didn't matter. I love him for many reasons but especially because he's not a faceless corporation on three floors of a skyscraper, he's a man – slight, grey-haired, with a thin tanned face, an exotic accent (he was born in Hungary) and a very dapper wardrobe.

That April morning over our bacon and eggs I told him about the literary sights fans wanted to show me.

'I've got the fare and enough money for incidental expenses,' I said. 'What I need is a free flat for a few weeks.'

'You can have my house!' said André, pleased. 'I'm going to China and India for a month, I leave on twenty-first July.' And he added: 'Workmen will be there, I'm having a new story added on to the house. But they'll be up on the roof, they won't bother you.'

Anyone who's ever had workmen building an extra floor to the house will find that sentence hilarious. But André and I were innocents and the plan seemed perfectly feasible to us. He described the house enthusiastically, gave me the address and telephone number and told me to land at Heathrow during office hours so his secretary could meet the plane and drive me to the house and turn over the keys to me.

As soon as he left, I got out my map and located the street he lived on. It was either in Chelsea or South Kensington (the map was a little vague) but it was unmistakably down below Buckingham Palace. I don't like it down there. My London begins up at Regent's Park and runs through Marylebone and Bloomsbury, Mayfair and Soho, on its way down to the Mall where it ends at St James's Park and Green Park. Everything below that, I regard as No Man's Land. But I rose above the fact that André lived in the wrong part of town and phoned my friends to announce that I had a London town house for three summer weeks.

That night I dashed off a letter to Ena Marks asking if she and Leo would like to spend a couple of August weeks driving hither and yon to meet my fans and see the literary sights they wanted to show me. Back came a cable: IT'S A DATE LETTER FOLLOWS ALL OUR LOVE ENA AND LEO.

I went down to British Airways and bought my ticket and then I wrote to the fans involved, giving them my arrival and departure dates and André's address.

A letter arrived from Ena, suggesting I send her a list of the fans' names and addresses so she could get in touch with them and start making up a touring schedule. She wrote:

> 'I have several painting commissions but I'm hoping to finish them by the time you come.' (Ena's a portrait painter, under her maiden name, Elena Gaussen.) 'Marcus the cat sends love. As for Leo, well, he is still making sorties to this planet when he can spare the time from whichever part of outer space he comes from.
>
> Your loving Ena'

I mailed her the list and asked her to keep my first week free for London fans, and to add Ayot St Lawrence to the list of tours just because I was panting to see it. The only other person I wrote to was Abbe.

Abbe had entered my life – for ten minutes – back in June of '71. A fan letter arrived from a young woman who said she'd just graduated from college and had been given *84* as a graduation present. The letter was funny. (She had graduated from Hunter College, which she spelled gravely 'Huntah,' giving it the Brooklyn pronunciation.) But what intrigued me most was the address. I could look out of the windows and see the apartment house she lived in, right across the street.

It was quicker to phone her than to write a thank-you note, so I called her and said:

'Why didn't you just hand the letter to the doorman?'

She said she hadn't wanted to be a nuisance – but since I mentioned it, could she leave her copy of the book with the doorman for me to autograph? I was on my lunch hour and I said:

'You can bring it over now if you want to.'

Her letter had been witty and relaxed. But when she came, she was solemn, round-faced and bespectacled – and suddenly I was looking at Myself When Young: easy and assured on paper, awkward and stiff in person. She was hunting for a job in publishing and I phoned a couple of editors for her, but before they got around to seeing her Abbe called to tell me she had a job at CBS. I congratulated her and then forgot about her. One year later, in July of '72, she phoned to say she was going to London for two weeks, and I wished her Bon Voyage.

She never came home. Or say that she took one look at London and discovered she *was* home.

The first London letter arrived in September telling me she had found herself a job working backstage in a London theatre.

'I'm tea-girl,' she wrote. 'I make tea for forty people – cast and crew – in a huge vat down in the basement. I also mop the stage before every performance and I sew an actor's tights back together when they split which they've done several times on this show.'

The theatre was paying her fifteen pounds a week and I didn't ask how she lived on it. I was writing *The Duchess* at the time and I used her as shamelessly as the theatre did. Abbe chased all over London for me, checking street addresses and bulletin-board notices and mews signs. She sent me the information in letters that jumped with the life of the 'hotel' in St Martin's Lane where she was living.

'It's really a rooming-house for theatricals run by ex-theatricals. The roof in my room leaks but it's not a big problem because when it rains, the manageress leaves a bucket in my room and the main leak is over the sink anyway.

'The walls are a bit thin. so when Derek, the man next door, starts snoring I just elbow the wall and he turns over. We've decided it's like being married only with a partition down the middle of the matrimonial bed. If I'm reading in bed and I laugh at something, he'll call:

'"Oo, wot is it, luv?"

and I have to shout the passage through the wall.'

When I was in London for the TV show I phoned her, and it took the hotel operator five minutes to connect me. Then Abbe said, slightly breathless:

'There's only one phone, it's in the lobby, they shout up for us. I had to run down five flights is why it took so long.'

During the three years since then, her letters had kept coming, though I don't think I answered one in four.

'My mother was here for Christmas. She took one look at my room and said: "I lived better than this during the Depression." Then she said: "For two hundred years, immigrants have been coming to the United States to improve their living standard. You emigrate back to

Europe to live in a tenement." Now she pelts me with letters on the subject. I am strongly considering writing *Deceased* on her next letter and returning it to sender.'

Then came a letter announcing she'd landed a permanent job at a West End theatre working the lighting board as assistant to the electrician. From then on I got to know the backstage crew, especially Ron, the electrician, and Beerbohm Tree, the theatre cat.

'After Beerbohm caught three mice we told the manager he ought to be paid, as he was the theatre exterminator, and the manager agreed to pay for his cat food.' Beerbohm got into a fight with another tomcat and needed an expensive trip to the vet for a bleeding eye, 'So we put him on payroll for one matinee as B. Tree, duties unspecified.'

The last letter I'd had reported that the St Martin's hotel had closed and Abbe had moved into Sandringham Flats – 'on Charing Cross Road of which you may have heard.' The flats had no elevators, no bathtubs and no showers. But her fourth-floor walk-up had a balcony 'and wonderful neighbours – mostly pub staff, writers, the Unemployed and ex-theatricals (a wig lady from films).' She didn't mind having no bathtub; she did mind having no phone.

'The phone company has heard a rumor that the building is to be torn down so they are arranging not to install new phones.'

That's Abbe, and when I wrote to tell her I had André's house for a month she wrote back:

'I'm looking forward to the Second Coming (well, the third). Please save your first Monday evening for dinner at my flat. Monday is my night off.'

By June, progress reports had arrived from Ena:

'Muriel Brittain is very excited. Cambridge is pencilled in for 13 August.' 'The Gommes are delightful. Winchester will be our first trip on 2 August.' 'The woman in Oxford seems a bit odd.'

I'd had a very friendly letter from the woman in Oxford so that last progress report baffled me and I phoned Ena. Leo answered and told me, in his impressive baritone, that Ena was down in the country painting a portrait.

'Has she straightened things out with the woman in Oxford?' I asked.

There was a pause.

'Ena,' said Leo, 'has everything under control.' And he added, 'We're both longing to see you.'

At the end of June, Doris in the Brighton bookshop wrote to say she would be going 'on holiday' on August 6 and hoped we could come one Sunday before then, and I phoned Ena again. Once more, Leo answered. Ena was visiting her mother, who had bronchitis.

'Do you know whether we have the last Sunday in July or the first Sunday in August free – and if not, can we switch one of them?' I asked.

There was a pause.

'Ena,' said Leo positively, 'would certainly know the answer to that.'

On July 19, six days before I was to leave for London, a letter arrived from André:

'Dear Helene,

'It seems the workmen will be taking over the entire house and you would be uncomfortable there.

'But come on the 25th as planned. My mother is in Switzerland for the summer and you will have the use of her flat in St John's Wood. Penny, my secretary, will meet you at Heathrow and drive you to the flat and turn over the keys to you . . .'

I got out my map of London and literally shouted for joy when I located St John's Wood. It was at the top of my Visitors' Map – right alongside Regent's Park and a lovely walk down along the park's Outer Circle to Marylebone. I dashed off notes to Ena, Abbe and the fans, and hoped my new address would get to London before I did.

Six days later, with a Nothing book, a date book and all my Best-Laid Plans, I took a night flight to London.

2 A.M. Tues./Wed. 25/26

The first great blessing of a borrowed flat is, if you've got jet-lag insomnia and you get hungry at two in the morning, Room Service hasn't closed for the night. I'm at the kitchen table, I've just had a ham sandwich and a glass of milk, thanks to Penny, who stocked the refrigerator with breakfast and lunch supplies for me.

The refrigerator isn't in the kitchen, it's out in the hall. Standing by itself inside the front door. This flat has several demented features. They stimulate me.

As we drove here from the airport I asked Penny if she had Mrs Deutsch's address in Switzerland so I could write and thank her for the use of the flat.

'Oh, she doesn't know you're staying there,' said Penny.

I thought I'd give myself a holiday from housework over here, so I said:

'Does she have a cleaning woman I could get to come in once a week?'

'Mrs Deutsch likes to do her own cleaning,' said Penny. 'She won't let André get her a housekeeper, and of course it worries him. Not that she's not perfectly healthy. But she's eighty-eight.'

I'll clean it myself.

I'm in a small apartment house just off Wellington Road, which seems to be the main avenue out here, very wide and tree-lined. It's a lovely suburb – old houses, old trees, quiet as the grave at night.

The front door of the flat is at the top of a long narrow hall that runs the length of the flat, with closets and a phone table on one side and all the rooms in a row on the other: bedroom, bath, kitchen and, way down at the far end, a large living-room.

I got stomped to death in a Customs mob for two hours so it was afternoon when we got here. There was a telegram under the door – WELCOME HOME ENA AND LEO – and a note from Judy Summers about touring Literary Chelsea tomorrow. Penny showed me over the flat and offered me my choice of beds. Mama Deutsch had her big double bed moved into the living-room so she could watch television from bed, but I'm sleeping in the single bed in the bedroom. If you've lived in one room all your life, a bedroom is the ultimate luxury.

As soon as Penny left I phoned Ena and she and I shouted at each other excitedly and she said she and Leo would pick me up for dinner at 7:30. Then Diana Athill phoned – she's André's partner – to say there's a Deutsch company lunch for me on Friday.

I don't sleep on planes so after I unpacked I thought I'd take a shower and then try for a nap. But after studying the bathtub I decided a shower wasn't practical. Mama has got the most crowded bathtub you ever saw.

There are thick steel rails with steel handles attached to both rims, for getting in and out: there's a broad wooden bench with steel handles, to sit on while you bathe; and in front of the bench there's a broad rack with soap, sponge, bathbrush and Johnson's Baby Powder. So between the small half-moon of unoccupied tub at the back and the shower nozzle at the front is a wood-and-steel obstacle course I was in no condition to run. I took a bath crouched in the back half-moon.

It wasn't till I stepped out of the bathtub and my toes curled around it that I noticed Mama's bathroom rug. It's an old Oriental, cut down to fit the bathroom floor. Dripping all over it, I also noticed there were no towels in the bathroom, so I went out into the hall and found the linen closet and opened the door – and my bones melted.

Every shelf is edged with a wide border of white lace, every bundle of sheets, pillow cases, towels and wash cloths is tied in wide pink satin ribbin and finished off with a great pink satin bow.

I can slave an hour wrapping one Christmas present and when I finish, the package looks as if I'd picked it out of a trash can, so I knew I'd be the death of that linen closet. But I'd seen a pile of freshly delivered laundry on the double bed in the living-room and there are enough towels and sheets there to last me.

You won't believe this but I just noticed there are Oriental rugs in here, too. In the kitchen. One covers most of the kitchen floor, and there's a little cut-down square piece of another one in front of the stove. You can sit a long time trying to figure out why anyone would want a piece of Oriental carpet in front of the oven. Some other time.

Leo and Ena came up to see the flat and by the time we went down to the lobby it was raining again. Leo had parked the car in the apartment house lot but having the manners of a stately grandee, he insisted on bringing it to the front door for us, And as soon as he left, Ena said:

'I'm going to sit in the back with you. Don't say anything about it. I can't sit in the front seat when Leo drives. You don't drive so you wouldn't notice it.'

'Leo,' she went on, 'drives straight down the middle of the street. So other cars give him a very wide berth and he's never had an accident. He has the lowest insurance rates in London so of course he thinks he's a very good driver. And I've had accidents, he's certainly not going to listen to me!'

Leo arrived with the car and Ena and I climbed into the back seat. I think the reason why I never noticed his driving is that Leo is so totally imperturbable, behind the wheel as anywhere else, and that kind of temperament inspires confidence in a nondriver. I also never noticed before that Ena is a compulsive back-seat driver. So the conversation on the way to the restaurant went like this:

'We've moved,' Leo told me. 'My mother died a year ago and left a flat in Park West which we thought we'd sell –'

'Leo, there's a couple crossing the street!'

'– but it's large enough for all Ena's canvases and there's a study for me –'

'Leo, you can't go through. You'll have to turn left.'

'– so we're in the process of getting rid of my parents' furniture –'

'Leo! Turn left!'

'– and moving our own things in, to see how we like it –'

'LEFT!'

Leo fell suddenly silent. That's when I noticed our car had stopped. We were in the middle of the street at an intersection and surrounded by heavy traffic. A bus coming toward us had stopped, and a car coming from the right and wanting to cross in front of us had stopped. The bus driver was leaning forward with his arms folded on the wheel, gazing at Leo. The driver trying to cross from the right was leaning out of his car window, staring at Leo.

Suddenly Ena heaved up out of her seat, flung herself over the back of Leo's seat, reached down and tapped his left wrist.

'THIS is your left hand,' she said.

And Leo said tranquilly:

'Thank you, my darling, if you hadn't told me I wouldn't have known.'

He surveyed the situation carefully, came to a judicious conclusion and turned left, and we drove the long way to the restaurant. Leo got out of the car, opened the back door and in his courtly fashion helped me out of the car followed by the frayed bundle of nerves beside me.

He isn't going touring with us. He said he has too much work to do. (He was a screenwriter for years, and a playwright, and somebody in Hollywood is interested in a modernized version of one of his scripts.) Ena says she knew all along he'd back out at the last minute: he hates sightseeing.

He wanted to know whether the BBC production of *84* had been shown in New York, and while we were talking about it I called the bookshop 'Marks and Co.' I thought it might sound odd to him, so I said:

'I don't know why, but I've never thought of it as "Marks and Company." On their stationery they never spelled out the word "Company" so I've called it "Marks and Co" for years, as if "Co" were a word.'

And Leo said in mild surprise:

'You were quite right. The "Co" didn't stand for company. My uncle, Mark Cohen, was my dad's partner as well as his brother-in-law, so they decided to call the firm "Marks and Co." The "Co" stood for Cohen.'

Over coffee, I got out my typewritten list and Ena got out her beautiful chart, with every route and destination in a separate color.

'Did I tell you the woman in Oxford's a bit odd?' Ena asked me.

'Yes, but that's all you said. Odd how?' I asked.

'Well, it seems odd to me,' said Ena. 'I telephoned her and introduced myself and asked what day she'd like to have us drive up to see Littlemore. And she said – she had a very tense voice – she said she thought it would be much better if Miss Hanff came alone by train.'

'Miss Hanff isn't going anywhere alone by train,' I said. 'She's afraid of getting lost.'

'I told her,' Ena went on, 'that I thought you'd prefer driving through the countryside and she said "Nonsense" in that tight voice. She said she would meet your train and put you up for the night and I was not to trouble myself further about it.'

'I'll call her tomorrow,' I said. And Leo said unexpectedly:

'Ena will call her. Ena's in charge of your schedule.'

'I really think it's better if I deal with her,' said Ena.

We put our lists and chart away and were waiting for the check when Leo said suddenly:

'I wonder what became of the sign that used to hang outside the shop.'

I thought of Dan Kelly in Omaha.

'Funny-you-should-ask,' I said. 'It's hanging on the short wall of my alcove, alongside all the books that came from there.'

'That's nice,' said Leo peacefully.

This kitchen's going to be my office; it's very sunny in the daytime and the table I'm writing on is solid and roomy. Mama's tea tray was on it: china cream-and-sugar, cup-and-saucer, small pot of honey and a knife and spoon neatly set out on a fresh napkin. I moved the whole tray on to a chair by the window out of harm's way. To anything breakable, I classify as Harm's Way.

Wednesday, July 26

Back in my late teens when I was acting with an amateur theatre group, I read a one-act play called *Two Passengers for Chelsea*. It was about Thomas and Jane Carlyle and I loved it. I'd never read Carlyle, so the next day I went to the local library and brought home his *History of the French Revolution*.

All I remember of it is that Carlyle never called Robespierre 'Robespierre', he called him 'Sea-Green Incorruptible Robespierre' – and I mean if Robespierre was mentioned four times on one page he was 'Sea-Green Incorruptible Robespierre' all four times. The whole book was so full of outraged capitals that reading it was like being continuously shouted at. When you finished you were just worn out.

But years later, somebody gave me a book of Jane Carlyle's letters. Till I read them I hadn't known what a huge literary lion Carlyle was, back in the 1840s and '50s. The Carlyle house in Cheyne Row was a literary salon, with Tennyson, Thackeray, Dickens, Emerson, the Brownings, all coming to pay homage to the Sage of Chelsea. Jane presided over the salon with great charm and wit, and her letters took you into that house and made you feel you knew her and Thomas very well. I hadn't known the house still existed and was open to the public – much less that everything in it was exactly as the Carlyles had left it – till Judy Summers took me there this afternoon.

Judy Summers is one of the rare souls who look exactly as their name sounds: small, dark-haired, pretty and in her twenties. She quit her job as a tour guide to enroll in a BBC training programme. She's learning to edit film, but what she really wants to be is a novelist.

'If I'm trained for a job that pays well, like film editing,' she said,

'I'll be able to work half the year and save enough to live on the other half while I write.'

She can probably manage it. Her parents own a house in St John's Wood, and Judy has a floor of it converted into a flat, rent-free.

The trouble with Literary Chelsea is that except for the Carlyle house, none of the literary houses you want to see are open to the public. We stopped outside one, for instance, and Judy pointed up to the third floor.

'D'you see those two windows on the left?' she asked me. 'They were the windows to Henry James's study.'

We stopped in front of another house and Judy jabbed an accusing finger at the living-room curtains behind which we could see someone moving.

'You'll notice there are people living there,' she said. 'They can do anything they like with that house! It's not a museum, it's not National Trust. And the powers-that-be hope you won't notice the plaque. The name on it isn't pure enough for the house to be preserved!'

The house belonged to Oscar Wilde.

Then we went to Cheyne Row and walked into a sitting-room that's exactly as the artist painted it in the painting reproduced in my book of Jane's letters. There was the busy wallpaper and busy slipcovers you know Jane chose because they wouldn't show the dirt and wouldn't wear out with too much cleaning (she was monstrous thrifty), and the horde of knick knacks on the mantel. And the small sofa where Nero, the family dog, sat for the only portrait in the painting Jane approved of.

What that painter put her through was a refined form of torture. Jane spent most of her time in the sitting-room; she had to do all her letter-writing, sewing and meal-planning there because it was the only room where her movements didn't disturb the Genius working upstairs in his study. Well, the painter wanted to paint both the living-room and part of the dining-room seen through the doorway – in microscopic detail – and he came two days a week for three months and then every day for six more weeks. And painted at Jane's elbow.

The chair is still there, near the door as it was on the day Jane jumped up from it when Leigh Hunt came.

The Hunts lived around the corner and Leigh used to drop in regularly. But he was sick one winter and was absent for so long that when he finally recovered and appeared in the Carlyle's doorway, Jane jumped up and kissed him. And a day or two later, one of the Hunt servants delivered a note. From Mr Hunt to Mrs Carlyle. The note read:

> Jenny kissed me when we met,
> Jumping from the chair she sat in;
> Time, you thief, who love to get
> Sweets into your list, put that in:
>
> Say I'm weary, say I'm sad,
> Say that health and wealth have missed me,
> Say I'm growing old, but add
> Jenny kissed me.

I think he was the only one who called her Jenny. Her friends and family, including Thomas, called her Jeannie.

The house is full of lovely panelled walls and spacious rooms, but the only other room I identified with was Thomas's study at the top of the house, because of what Jane went through to build it.

She spent half her time trying to keep the house quiet so Thomas could work in peace. She kept herself and the servants out of earshot, she bribed and threatened the neighbours into selling their noisy poultry and playing their piano only at specified hours – and still the house wasn't quiet enough. So one season when Thomas went away on a three-month lecture tour, Jane decided to surprise him by building a new study for him at the top of the house. She hired workmen to build new walls, new windows, new fireplace, and when the workmen were too slow, she pitched in and helped them build it. Then she installed Thomas's desk and bookshelves and made curtains and cushions and slipcovers – and completed the study triumphantly the day before Thomas came home.

He couldn't work in it. It wasn't quiet enough.

So Thomas magnanimously went away for another month, to give Jane a chance to rip out the new walls and the new fireplace and help the workmen instal soundproofing. After that, it was finally quiet enough for Thomas to finish his definitive five-volume life of Frederick the Great.

Jane was a pretty fair writer herself. I can't quote any of the letters from memory, but I've got a passage of her journal by heart. Carlyle was infatuated with a Lady Ashburton and the infatuation lasted twenty years, at least, until the lady's death. Lord and Lady Ashburton lived at Bath House.

> 'That eternal Bath House,' Jane wrote in her journal. 'I wonder how many thousand miles Mr. C. has walked between there and here. Oh, when I first noticed that heavy yellow house, without knowing or caring who it belonged to, how far I was from dreaming that through years and years, I should carry every stone's weight of it on my heart.'

We're doing the Abbey on Saturday. Ena wants to tour the Tower with us and she's painting somebody on Saturday.

Harrow tomorrow.

Thursday evening, July 27

Peter Astaire called for me at eleven A.M. as planned. He came alone. He's beautiful in the way all English public school boys seem to be at fifteen: dark hair carefully cut to frame a chiseled face, beautiful manners – and absolute self-possession.

'My mother will meet us at the tube station in half an hour,' he said. He told me his father and two older brothers went to Harrow, which made me nervous. I had a feeling my best pantsuit wasn't suitable for lunching with the wife of one Harrovian and the mother of three more, but I couldn't help it. I'm stuck with heavy clodhopper shoes and I don't wear skirts or dresses, they look hideous with oxfords.

'We lived in St John's Wood when I was small,' he said. 'I thought I'd take you on a tour of the neighborhood and show you where to find everything that's not in the High Street. The High Street's just round the corner, you'll find that easily. All the shops there are good.'

And we set off on a tour of what wasn't on the High Street. He took me to the post office and showed me how to use the stamp machine. He pointed out the best dry-cleaner's, the fastest dry-cleaner's, the launderette, the off-license (liquor store) – 'There's one in the High Street but this one's a bit closer if it's raining or near closing time' – and the 'local', the pub he said was 'the best in St

John's Wood.' Then we walked to the tube station.

There was no middle-aged woman waiting for us. What there was, sitting behind the wheel of an Alfa Romeo, was a slim, pretty redhead in her thirties, in an unpressed linen dress the colour of the freckles on her nose.

'This is my mother,' said Peter. And the redhead said, 'I'm Lesley,' and stuck out a hand shyly.

'You must have been a child bride!' I said as I climbed in the back seat. Lesley said:

'Almost. I was married at eighteen and had my oldest son at nineteen.'

We had lunch at what both of them told me was 'the best fish-and-chips pub in London' and then drove to Harrow-on-the-Hill in bright sunshine. It was a short drive through green suburban country. Then the car climbed a long uphill road. At the top of it, there was Harrow-on-the-Hill, a picture postcard. You come first to the King's Head Hotel, built in 1535, and a few yards from it, a gibbet with Henry VIII's portrait (the king's head) hanging from it, which seemed a kind of ambiguous compliment to the school's founder – or patron, I'm not sure which.

Just beyond the hotel on a rise above a great lawn is Harrow School. It's a red brick mansion, with two imposing white stone staircases, one on either side, curving up to the white arched door, and a white turret clock set in the red brick above the door. While Peter mounted the steps and rang for the caretaker, Lesley and I waited on the lawn below. I told her how impressed I was with his aplomb.

'He wouldn't let me come to your flat with him,' she told me. 'He said: "I think Helene and I ought to have a little time to ourselves first, Mother. We'll meet you at half-past eleven."' So she'd waited meekly at the tube station.

The caretaker came to the door and we saw him and Peter in conversation. The conversation lengthened. Then the caretaker went back into the school building, closing the door behind him, and Peter came slowly back to us.

'The caretaker says he's not permitted to allow visitors to go through the building in summer when the school's closed,' he said. 'Not even with a Harrow student to escort them.' And then he said:

'If you don't mind sitting on the grass, I can tell Helene all about the school and answer any of her questions.'

My heart went out to him. He'd counted on showing me Harrow. But without batting an eye he proceeded to give me a history of the school – 'Lord Byron, Winston Churchill and King Hussein all went to Harrow' – and then told me about the dormitories, called Houses.

'You're put down for a certain House by your parents as soon as you're born. My father and brothers were all at Headmaster House, so of course that's where I am.'

He said the salaries paid to teachers – called 'masters' – are 'appalling.'

'Harrow attracts some of the best masters because it pays the best,' he said. 'But even at Eton and Harrow, the masters must have small private incomes to manage decently. At Oxford and Cambridge the pay is so poor most of the professors are impoverished.'

He said most of the kids smoke pot – 'and we all know which masters drink.'

He confirmed something I'd guessed from what little I'd read about English schools, and it baffles me. There's no such thing as a graduation ceremony – not at Eton or Harrow.

'You stay until you finish the course and then you leave.'

What baffles me is where, in the former English colonies I live in, the great American Graduation Day came from. We make so much of high school graduations and college commencements we must have got them from somewhere.

After the lecture, Peter took us for a walk along the High Street – a hilly road lined with shops in Tudor houses. He pointed out 'the tuck shop' (candy store) and the restaurant – blandly named 'The Old Etonian.' Then we went into the official school clothing store so Lesley could order a few things Peter needed. While we stood at the counter, she and Peter conferred, and then Peter announced they were buying me a Harrow School shirt. It's white with a thin blue stripe – in the kind of fine sheer wool I haven't seen since nylon/orlon/dacron and all their miserable ilk took over the world.

We left the High Street for a wider avenue lined with the Houses. They might be turn-of-the century New York mansions or small-town city halls, red or grey stone buildings with white-columned doorways and none of the institutional look of American dormitories.

We drove back to Kensington. Peter wanted to show me his books about New York and Lesley wanted me to have tea in their garden. I'd heard about Cassius, the family terrier, and as Lesley put her key in the lock an outraged high-pitched barking started on the other side of the door. I figured it was hearing my strange voice that set him off so I stooped down and lifted the mail slot. All I could see through the opening was a white tail waving, but I called:

'Hi, Cassius!' From which Cassius concluded we must have met somewhere and become friends, and when we walked in he greeted me with enthusiasm.

It occurs to me I do exactly the same thing. Some out-of-town fan will phone and say:

'Miss Hanff? It's Mary Jones from Seattle.'

And I don't know her but she obviously knows me so I say:

'How are you?' With enthusiasm.

Rain routed us out of the garden and when I left I wished them better luck with the weather in Cornwall; they're off on a two-week vacation tomorrow.

Friday, 28th

I just went marketing in St John's Wood High Street. You're walking along an ordinary twentieth-century street, you turn right, into the High Street, and you're back in Jane Austen's day. It's a two-block stretch of small, sedate shops with decorous shop windows – no big signs, no gaudy displays – all of it looking so gentle and well-bred you want to take slow, ladylike steps. I walked up one side of the street and back down the other, past bakeries, meat markets, vegetable markets, gift shops, florist shops, china store, dress shop, shoe store, stationery store, an optometrist's, and two small supermarkets.

I went into one of the supermarkets and I didn't hit trouble till I'd filled my cart and pushed it to the checkout counter. I put all my purchases on the counter and the clerk added up the total and I paid him. I waited for him to pack everything in bags but he just stood there, and the two of us stared at each other, both waiting. Finally he said:

'Where's your bag?'

In London you take your own plastic bag to the supermarket with you. I explained I hadn't known this, and the clerk produced a couple of bags from a hidden supply and packed everything, but he made it clear I'd ruined his morning.

When I got back here and put my coffee and tea and crackers in the kitchen supply closet, I found Mama's bag supply. On the inside of the closet door there's a round nylon net bag stuffed to globe size with hundreds of plastic bags, each one folded neatly very small. She must have been saving them for twenty years.

Then I watered the 47 plants – every windowsill is crammed with them – and went into the bedroom to dress for the Deutsch company lunch. The bedroom has my favorite batty feature.

The room is dominated by a massive free-standing mahogany wardrobe Mama must have brought with her from Hungary fifty years ago. It's finished off at the top with an intricately carved railing. Well, behind the railing, lined up in a neat row are five empty egg cartons. Three paper, two plastic. If you're sitting on the bed putting on your pantyhose you can waste a lot of time staring at those egg cartons trying to figure out what they're doing there.

If you need to buy pantyhose over here, you ask for 'tights.'

Later

André's offices are in a five-story brownstone on Great Russell Street and the top floor is a large empty room reserved for literary sherry parties and company lunches. Diana, André's partner, presided at the lunch and everybody was there: Bill the sales manager, Piers the negotiator, Pam the Juvenile editor, and my personal Prince Philip, Deutsch's business manager and my private banker when I'm here. 'Oh, don't bother the bank, dear,' he says, and doles out cash to me every week and deducts it from my next royalty check. This company lunch would not be possible in New York because, though your editor is in a New York skyscraper, if your publisher is Lippincott, the sales manager and business manager are in Philadelphia. If it's Doubleday, they're out on Long Island. If it's Little, Brown, they're in Boston.

Futura, the paperback house that publishes my books over here, is also having a company lunch for me. Next Friday.

Saturday, July 29

Do not put off paying for that crypt or grave you ordered for yourself. Consider what happened to Ben Jonson.

Ben knew he'd be entitled to burial in Westminster Abbey and he reserved a grave there for himself and he never paid for it. Well, when he died he had a fine funeral and then the mourners went home and left Ben to be buried in his crypt under the Abbey floor. But the grave-diggers knew he hadn't paid for it, and they weren't going to waste valuable grave space on a deadbeat. So they opened the grave and slid Ben in, upright, and propped him in a corner, to keep the grave available for a paying customer.

This was in 1637 but nobody knew about it till 1793.

'In 1793,' reported Judy, 'the grave was opened to put a man named John Hunter in it – and the grave-diggers saw Ben Jonson's red hair sticking up out of the corner.'

'What did they do with him?' I asked.

'Nothing,' said Judy. 'They just left him standing there.'

You think of the old bromides about Eternal Rest – 'How sleep the brave who sink to rest'; 'We shall rest, and, faith, we shall need it – lie down for an aeon or two . . .' They all go right out the window when you realize Ben Jonson is spending Eternity standing up.

He had no luck whatever in Westminster Abbey; even the plaque in his memory has to be hidden away in a side wall where the Abbey hopes nobody will see it because the eulogy on it begins 'O rare Ben Johnson', and that ain't how he spelled it.

Still he was a lot luckier than Oliver Cromwell. Judy took me into the Henry VII Chapel and pointed to a sign:

'The Burial Place of Oliver Cromwell'

'It's his burial place, she said, 'but it's not his grave.'

The Lord Protector was buried there in 1658 with great pomp. But two years later came the restoration of the monarchy. And Charles II, whose father had been beheaded by Cromwell, had the body dug up and sentenced to be half-hanged, drawn and quartered for high treason. So Cromwell's decomposing corpse was publicly disemboweled and carved up. Thousands of Londoners came to the festivities.

I saw the tomb in which Elizabeth and her half-sister Queen Mary are buried together, in spite of the fact that Elizabeth was sent to the

Tower on Bloody Mary's orders. She wanted to write to Mary and ask to be put to death by a French executioner's sword instead of an English ax, because a sword sliced a head off in one clean blow and an ax didn't. How Elizabeth knew this is that when she was three years old, her mother, Anne Boleyn, had died by a French sword and somehow Elizabeth learned it had been a quick, clean death. When she was eight, the one stepmother she loved – Catherine Howard – had her head clumsily hacked off by repeated blows of the ax.

I was very moved to find memorials to two American writers there:

> Henry James, O.M.
> Novelist
> New York, 1843
> London, 1916

> Thomas Stearns Eliot, O.M.
> Born 26 Sept., 1888
> Died 4 Jan., 1965

On the way to the Abbey, we stopped at the Hotel Cadogan – Judy having discovered I love Oscar Wilde's plays and *The Ballad of Reading Gaol*. The hotel is still elegant and expensive but Judy said that back in the 1890s it was the most exclusive hotel in London.

'This is where the police came to arrest him,' she said. 'One of the arresting officers stepped up to him and said in a low voice:

'"Please come quietly, Mr Wilde, this *is* the Cadogan."'

We're doing the Tower next Friday if Ena can make it.

Abbe just phoned to confirm dinner Monday night.

'222 Sandringham Flats, Charing Cross Road,' she said. 'Are you sure you can find it?'

I told her not to insult me.

Brighton tomorrow.

Sunday, July 30

It was raining this morning when Ena came and we called Doris in Brighton. She said it was raining there, too, and she and Ena agreed that Brighton was a town to see on foot so we waited to see what the weather would do.

Ena loves Mama's kitchen mantel. It has a long row of Mama's treasures – painted china plates, pewter cream-and-sugar, souvenirs André brought her from faraway places – with kitchen necessities tucked unobtrusively between them, and even those – spice jars, soap dish, cleaning cloths – are all carefully chosen and arranged. One item baffled me. The centrepiece is a polished pewter teapot, and on one side of it, hanging down on a short string, is a large round medal with 'Mary' (Mama's name) on it. But on the other side there's a round Christmas tree ball, also on a string.

'Why would she hang a Christmas tree ornament up there?' I asked Ena.

'For balance,' she said. 'Mama likes symmetry. She probably couldn't find anything else the same size and shape as the medal.'

Ena made a detailed drawing of the mantel for me and entertained me with Leo stories while she worked.

'We had a cottage in Dorking last summer, it was on the water, and one day Leo decided to take the dinghy out and read while he floated.

'He piled his books in the dinghy carefully – you know how measured his movements are; none of this was hurried – he piled the books very neatly, edge to edge, and then he stepped majestically into the dinghy. But he didn't step into the middle of it the way anyone else would. He stepped on to one end of it. And the other end rose very slowly into the air – and Leo, in absolute slow motion, went perfectly head-over-arse into the water. It was lovely to watch!' And she went off into peals of laughter at the memory.

'Did he get mad when you laughed?' I asked.

'Oh, no, not Leo!' said Ena. 'He just picked himself up, dignified as ever. Then he shook the water out of each book, piled them carefully back into the dinghy and then stepped into the middle of it, dripping wet but majestic as ever, and sailed off.'

She said he also decided to take up horseback riding down there.

'On the day of his first lesson he got on the horse with a cigar in his mouth. It was all right: the horse refused to move. Either he didn't like the cigar smoke or he didn't like Leo.' And she was off on another fit of laughter. 'The instructor was quite upset and embarrassed but Leo wasn't perturbed in the least. He just handed me his cigar and politely asked for another horse.'

At one o'clock it was still raining in both cities and we postponed

Brighton till next Sunday. Doris insists she's not leaving on vacation till Monday.

Monday, July 31
lunchtime

I rose up early this morning to clean the flat and started by putting the kitchen and bathroom Oriental rugs out in the hall so I could scrub the floors. Then I went looking for the bucket. I looked in every kitchen and hall closet. No bucket anywhere. What I found instead was a toy-sized Bissell rug-shampooer so light a child could push it – and bottles and bottle of carpet shampoo. Even so, it wasn't till I was wiping the steel handrails on the bathtub that the obvious hit me.

Mama must be arthritic. She can't bend and straighten easily or she wouldn't need the hand rails. So of course she can't get down on her knees to scrub floors. But she was by God gonna do her floors herself – even if it meant cutting down her Oriental rugs to fit them, including an extra patch of rug in front of the stove.

Ena phoned; she switched dates so she can do the Tower with Judy and me next Friday. I called Futura to ask if I could bring her to the company lunch and Futura said: 'Any relation of Marks & Co. is welcome at Futura.' I figure if she's along, she'll get me out of there in time to meet Judy at two.

It's raining and Ena insists on driving me in to Charing Cross Road tonight for dinner with Abbe. She said she's meeting Leo in town anyway.

9 P.M.

I've given up sitting by the phone waiting for Abbe to call and ask what happened. I'm in the living-room. I thought if I watched TV it might calm me down but it didn't. I turned it off and I'm just sitting, cursing the London phone company for not giving Abbe a phone.

Charing Cross Road is two streets long. Ena drove slowly down it, peering out the window on her side while I peered out the window on mine, looking for Sandringham Flats. There was nothing that looked like an apartment house. In spite of the rush-hour traffic Ena circled around a couple of one-way streets and then drove back down Charing Cross Road slowly, twice, and neither of us found any sign of Sandringham Flats. Finally I told her to drop me at the upper end of the road and I'd find the place on foot.

Ena drove off and I walked slowly down one side of the road and then slowly back up the other side, but all I passed were small shops, none of which carried the numbers 222 or the name Sandringham Flats, and I blame Suburbia for what happened next.

The bookshops had closed for the day, but most stores were open – record shops, souvenir shops, a photo store, a couple of fast-food places. I went into the first one and asked the clerk if he could tell me where Sandringham Flats was. He'd never heard of it.

'D'you have the street name?' he asked me.

'It's on Charing Cross Road,' I said.

This shook him. He gawked a minute and then shouted to somebody in the back:

'Billy! Lady's lookin' for Sandringham Flats!'

Bill never heard of it.

I went into every single open store on both sides of Charing Cross Road – and not one clerk or manager could point out an apartment house on the street they both worked on five days a week. I thought it was only in New York that suburbanites took a commuter train every morning into the ciy, worked all day in stores or offices and took the commuter train home in the evening without ever seeing or learning anything of the street they worked on.

At seven, I was still wandering up and down Charing Cross Road. At seven-fifteen, I went into one of the snack bars and ate a sandwich standing at the window in case Abbe came by looking for me.

At eight, I took a cab back up here and sat by the phone – in tears – hoping she'd call from a phone booth.

Of all the roads in London I had to get lost on that one.

Tuesday, August 1

Abbe phoned. She said she 'hung around the gate' for an hour and then went up and ate her company dinner by herself.

'What gate?' I said.

'There's an entrance gate with the name cut into it, but it's iron and so old and dark nobody can see it,' she said. 'You're not the first one who couldn't find us. I keep bringing it up at tenants' meetings and demanding we put up a large modern sign. But there's always some elderly wardrobe mistress who says: "People who can't find us don't deserve to." That's why I asked if you were sure you could find it. If you hadn't been so superior about it I'd have given you directions.'

I'm taking her to theatre and a late dinner next Monday to make up for it. She'll meet me in front of 84, Charing Cross Road:

'You can find *that*?'

Wednesday, August 2

Now I know why it's rained every day since I landed. It must have rained on July 15, which is St Swithun's day. I just read the booklet the Gommes bought me at Winchester Cathedral. St Swithun is the cathedral's patron saint and what it says in the booklet is:

> St Swithun's Day, if thou dost rain,
> For forty days it will remain;
> St Swithun's Day, if thou be fair
> For forty days 'twill rain nae mair.

– sort of a summer Groundhog's Day.

We met the Gommes at an inn for lunch. Jim is a retired headmaster, and Jean bowled me over by telling me she grew up in one of the Nash Crescent houses in Regent's Park back in the days of large families and nannies and live-in servants.

We went to the cathedral after lunch and the Gommes took me straight to Izaak Walton's little alcove. The main feature is a three-panel stained-glass memorial. A neat sign underneath it says:

> 'The Gift of the Fishermen of the World.'

You stare at the sign and imagine all the anonymous fishermen from Maine to Dover to Marseilles to the coasts of Scotland and Australia and California and Newfoundland chipping in their pounds and francs and dollars to create a memorial to the world's most famous Angler.

The central panel was of portraits of the 'fishers of men' whose short biographies Walton wrote in the Lives. But the pane I stared at longest was the one with a portrait of Izaak himself. He's sitting reading with his fishing-rod, net and creel beside him. And the serenity of the face reminded me of his line about the milkmaid:

> 'She does not worry about things which will not be.'

Considering that he lived from King James I's day, through the beheading of Charles I, then helped an Anglican churchman escape from Lord Protector Cromwell and lived on into the Restoration, he must have spent most of his life not worrying about things which might have happened to him but didn't.

Ena and the Gommes had tactfully left me alone in there and I started down a long side aisle looking for them, with one eye on the stone graves I was walking on. That's how I came on Jane Austen's grave. To look down at a spot in a stone floor and know that Jane lies buried beneath it can shake you. Then I read the long inscription her brothers and sister wrote for the tombstone and got apoplectic.

> 'The benevolence of her heart, the sweetness of her temper and the extraordinary endowments of her mind obtained the regard of all who knew her, and the warmest love of her intimate connections.'

– and another paragraph about the family's grief and their confidence that her soul would be 'acceptable in the sight of her Redeemer.'

The whole epitaph was the sort of effusion any family might write about any sister. No indication whatever that this particular sister wrote books – that 'obtained the regard of' a helluva lot of people who *didn't* know her.

Then we drove to Jane's house at Chawton, and the tablet on the brick wall there made up for the family's oversight.

JANE AUSTEN
Lived here from 1809 to 1817 and hence all her works were sent into the world. Her admirers in this country and in America have united to erect this tablet.

And you open the door and walk into the house whence all her books were sent into the world.

The door of the sitting-room has been carefully trained to creak for

558   THE HELENE HANFF OMNIBUS

tourists who know that it creaked in Jane's day and she wouldn't let anyone oil it because the warning creak told her company had come and gave her a chance to hide her current manuscript before the visitors entered the room.

We climbed the stairs to Jane's bedroom. There's a dress of the period lying across the bed and several more on mannequins. One white muslin dress with puffed sleeves and an embroidered bouffant skirt reminded me of Lydia Bennet's moronic note telling her friends she was eloping with Wickham and asking them to have a servant 'mend a great slit in my worked muslin gown.' And we saw the white housecaps Jane wore, including the one from which she looks out at you in the portrait in the front of most editions of her books. On one of the upstairs walls, in a small frame, there's a letter written by Jane to tell her brother Edward that their father was dead, breaking the news so gently the letter carries its own balm.

'Our dear father has closed his virtuous and happy life in a manner almost as free of suffering as his children could have wished . . .'

When we came downstairs we went out to the back yard to see the bake-house, the copper-lined pit for washing clothes and the huge iron wash basin near the pump. I wish I'd thought to ask the caretaker about a kitchen item Jane mentioned. In one of her books, she described a kitchen as being fitted with all the latest modern conveniences including 'a hot-closet.' I'd love to know what a 'hot-closet' was.

The Gommes took us home to their airy country house in Farnham for tea. The living-room has a stone fireplace with armchairs and a sofa in a semicircle in front of it. But the weather was clear and we had tea in the garden – scones and jam and strawberries and double-cream – and they'd gone out and bought gin and vermouth for me in case I wanted to top off tea with a martini.

A two-minute walk from the house is a small cottage, 'where,' said Jean Gomme tranquilly, 'one of us will live when the other one dies.'

Ena's still having trouble with the woman in Oxford.

'I talked to her again last night,' she said. 'I told her we'd like to come down on Tuesday or Wednesday of next week and asked which of the two days was more convenient for her. And she said: "Just tell

Miss Hanff to take the ten o'clock train on whichever day suits her. She can let me know by postcard."'

So I just wrote her a friendly letter saying it seemed silly to come by train when Ena had offered to drive me through the countryside, and we'd like to come on Tuesday and would arrive about noon and I was very excited about seeing Littlemore.

Friday, August 4

Once upon a time, two children eight years old – a girl named Elizabeth, a boy named Robert, called Rob – were introduced to each other and told that they had been born on the same day and at the same hour and that Fate would therefore give them parallel destinies. They grew up in the same small circle of noble families, so, when the twenty-year-old Elizabeth was taken as a prisoner to the Tower she knew that Rob was already a prisoner there.

That's the beginning of the romance of Queen Elizabeth I and Rob Dudley, the only man she was to love till the day she died.

(Don't annoy me with Essex. Rob Dudley died at fifty-eight, and Elizabeth turned for solace to his asinine stepson, Lord Essex. But she didn't hesitate to have Essex put to death when he tried to overthrow her. And at her own death, when the locked box she always kept on her bedside table was finally opened, all it contained was a letter from Rob with the notation in Elizabeth's hands: 'The last letter he ever wrote.')

I'd told Judy what I wanted to see most in the Tower and she took Ena and me to the Beauchamp Tower first. At the bottom of the entrance stairs she showed us the name, 'Robart [*sic*] Dudley', which Rob cut into the stone before climbing to his prison quarter. The winding stone staircase is fearsome, You climb steep steps between huge stone walls that get grimmer and darker at every landing.

We came to Rob's landing and Judy led the way into 'the Dudley apartments' – a bland name for a sixteenth-century prison cell with stone walls several feet thick. You try to imagine what it was like when darkness closed in and candles threw long shadows on the grey stone walls.

There's a narrow outdoor walkway outside the Dudley apartments connecting the Beauchamp Tower to the Bell Tower, where Elizabeth was held. Every day, with two guards in front of her and two behind,

Elizabeth was allowed to walk the length of the passage for exercise. When she reached the far end, she was outside Rob's room. She knew he was listening behind the stone wall and could hear her footsteps, and her voice if she spoke to a guard, and would be cheered by her presence as she was by his. On that walkway I paid homage to the two of them for all I owe them.

It's my belief that if Elizabeth hadn't encouraged Sir Humphrey Gilbert and Sir Walter Raleigh to explore the New World, I'd have been born speaking Spanish instead of speaking (unrecognizably, to be sure) the tongue that Shakespeare spoke. Well, that's of importance to nobody but me. What's important to half the world is that thanks to Elizabeth, Shakespeare was free to speak the tongue that Shakespeare spoke, as an actor/playwright on a public stage. She was the first English monarch who loved the theatre and encouraged it instead of ordering sheriffs to hound the players out of town. Now Rob Dudley wasn't exactly anybody's parfit gentil knight. He was devious, calculating and untrustworthy, whether he ordered his wife's death or not. (She either fell down a long flight of stairs, or was pushed down them by a servant at Rob's suggestion.) All that matters to me about Rob Dudley is that he was the Earl of Leicester, patron of Shakespeare's company.

From Rob's landing we went to the White Tower, where the main torture room and the dungeons were, but there's nothing to see there anymore. The dungeons are closed to the public now, and the torture devices have been replaced on the torture room walls by ancient weapons and suits of armour. Which was fine with me. I'm not just crazy about torture chambers, and I've read more than I wanted to know about men and women having their legs and arms stretched on the rack till every joint was pulled out of its socket and every bone broken.

We went out of doors to Tower Green, a lovely small park where royal beheadings took place, including those of three young queens: Anne Boleyn, Catherine Howard and Lady Jane Grey.

Weaker Sex note: Lady Jane Grey, aged sixteen, went to her execution with what witnesses called superhuman grace and courage. She comforted the clergyman who was there to comfort her and asked the swordsman for instruction so she could place her head on the block correctly.

Her nineteen-year-old husband (Rob Dudley's brother) cried all the way to the scaffold.

Her father was another winner. He'd forced Jane to accept the crown she didn't want and wasn't entitled to – and as soon as she was arrested, he denounced her, to save his own skin.

The Royal executions on Tower Green were private. Ordinary traitors were executed on Tower Hill, outside the Tower precincts, and the block was on a scaffold built good and high so ten thousand Londoners could see the show. They jammed the Hill and perched in trees to get a good look at the ax or sword as it fell, and see the head roll off and the blood gush out. Then they stampeded up to the scaffold with pieces of rag to dip in the blood. You wouldn't believe how many diseases were cured by the blood of executed traitors.

I finally found out what the 'Order of the Bath' means. Meant. Judy took us to a 900-year-old church on the second floor of the White Tower called the Chapel of St John.

'This is where the Knights of the Bath prayed before their investiture,' she said. 'After the service, they were ushered into an adjoining room where they stripped and bathed in wooden tubs. As they sat in their tubs the King entered, tapped the bare shoulder of each man with a sword and declared him a Knight of the Bath.'

Then Queen Mary ascended the throne, followed by Elizabeth, and the ritual had to be abandoned since no female monarch could be asked to enter a room full of naked men sitting in bathtubs.

No other tourist attraction I've ever heard of has the grotesque contrasts of the Tower. The sumptuous royal apartments where monarchs once stayed from the day they inherited the throne to the day of their Coronation were above torture rooms and dungeons and had a fine view of the bloodletting on Tower Green. I was glad we didn't line up to see the Crown Jewels; it would have been like seeing the Taj Mahal and Auschwitz on the same day.

We rescued my beautiful flowers from the Tower cloakroom, lugged them to Brown's Hotel, and checked them at the cloakroom there while we had tea. They were half dead when I got them home but they're in water and recovering. They were presented to me at the Futura company lunch.

Futura has the youngest executives I've ever met. They're all in their twenties, sleek, groomed, buttoned-down young men of the kind called Upwardly Mobile at home.

I sat next to the editor-in-chief and he told me he's sorry they published *84* and *The Duchess* in one paperback volume.

'We thought *84, Charing Cross Road* was too short to publish by itself at the usual paperback price,' he said. 'Now we know we could easily have sold the two books in separate volumes and of course we'd have done much better financially.'

So I told him my Writer's Economics:

'Every reader who buys your paperback with the two books in it writes me a fan letter and I write a thank-you note to each of them,' I said. 'My thank-you note costs twenty-two cents; my royalty on the book is eleven cents, so every time somebody buys the book I lose eleven cents.'

And he said:

'You're lucky to be getting eleven cents. If the paperback contained one book instead of two, you'd get only seven cents.'

On my back he's Upwardly Mobile.

Monday, August 7

Brighton was rained out again yesterday. Doris was so disappointed. I think she postponed her holiday for a weekend just to show it to me. Ena says she's going to drive me down on the first sunny day we have free. She didn't tell me before that she knows the city and loves it.

A letter in the mail from the woman in Oxford. She's been called out of town by the illness of a cousin and she can't say how long she'll be gone. She's so sorry to miss meeting me.

Well, she's not the first puzzle I've run into in my life. I tell myself with fans as with the weather, you win a few, you lose a few.

Midnight

Abbe met me outside the empy storefront at 84 – which the owners won't let to anybody because they want to tear it down. It's a good thing she knew me because I'd have walked right past her. She's acquired a slim figure, lustrous long hair, contact lenses and complete self-possession. And the damnedest English accent you ever heard. Most of the time she speaks with the impeccable accent she hears onstage. Then she'll come on something that surprises her and say: 'Oh, Gawd!' in the half-cockney she must hear backstage.

You'll never stumble on Sandringham Flats, you have to know where to look for it. It's not on Charing Cross Road, it's set back behind it. It's a long row of flats in a heavy brown building with high iron gates. On the fourth floor, Abbe led the way across the walkway into her flat.

The real estate developers keep declaring Sandringham Flats unfit for human habitation, and Abbe knows she won't have hers for very long: there's a rumour that the telephone company was right and the flats on Abbe's side of the street are to be torn down soon. It's a pity. She has a bright, clean apartment – living-room, bedroom, kitchen and 'loo.' She painted all the rooms herself, she bought carpeting and cut it and tacked it down very professionally and she's created a warm and attractive home. With no bathtub and no shower stall.

'I don't know why Americans make such a fuss about bathtubs,' she said testily. 'You get just as clean taking sponge baths.'

'Americans' forsooth.

Wednesday, August 9

I just read the booklets I brought home from Brighton last night, all about Prinny and Mrs Fitzherbert, and Prinny is now, after Elizabeth I, my favourite English monarch.

'Prinny' was the nickname of the Prince Regent who became George IV. When he was young he fell in love with a pretty Catholic widow, Mrs Fitzherbert, and since the English constitution forbade the future king's marriage to a Roman Catholic, young George married Mrs Fitzherbert secretly. When he became Regent, he regretfully stopped living with her, and by the time he was crowned George IV he'd made a proper royal marriage. Without benefit of a divorce. The marriage was unhappy and the King – still called Prinny by his friends – consoled himself with a string of mistresses. But when he died, it was Mrs Fitzherbert's portrait they found in a locket around his neck.

What I love most about this story is the vision of Mrs Fitzherbert going placidly through life knowing the Queen of England was married to a bigamist. All of which has nothing whatever to do with why Prinny's my second favorite monarch.

He had a consuming passion for architecture. As Prince Regent he commissioned John Nash to turn an old house at Windsor into Windsor

Castle, and then directed him to cut a great royal swath through the green fields of London. On Prinny's orders, Nash built a long avenue – calling it Regent Street, of course – with a fine mansion at its lower end and at the top end Regent's Park, with facing crescents of white houses flanking the entrance, and a series of terraces of tall white houses along the Outer Circles of the park. All this and Brighton Pavilion, too. But Doris was right. You don't go to Brighton just to see the Pavilion.

It was a beautiful day and Ena and I drove down before the weather could change its mind. Outside Brighton we came to a detour and went through a lush green suburb called Hove, along a boulevard lined with red brick Victorian houses with white-trimmed bay windows and white porches. Then we turned a corner and suddenly there was the sea, very calm and blue, and Ena said:

'This is Brighton.'

When I was a child, my family took a house in Atlantic City every summer. I'd never liked it much – but by the time Ena parked the car inland, I was suddenly wild to get back to the seashore and we went there first.

It looked both strange and familiar. 'The boardwalk' above the surf in Atlantic City is literally made of wooden boards built on wooden stilts. In Brighton, the promenade deck is concrete and the railing is wrought-iron. Then I looked down at the 'beach,' and got a jolt. It's not made of sand, it's made of pebbles – thousands of them as far as the eye reaches along the shore. And sunbathers stretched out on the burning hot pebbles as peacefully as Indian holy men on beds of nails. We strolled along the promenade, past a row of Victorian beachfront hotels smaller than the Atlantic City palaces of my childhood but just as gaudy. One of them had bright red awnings at every single window. I couldn't remember when I'd last seen an awning.

When we left the beachfront, Ena took me through hilly little shopping streets, more Cape Cod than Atlantic City, with small curio shops, gift shops, snack bars all pasted up against each other in winding rows. Then we came to a big corner store that sold nothing but Brighton Rock.

'I always thought Brighton Rock was a boulder, like Plymouth Rock,' I told Ena.

'It may well have been, originally,' said Ena.

What it is now is hard candy. It comes in great, round, flat lollypops, but mostly you buy it in long striped rolls like miniature barber poles. Red-and-white, red-and-green, red-yellow-and-green, six inches long or two feet long, it's as unique to Brighton as salt-water taffy is to Atlantic City.

What moved me unexpectedly was that the Brighton Rock candy palace looked exactly like the salt-water taffy stores. It was large, open on all sides and swarming with teenagers in bathing suits and bare feet. Some of them had 'punk' orange or purple hair, some of the boys had shaved 'skinheads' – but they were essentially the same teenagers I'd looked up to when I was eight years old, the same thin tanned bodies, the same exuberant self-absorbed faces as they jostled their decorous elders. The proper middle-aged patrons were the same, the holiday atmosphere was the same – and from the opposite shore my eight-year-old self never dreamed she'd see, the blue Atlantic was the same.

I still think the Pavilion's Moorish domes are a monstrosity.

They were painted a gaudy green that clashed with the grass of the surrounding lawn. Ena said the domes are painted a different color every year or two. But step inside, and the difference between Prinny's Pavilion and the over-stuffed stately homes and palaces I'd seen is extraordinary. No dark mahogany rooms smothered in heavy furniture, no massive oil paintings cramming every wall. The Pavilion is all uncluttered grace and light.

In the state drawing-room, for instance, the cream-colored walls are decorated with only an occasional mirror bordered in thin gold. There are water-green satin drapes at the long windows, curved chairs covered in the same green satin, and green satin settees with thin gold-leaf borders in small alcoves under white arches.

We went into a second drawing-room with bare white walls intersected by gold-leaf panels, and here and there Chinese stands painted in delicate patterns of lavender and rose, holding five-pronged candelabra. All the state rooms have the same uncluttered simplicity – in spite of the appalling amounts of money Prinny spent on them. (Upstairs, Queen Caroline's bedroom positively jumps with chinoiserie. Her taste in furnishings was fussier than her husband's.)

According to the booklets, it's because he spent so much money on architecture and palace interiors that Prinny has been an unpopular monarch for two hundred and fifty years. He spent fortunes on palaces and parks at a time when England needed all the money it could raise to finance the Napoleonic War.

Well, the Napoleonic War was followed by the Crimean War and the Boer War and the First World War and the Second World War and they're all long gone.

The Pavilion at Brighton and Windsor Castle and Regent Street and Carlton House Terrace and Regent's Park and the Nash Terraces are all still here. Blessings on your far-sighted spendthrift head, Prinny.

Thursday, August 10

A young reporter came to interview me this afternoon. She'd never been in a flat in St Johns Wood before so I showed her all of it and explained my absentee hostess was André's eighty-eight-year-old mother. I'd made coffee for us and I said:

'Do you mind if we have coffee and the interview in the kitchen instead of the living-room? It's so far down the hall I got tired of running back and forth to hot up the coffee so now I never leave the kitchen.'

'I'm sure Mrs Deutsch has all her meals in the kitchen,' she said. 'She's probably not able to carry heavy trays down the hall.'

'She doesn't know how lucky she is to have a kitchen big enough for a table and chairs,' I said. 'I wish I did.'

'Well, you wouldn't be willing to put your refrigerator out in the hall to make room for it,' she said.

Oh.

Friday, August 11

'Mr Bernard Shaw regrets he cannot answer mail or acknowledge books sent to him because if he did, he wouldn't get any work done. But he thanks the sender . . .'

The form letter is framed on a wall in Shaw's house at Ayot St Lawrence and when I read it I thought it was the perfect solution to fan mail. Then I saw the catch. The letter only saves time for an author who can afford a secretary to read the mail, have copies of the form letter made, insert the letters in envelopes and address, seal, stamp and mail them.

Even if I had the money I couldn't answer fan mail with a mimeographed or Xeroxed form letter. But then, I feel very popular when I get ten or twelve letters a week. Shaw got two hundred a *day*. For thirty or forty years.

Ena drove me down and there were 'Shaw's Corner' signs all along the way. They're needed, because the house is in a wood, hidden both from the road and from the few neighboring houses. Being a big-city dweller, I couldn't live there all year round but neither did Shaw till he was very old. He was still writing to Ellen Terry from a London flat in 1938 and he was past eighty then.

Charlotte, his 'green-eyed millionairess,' obviously shared her husband's plain taste. The furnishings are those of any modest country house. Then you look at the framed photos on the mantel and you know this is not any modest country house. The framed photos are of Lenin, Ibsen, Stalin, Yeats and O'Casey.

There's a portrait of Charlotte above the mantel. There were no photos of Ellen Terry and Mrs Pat Campbell. I thought Shaw might have put them on the mantel after Charlotte died. Then I read the Ayot booklet. It said that after Charlotte died Shaw kept her ashes for the seven years he outlived her, and left instructions that when he died his ashes were to be commingled with hers and scattered over the garden.

I don't know how many writers were contemptuous of that marriage because it may have been sexless. Edmund Wilson was one of them. How many wives did he have? Five?

'*Let me not to the marriage of true minds admit impediment.*' There's a study in the house, which is not where he worked. But there's a large desk in it – and even though it's obvious staging-for-tourists, Shaw's large china teacup and saucer and his gold-rimmed spectacles lying on the desk mesmerize you. It took all my willpower not to touch them.

There are wonderful cartoons of him on all the walls and a Rodin bust of him and a prankish marionette figure from the National Theatre's production of *Shaks.* vs *Shaw.* They borrow it back whenever they revive the play. And in a glass case, what must be a priceless possession: the prayer book of Charles I, printed a year before he was beheaded.

Then we left the house and walked down beyond the garden to his workroom. The Hut.

It's just that. One room, with a plain wooden desk, a straight chair, a telephone and nothing else. You stand there, imagining him writing in perfect solitude and quiet – and then ruin the whole romantic image by remembering that Shaw wrote plays on clattery trains en route to speaking engagements on behalf of Socialist candidates or causes. He could write a play in bad light on a lurching, noisy train – in such clean, clear shorthand that when he got off the train with the final scene finished, he could mail his shorthand notebooks to his secretary in London knowing she'd have no trouble transcribing them, so that when he got home the play would be typed and ready for correction. He could write anywhere and under any conditions, and turn out a nearly perfect play in one draft and in less than one month.

I wish I knew who it was that corrected the old definition of genius.

'Talent,' whoever-it-was said, 'is the infinite capaciy for taking pains. Genius is the infinite capacity for achievement without taking any pains at all.'

It'll probably turn out the person who said it was Shaw.

Saturday, 12th

There's a little market across the street I never use since I love the High Street. But today I just needed coffee and eggs and I stopped in there. I was the only customer and when the owner saw me reach for my brand of coffee he got it down for me from a high shelf.

'Are you visiting in the neighborhood?' he asked.

'I'm staying across the street in Mrs Deutsch's flat,' I said.

'Oh, Mrs Deutsch!' he said, pleased. 'She used to buy Continental coffee, too. But these days she buys the Instant.'

There was a big bin of eggs, several brands, so I said:

'Which eggs does she buy?'

'Oh, she won't buy my eggs!' he said, grinning. 'She likes her eggs fresh from the hen! She has friends drive her out to a farm for them.'

I came home, stopping in the kitchen to put the coffee away. I stared at the long mantel where nothing unsightly was allowed in plain view. And when I went into the bedroom, I saluted the empty egg cartons lined up on top of the mahogany wardrobe in the Spare Room, waiting for their next trip to the farm.

Sunday, August 13

Ena drove me to Cambridge along country roads, cows to the left of us, sheep to the right and a wild sky that looked as excited as I felt: bright blue with sunny white clouds, but above and behind them, huge grey-black storm clouds. Following Muriel Brittain's meticulous directions, Ena found Jesus College and the parking lot with no trouble. We started to climb Stairway No. 7, and were less than halfway up it when Muriel came running down to meet us. She's very small and light on her feet, with a light voice to match.

'We'd better go right in to lunch before the Hall closes,' she said, and led the way into a large, long dining hall. It had a vaulted ceiling with immensely thick oak beams, and three dining tables that ran the length of the room, one along each side wall and one down the middle of the room, each with a long bench instead of chairs.

'It takes two sittings to feed the whole College at dinner,' said Muriel.

Lunch was cafeteria-style and we got our trays and settled at a nearly empty table against one wall. At the front of the room, running the width of it, was the High Table for the 'Fellows,' and Muriel pointed to the two huge framed portraits on the wall above it. One was of Henry VIII, the other of Thomas Cranmer.

'Cranmer was an undergraduate at Jesus College a few years after it opened,' she said. 'And then he was elected a Fellow.'

On the wall opposite was a portrait of an Archbishop of York who, said Muriel, was Laurence Stern's great-grand-father. 'They were both Jesus men.'

'Laurence must have become a clergyman because it was the family profession,' I said. 'I've always had a theory that he got the idea for *Tristram Shandy* standing on the church steps greeting the members of the congregation as they filed out after Sunday services, and listening to their long-winded stories that kept wandering off on tangents and never got to the point.'

Coleridge was also a Jesus man. I said I hadn't known that, and Muriel said, mildly exasperated:

'Well, he never finished, you know. He kept running away and coming back, and running away and coming back. Then he ran off to fight in the French Revolution and that was the end of it.'

From her tone, you'd have thought it all happened last year.

You don't call Cambridge students 'students,' you call them 'pupils' or 'undergraduates.'

I told her that at home 'pupils' are grade-school children. As soon as they start high school they're students and they're 'the student body' clear through college.

She informed us solemnly that the full name of the college is 'The Ancient and Religious Foundation of the Blessed Virgin Mary, Saint John the Evangelist and the Glorious Virgin Saint Radegund, Commonly Called Jesus College.' It was originally a Benedictine convent and its cloister dates back to the eleventh century. Saint Radegund lived in the sixth.

'She was the daughter of the King of Thuringia,' said Muriel. 'She was carried off by the Franks who married her forcibly to their King Clothair – a right bad lot who murdered her brother.'

I forget how this made her a Glorious Virgin.

After lunch, Muriel walked us past a small alcove with a serving counter in front of it and said:

'This is where the nuns queued up for their daily ration of beer.'

As we started up the staircase to Q's rooms I asked her the difference between a 'don' and a 'fellow.'

'At Cambridge,' she said, 'the teaching staff are dons. But a don has no college rooms of his own. He has to find lodgings in town until he's elected a Fellow by the Fellows of his College. Then he gets a home here, but only for himself. There are no rooms for his family.'

'So all the years Q taught here, he had to leave his family in Cornwall,' I explained to Ena. 'He had a wife and a son and daughter. His son fought through World War I without being wounded, went to Berlin in 1918 with the Occupation Army, and in one weekend there, caught pneumonia and died.'

At the top of the stairs, Muriel unlocked a door and opened it and I followed her into Q's Common Room. His big armchair was in front of a grey stone fireplace. I heard Ena admiring the plum-colored damask wallpaper and mahogany furniture but I don't remember seeing them. I was finding a way around the furniture to get me closer to the photos of Q on the mantel.

'Your husband didn't say in his book how he came to know Q,' I said.

'Freddy came up as an undergraduate in 1919,' Muriel said. 'Q sort of adopted him.'

She must have been a generation younger than Freddy. He'd be in his eighties now; Muriel can't be out of her fifties.

She and Ena disappeared into the kitchen to make tea and I blessed them both for their tact in leaving me alone in the room for a few minutes. I went up to the mantel to look at the photos – there were several of him. It was a very kind face, weatherbeaten granite like the photo above his obituary notice in the *Times*. I imagined him lounging in his armchair with his students around him. They used to come there during the day as well as in the evening.

Muriel came in with the tea tray and Q's tobacco jar. Then she made me sit in his armchair for tea.

'I've read stories,' I said, 'about how much he resented women in his classes when they were first admitted to Jesus.'

And Muriel said with energy:

'That's all nonsense, I don't know who started that story! He was as kind and generous to women undergraduates as he was to everybody else! And the women were all charmed by his passion for clothes. Did you know he changed his attire three times a day? He had ties to harmonize with all his bowlers. Here, I'll show you.'

She went to a closet, rummaged in it and then held up a dashing green bowler and matching tie. Then she brought me a dark brown bowler.

'This was his favorite,' she said – and laid it in my lap.

It shocked me. Now that I knew he hadn't resented women students I felt less an intruder. I was shocked just the same, at sitting in his chair with his favourite hat in my hands. There was a kind of violation in being so familiar with his ghost.

And then I remembered something he'd said once, in a lecture. I don't remember what the subject of the lecture was, but he said he was offering his own view of it because 'sometimes the clearest visions are those seen through the eyes of a friend'. And he had added: 'If that word be presumptuous, you must forgive me.'

I'd loved him for that line when I first read it, because I was reading it in an edition printed expressly for American readers; knowing Q, I knew he'd edited it – and he'd let the line stand. If he saw himself as my friend I had a right to be there in his Common Room where his pupils had always been welcome.

Muriel took us through the rooms – the tiny kitchen, the bare, narrow bedroom as Spartan as a monastic cell. Most of his novels were about Fowey in Cornwall, where he lived, and looking at that monastic cell, I wondered if they'd been written out of homesickness during every year's long exile in Cambridge. But I think the exile was voluntary. He loved teaching.

We were there for three hours. By the time we left, I was convinced Q knew I was there and was pleased (and amused) that it meant so much to me.

It was nearly five years later that a letter came one morning from a Londoner named Cecil Clarabut.

'Dear Miss Hanff

'Since he has meant so much to you I jot down a few memories of Q. He was the first professor of English Literature at Cambridge and was not lecturing very much when I arrived there, always without notes because of his poor eyesight. The style was the man: he spoke very much as he wrote, in a gentle and urbane manner.

'He dressed often in tweeds, looking more like a countryman than a don . . . He had a vast library which afterwards passed to the English department, situated in a block of lecture rooms known as the Divinity School opposite the entrance of St John's, and it was a particular pleasure for a group of us reading for the honours course (tripos) to sit round a big fire and listen to him weekly as he smoked. Though he began as a Cornish writer, his power to evoke the Dorset atmosphere of Thomas Hardy made him seem a Wessexman and he made the brooding power of Egdon Heath unforgettable.

'Years later I saw him last in retirement, walking in the cool of his garden at Fowey . . .'

5

'Then to the well-trod stage anon ...'

I   Out of Sight, Out of Mind

The letter from London was addressed to Flora, my agent, and she read it to me over the phone, on a December day in 1980,

> 'Dear Miss Roberts,
>   'I am interested in adapting the book "84, Charing Cross Road" for the stage, in both writing and directing it, though of course the words would be Ms Hanff's ...
>
> James Roose-Evans'

I told Flora to do whatever she thought best about the contract he proposed, and hung up and forgot about it. James Roose-Evans's letter lay outside my private universe, which, that December, contained nothing but Eyes. Cataracts had developed on both of mine. And since you may one day find yourself in the same situation, I pass on to you the two incontrovertible facts about it.

Fact One: Cataract surgery is simple, painless and (except with implants) risk-free; sight is easily restored by cataract spectacles, contact lenses or implants; the whole procedure is common, routine and nothing to worry about.

Fact Two: Fact One applies only to cataracts on the eyes in somebody else's head.

Never mind that when I took a bus down to Gene's 48th Street office on a rainy day, I had to get off at 57th Street, which I recognized by its width, and walk the remaining nine blocks in the rain, counting as I went, because I could no longer read street signs.

Never mind that at night I fell over curbstones I couldn't see, and down the fuzzy white stone steps at Lincoln Center – or that when I went Christmas shopping I fell down the blurred escalator steps at Saks and walked into a glass wall at Bloomingdale's. Never mind that marketing for Christmas dinner was a nightmare of blurred colours and fuzzy print on supermarket boxes, and price tags I couldn't read.

All of it was preferable to a surgeon's knife coming at my good right eye and maybe slipping when it got there. My left eye had always been nearly blind, I didn't worry about that one; but it made the right one indispensable. I was a writer, I lived alone and did my own cooking and housework. I could still see to type and when anybody asked when I was going to have my eyes operated on I said flatly:

'When I can no longer see to work.'

In January, a charming letter arrived from James Roose-Evans to say he was hard at work on his adaptation of *84, Charing Cross Road*, which he hoped to produce at a summer theatre festival.

On a morning in February, I put paper in the typewriter, to answer a letter from André that lay alongside the typewriter. I glanced at the letter and saw, instead of typewritten lines, the dreaded blur. I got a magnifying glass and sweated out the answer. But Push had come to Shove. The next day I went shopping for an eye surgeon. I found one I trusted and set dates for two operations, the first on my half-blind left eye for the end of March, with the one on the right eye to follow at the end of April.

From the day I committed myself, I woke every morning promptly at five with an attack of panic and terror – euphemistically known as an Anxiey Attack – which lasted two hours. By March, the Anxiety Attacks were taking up most of the day.

That March, I got a phone call from Celeste Holm. Back in the *Oklahoma!* days, Celeste had been the easiest of all actresses for a timid press agent's assistant to interview. She was salty and pithy and down-to-earth and I liked her. Then she went to Hollywood and it was thirty years before I saw her again. In the mid-seventies she'd phoned to say she wanted to give her father an autographed copy of *84* for Christmas and would I have lunch with her? We met for lunch, and after thirty years of Hollywood stardom, she was still salty and pithy and down-to-earth.

Now she said on the phone, 'I'm giving an *Oklahoma!* reunion. I'm inviting everybody who was connected in any way with any of the companies – three hundred so far. Are you good on your feet? Can you come and give a shorter version of the *Oklahoma!* story you told in *Underfoot in Show Business*?'

The reunion was to be held on March 31 – the anniversary of the show's opening – and I had to decline: I'd be in the hospital that day.

The nearly blind left eye was operated on successfully on March 30.

In April, a letter from James Roose-Evans announced that his adaptation of *84* was finished and that he hoped to produce it at the Salisbury summer theatre festival. I don't remember whether I answered him. James Roose-Evans's petty affairs couldn't compete with the panic that occupied all of April till the surgery on the thirtieth.

The operation was wildly successful. 'Wildly' because I'd expected to wake up blind till I was given spectacles – and I didn't. Having been very nearsighted all my life, I discovered, when the patch came off my eye, that I could see as well as I'd ever seen without glasses. I woke up to the same fuzzy world I'd always seen. There was only one small hitch.

'You won't be able to read for a month,' the surgeon warned me as we parted. 'Come back in a month and I'll give you a prescription for glasses.' He offered me temporary cataract spectacles to wear on the street, but I'd heard these were difficult to get used to and I knew I could manage without them. In a month I'd get permanent spectacles for both reading and distance wear.

I left the hospital and rode home in a friend's car in a state of blissful relief. I could live without reading for a month, surely? Surely. I got out of the car, floated into the lobby and was welcomed by the super and the doorman. Then I went into the mail room to pick up my mail.

The long rows of mailboxes were still there – but the boxes no

longer had numbers on them. I called the doorman and he came and
showed me which box had 8-G on it in invisible letters. I opened the
box and took out of it a pile of blank envelopes. I carried them to the
elevator, stepped into it and confronted a double row of buttons
which no longer had floor numbers on them. I called the doorman
again and he came and showed me which button said 8 and I
memorized its position. By which time I was shaken enough to want
to call my best friend, and as soon as I'd let myself into my apartment
I hurried to the phone. But of course, the phone dial had no numbers
on it. Neither did the clock. Neither did the radio.

'*You won't be able to read . . .*'

Friends and neighbours flocked to the rescue. My friend Lolly took
a morning off from her insurance business every week to do my
marketing and go through the mail, pulling out the doctors' bills and
medical insurance forms, writing checks for me and showing me
where to sign them in invisible ink. And not for the first time did a
New York apartment house turn out to be a life-support system.
Neighbors dialled the phone for me, set the oven for me, wrote
cheques to cash for me and took them to the bank and cashed them
– and folded the dollar bills into separate piles so I'd know the ones
from the tens.

Meanwhile, it was May – and I discovered I could see curbs and
traffic lights clearly. I'd had months of practice at finding my way
around town without being able to read signs by memorizing
landmarks and I began walking all day long, through Central Park and
all over town, without mishap if not exactly without incident.

There was, for instance, the beautiful brown-and-white collie who
came toward me one day in the park and who, as I stooped to pet
him, turned into a brown suitcase in a man's white-cuffed hand. And
there was the lovely Saturday afternoon when I was sailing
insouciantly down Fifth Avenue and saw ahead of me a large pink
banner streaming down the familiar steps of St Thomas's church. St
Thomas's has wonderful choral concerts and I hoped the banner was
advertising one of them, as the crowd at the side of the steps seemed
to indicate. The crowd blocked my way and I detoured around it and
down to the curb – just as a limousine door opened and a misty white
bride walked into me. That's when I saw that the large pink banner
had turned into six pink bridesmaids lined up in formation on the

church steps. I fled to the far side steps of the church, and having no prior engagement, went to the wedding.

I couldn't bother friends and neighbors with any mail that didn't contain bills or checks and I ignored the growing unopened pile, including a large manila envelope. But June finally came and I went down to the surgeon's office, got prescriptions for cataract spectacles and carried them – all unsuspecting – to the optometrist. On the day I picked them up he said to me:

'You'll want to practise with these.'

He was wrong. I never wanted to practise with them.

When I say that the first time you put on cataract spectacles they magnify everything and distort everything, I mean that when I put them on, my typewriter was instantly the size of an Alfa Romeo – and when I headed for the kitchen for the martini I suddenly needed the kitchen door, big as a wall, curved menacingly outward toward me at a ninety-degree angle.

I took the damned things off and made my martini without them. Then I scooped up the pile of mail, settled in the armchair, put the spectacles back on and reached for the large manila envelope. I took out of it James Roose-Evans's script of *84* and all I can tell you about it is that it was huge. I never knew the mere size of things could be so intimidating. When I turned toward the ceramic ashtray at my elbow, it had become a great vat and I shrank from it.

A couple of nights later I tried wearing the Fun House mirrors on the street and promptly fell over a curb that looked two feet closer than it was. I was also nearly hit by a cab zooming around a corner I couldn't see, because cataract spectacles give you 'no peripheral vision,' a smooth phrase meaning that if you look sideways out of them you fall off the edge of the world.

Somebody told me that contact lenses didn't distort and magnify the world and the minute I heard this, I phoned my surgeon.

'I want contact lenses,' I said.

'Good! Fine!' he said. 'Come back in two months when your eyes have healed.'

In July, James Roose-Evans wrote to say that *84* would open in Salisbury in August. Was I coming over for it? No, I wasn't. The letter might have come from some other planet for all it had to do with me.

In August, the surgeon pronounced my eyes healed and sent me across the hall to Dr Siegel, the lens expert. He inserted soft contact lenses in both eyes and the miracle happened: the world was instantly bright and clear and of normal size again. And I had enough peripheral vision to protect me from berserk New York cab drivers.

However: Soft contact lenses are tiny, almost invisible rounds of plastic, and you position one on the tip of your index finger and insert it deftly in your eye. You insert it deftly in your eye if you're deft. If you're not – I am not – you stand at the bathroom sink and, wearing the Fun House mirrors, position the tiny round of plastic on the tip of your index finger. You remove the spectacles and raise your index finger toward your eye – whereupon the lens flies off it, into the Great Beyond. You don't know whether it flew upward and landed on the top of the shower curtain, or downward to lodge somewhere in your shaggy bathroom carpet. You put on your cataract spectacles and turn the bathroom upside down and you don't find it. Three days later you may find a dried speck of something under the doorstop but when you put it in lens fluid to soften you discover that what you found isn't a lens, it's half-a-lens.

I lost eight in the first month. Two a week, regular as clockwork. There was a ninth that I can't properly call Lost since I know where it is. My bathroom was freshly painted at the end of August and one morning as I lifted my index finger to my eye, the lens flew off it and landed on the wall behind me where it attached itself to the sticky white enamel. It's still there. It gleams at me on Saturday mornings when I'm cleaning the bathroom and wipe down the wall. When I'm feeling pleasant I say hello to it.

Plus Which. (And I really felt sorry for Dr Siegel, a man of infinite patience, good humor and optimism, because as time went on the Plus Which wore even him out.)

The day he first put the lenses in for me, he asked me how they felt.

'Wonderful,' I said, 'except the right one feels as if it's going to drop out.'

'That,' said Dr Siegel, 'doesn't happen.'

We left his First Avenue office together. He was going on vacation, I was going to walk over to Fifth Avenue, to shop for the first time in six months. I got as far as Madison and was halfway across it when the right lens dropped out on my cheek. I couldn't see it, of course; I could only feel it. Clutching it between thumb and forefinger, I hailed a cab and went home and (in not much more than a couple of hours) put it back in.

From then on, the right lens dropped out two or three times a day. I phoned Dr Siegel's assistant, who said conversationally: 'Your eye appears to be rejecting the lens.'

In extremis, I called Bud, my personal doctor, and wept into his sympathetic ear.

'A lot of my patients have eyes that rejected the lens at first,' said Bud. 'The lens is a foreign substance and the eye wants to be rid of it. But if you insist, your eye will finally accept it. Okay?'

Okay. I mapped out a programme for Insisting. I was fairly good at self-hypnosis and I'd read an article about biofeedback. I began hypnotizing myself and giving my right eye biofeedback instructions under hypnosis:

'The lens is not a foreign substance, it is a house-guest! It is there to *help* you! You will regard it as a FRIEND!'

My right eye listened to this spiel three times a day for half an hour each time and went right on throwing the lens out – in the bank, on somebody's terrace, at the supermarket checkout counter.

By September, the wonderful reviews of *84* sent to me by James Roose-Evans from Salisbury meant far less to me than the new technique a friend taught me for inserting the lenses. (It's the mountain-to-Mohammed technique: you don't lift your finger to your eye, you lower your eye to your finger.) I began putting them in without losing them – with the aid of reminder signs Scotch-taped to the bathroom wall:

STOPPER IN SINK.

JOHN LID *DOWN*!

STAND PRESSED AGAINST SINK SO LENS DROPS *IN* IT.

When I found that last one in a desk drawer months later, STAND had been crossed out and SIT substituted, with the word CHAIR printed at the bottom in case I didn't know what SIT meant.

In September, André Deutsch came to breakfast and said briskly:

'Darling, I want you to write me a short, funny book about cataracts.' He was lucky I didn't throw him out the eighth-floor window.

In October, James Roose-Evans wrote to say that he had sold *84, Charing Cross Road* to a London West End producer named Michael

Redington. I wrote and congratulated him, and went on trying to hypnotize my right lens, which went on dropping out.

Early in November, Sheila Murphy phoned. Sheila was André's press agent.

'Michael Redington,' she said, 'is opening *84, Charing Cross Road* at the Ambassadors Theatre on Thursday, 26 November. He wants to bring you to London for a week before the opening to publicize the show. He'll pay all expenses. Isn't that lovely?'

I had visions of the right lens dropping into oblivion in Heathrow Airport and the spare lens dropping out on the sidewalk the next day, leaving me at the mercy of the Fun House spectacles for the rest of the week. I opened my date book to November 26 and saw my excuse.

'I can't come,' I said. 'November 26 is Thanksgiving Day. It's a big holiday, I have commitments here on Thanksgiving.'

'Michael will be so disappointed,' said Sheila. 'He's so anxious to have you come! Will you think about it?'

I said I'd think about it and we hung up. My friend Richard was having coffee with me at the time, and since he's one of the friends who come here to Thanksgiving dinner I explained the conversation to him. Richard is a laconic man and usually imperturbable, but he stared at me in disbelief.

'After all the years you spent trying to crash the theatre as a playwright,' he said, 'somebody's made a play from your book, it's opening in the West End – and you're not going to the Opening?' And he added drily: 'Your "commitments" will have you committed if you don't go.'

And I think that's when it finally dawned on me that what James Roose-Evans had been slaving over, all these months, had something to do with me.

'I have to go, don't I?' I said.

But I lay awake a long time that night dreading the trip, and when Sheila Murphy phoned the next day she had to cope with a cranky five-year-old who after much pleading, says All right, she'll go to the dentist, but she has to wear her pink dress and she has to take her doll along and she has to have ice cream afterward and they can't take it home, she has to have it in the ice-cream parlour.

'Michael,' said Sheila, opening negotiations, 'will put you up at any hotel you name.'

'I don't care what hotel it is but it has to be a good one, I'm sick of cheap hotels,' I said. 'And it has to be in Marylebone. If I'm coming to London for a raw November week, at least I'm going to be in the neighborhood I like best.' (I didn't think there were any hotels in Marylebone; it's residential.) 'If he can't find a good hotel in Marylebone I'm not coming.'

'He'll find one,' said Sheila.

'And I'm not taking a night flight where you walk around like a zombie with jet-lag for two days,' I said. 'There's only one day flight I know of, it's BA. If he can't get me on that I'm not coming.'

'If he can't get you on that,' said Sheila tranquilly, 'he'll fly you Concorde.'

So then of course I prayed the BA flight would be sold out. But God doesn't hear greedy prayers and Sheila phoned back a day later to say I was booked on BA's 10 A.M. flight for Wednesday, November 18.

'You're at the St Georges Hotel,' she said. 'I went round to see it and it's lovely. It's in Marylebone.'

That afternoon an enormous bouquet arrived. From Michael Redington – to thank me for letting him give me a free trip to London. And the five-year-old cabled graciously:

THANKS FOR BEAUTIFUL FLOWERS TELL B.A. MUST HAVE WINDOW SEAT IN SMOKING SECTION

Sheila phoned the next day to report:

'BA has reserved you a window seat in the smoking section.' Then she said: 'Leo and Ena Marks have money in the show. And André Deutsch Ltd has money in it.' And she added in a voice heavily casual, 'I'll have you know the Press Department has fifty quid in it.'

Suddenly I had tears in my eyes.

On the Sunday before I was to leave for London the right lens dropped out in a box at Lincoln Center. On Monday I turned up in Dr Siegel's office and said Do Something.

He sat me down at a little machine and peered into my eyes through a magnifying glass.

'Oh, that's interesting!' he said. 'I can see the stitches! Tissue has grown over them in your left eye – but they're visible in your right eye and they're pushing the lens around!'

And he sent me across the hall to the surgeon's office. The surgeon sat me down at another machine with my chin on a metal chin-rest and my eyes in little metal frames, and examined my right eye. Then he picked up a little scissors. As his hand with the scissors in it came straight at the naked eyeball of the only eye I see with, he said in a measured doomlike monotone:

'DON'T MOVE'

and I sat frozen while he snipped ten or twelve stitches out of my eye. I left that office bathed in sweat but so full of joyful relief that in spite of the raw November wind I started walking the forty blocks home.

'Well, of *course* the lens dropped out on your way home!' said my friend Nina in her positive way, as I came weeping into the lobby. 'Your eye is puffy from the irritation of having the stitches taken out! The puffiness will be gone in a day or two and it'll never drop out again!'

She was right. Though it would be a month before I dared to believe it, the nightmare was finally over.

On Tuesday night I packed a suitcase with my best clothes and my two most prized possessions: an extra pair of contact lenses, and the miserable cataract spectacles without which I couldn't see to clean the lenses or position them on my index finger. The strange thing about the spectacles was that sometimes, when my eyes felt gritty at the end of a long day, I found myself taking out the lenses an hour before I went to bed and wearing the specs to watch the late-night TV news. And when I went out to the kitchen to wash the coffee pot or get a glass of milk, the kitchen door no longer curved menacingly outward. The spectacles had adjusted to me.

On Wednesday morning, I took the plane to London.

II   Centre Stage

Dieter, a Deutsch editor, met me at Heathrow and drove me to the St Georges, but it was too dark and rainy for me to see where it was. We had drinks in an attractive top-floor restaurant, then Dieter left and I took the elevator down to my room, turned the key in the lock and – appropriately for Cinderella – at exactly midnight walked in. From that moment, the trip had a dreamlike unreality it never lost.

I wasn't in a hotel room, I was in the living-room of a suite, with a deep sofa and armchairs, a bar-stocked refrigerator in one corner and a colour TV set in the other. There were bouquets with cards stuck in them on the coffee-table and both end tables, there were letters and greeting cards propped up on the mantel, there was a supper tray of cold meats and salads protected under plastic on the coffee-table in front of the sofa.

My suitcase had been deposited in the bedroom and when I went in there to unpack, I saw beyond it a dressing-room – its long dressing-table fitted with two small sinks, two bright table lamps and two tufted chairs, expressly designed for guests with contact lenses and ten thumbs.

I unpacked, had a leisurely bath, put on a robe, sashayed in to supper and read the cards and letters as I ate. The card in the most breathtaking bouquet – an enormous profusion of buds and flowers – was from Michael Redington and said he hoped to see me at the theatre at four on Thursday. There was a note from Ena to say she'd call me in the morning, and a note from Abbe enclosing press clippings about the show:

'Elizabeth Taylor's in town for her opening but you and *84* are getting much more publicity. Liz, eat your heart out.'

There was a letter from James Roose-Evans to say he was giving a luncheon for me at the Garrick Club on Sunday. There was a letter from Sue Hyman, the show's press agent, with two typewritten pages of interview dates attached. And I hadn't even brought a notebook to use as a date book.

Lying next to the supper tray was a copy of the Celebrity Bulletin. I hadn't seen one of those since the Theatre Guild days. I ran my eye down the alphabetical list of Who Was In Town This Week – and the two names, one after the other, jumped out at me:

Helene Hanff

Celeste Holm

'Look it that, I'm a celebrity,' I thought. Celeste wasn't in London, she was in Nottingham rehearsing *Lady in the Dark*. I had a sudden urge to phone the number given in the Bulletin – till I realized it was one-thirty A.M. I finished my coffee and floated off to bed.

After breakfast the next morning – in style, in the living-room – I thought I'd better buy a notebook-datebook before the first interviewer arrived. I went down to the lobby, walked out to the sidewalk – and stood and stared; I was standing on the corner with the London view I loved best. The St Georges was at the top of Regent Street, looking up the wide avenue of Portland Place to the Nash crescents flanking the entrance to Regent's Park. They beckoned in the misty rain and I walked out to them – and then had to run all the way back to Mortimer Street to pick up a notebook, getting back up to the suite two minutes before the first interviewer arrived.

They came all morning, with just time for a late lunch before Sue Hyman arrived at three. She was a pretty woman in her thirties, a wife and mother and head of her own PR firm, and awesomely efficient.

'A car will be here to take you to Thames Television at eleven. A car will be waiting there for you at twelve to take you to . . .'

I wasn't even allowed to walk down Regent Street to the Ambassadors Theatre five minutes away on foot. 'A car will be here . . .'

It was, and it dropped me in front of a theatre plastered with posters advertising the show. With my name on them in big block letters. Thirty years after I'd given up trying to write plays, my name on those posters was too far-fetched to be real. It was just part of the dream I was living in.

Michael Redington was waiting for me in the lobby and he drove me home to his house in Westminster for tea.

Michael is one of those rare gentlemen to whom the word 'sweet' applies. He was lean and sandy-haired and he must have been in his late fifties ('I was company manager for the Lunts when they toured Australia in the forties' he told me), but he looked younger; maybe because after working in the theatre all his life, he was still stagestruck, he still had a youthful enthusiasm about it. He'd been a company manager and press agent for years; he was now finally a producer and when he said '84 is my first West End production!' you could hear the exclamation point.

I told him his flowers were dazzling and he said:

'Ann, my wife, is a florist. She plans a bouquet so that when the flowers blooming today begin to die, a group of buds will be just ready to open. One variety won't open till your last day.'

He spent an hour – he could have spent six – showing me his collection of theatre photos and programs, and he gave me one of his favourite theatre books to take home. It's called *Time Was*; it's the memoirs of a costumer and set-designer named Graham Robertson who worked in the London theatre of Ellen Terry and Henry Irving, Sarah Bernhardt and Oscar Wilde, and I love it.

There was a lunch interview on my schedule for Friday and the name of the interviewer conjured up a memory of my first morning in London ten years before. I'd gone up the street from the hotel to André Deutsch's office to be interviewed by 'a bouncy young reporter from the *Evening Standard* named Valerie Jenkins,' it said in my diary. Since then, Valerie had become one of the best-known newspaper columnists in a city that still published eight daily newspapers. She was listed on the schedule as 'Valerie Jenkins (Grove).' When she arrived, she seemed as young and bouncy as ever, though she told me she and her husband – a fellow newspaper writer – had three daughters.

She drove me out to a north London restaurant near where she lived, and as we finished lunch and the interview she said: 'Do you mind driving back to the house with me? Lesley, my mother-in-law, wants to meet you.'

And I call blessings down on Lesley's attractive head because if she hadn't wanted to meet me, I would never have got to see that house. To walk into Valerie's house is to walk back into another time and another world.

We met Lesley in the sitting-room – big and old fashioned with small sofas and armchairs in bright flowered slipcovers and a massive fireplace at one end. Then Lesley and Valerie took me on a tour of the house. There was a library cheerful with white bookshelves and a water-green carpet; a big dining-room with knotty pine table and chairs, a red brick fireplace and hand-painted plates in immaculate rows above the mantel; and a children's sitting-room – 'the day nursery,' said Lesley, as if Queen Victoria weren't dead – with child-sized table and chairs, including a child-sized rocker, William Morris wallpaper and old-fashioned toys: alphabet blocks, toy animals, a rocking horse.

But it was the levels of the house that gave it its nineteenth-century flavor. You go down half a flight from the sitting-room to the 'day nursery' and down another half flight to the kitchen and dining room. You go up half a flight to the guest bedroom, up another half to the master bedroom, a third to the 'night nursery' and a fourth to Lucy's room. ('Lucy, being six,' explained Valerie, 'decided she was too old for the night nursery.') At the top of the house were two large bed-sitters – one in green and white for Lesley when she visits, the other in pink and white for Nanny.

Because of the levels, the house was full of small landings and hidden nooks for playing hide-and-seek on a rainy day. And of course there was a back garden, and of course Nanny and the two smaller children had gone walking, accompanied by the family dog. They came back just as I was leaving – and Nanny confounded all my notions of nannies by being twenty-two and very pretty.

The aura of that house – the sense of a bygone security that conjured up Louisa May Alcott's world – was to stay with me for months. So was the astonishment that it had been created by parents who were 1980s newspaper reporters. Their breakfast and dinner conversations aren't calculated to shield their children from the modern world. They just don't let the modern world rob childhood of its birth rights.

On Saturday, Abbe phoned and I told her to come to the hotel and have dinner with me on Sunday night.

'Phone before you come to make sure I'm back,' I said, 'James Roose-Evans is giving a luncheon for me at the Garrick Club and I don't know how late I'll be there.'

'Oh Gawd!' said Abbe. 'The Garrick is the most prestigious theatre club in London! Only the best names are elected to it – and no one can set foot in it who's not a member or guest of a member.'

Michael drove me to the club, in the heart of the theatre district, and sure enough, when he opened the imposing front door, a doorman loomed up instantly, barring the way for all his courteous 'Good morning.'

'We're guests of Mr James Roose-Evans,' said Michael. And the doorman stood aside, gestured toward a grand staircase and said:

'They're in the Morning Room. Go right up.'

We crossed a wide foyer and began to climb the broad mahogany stairs, stopping now and then to look at the wall alongside us, with its massively framed portraits of legendary London stage stars, painted in the costumes of their most famous roles, some against the backdrop of the stage sets used in their grandest scenes.

The floor above opened into a museum hall filled with glass cases of theatrical memorabilia. I yearned to stop and examine everything in every case, but Michael led the way past them and into the Morning Room. It was a large, comfortable clubroom with easy chairs grouped around small tables. The walls of the room were crammed with more framed oil portraits of theatre celebrities, the narrow spaces between them filled with miniature portraits.

Michael led the way to a small group having drinks at a table by the long windows, and a big, benign-looking man with a middle-aged bespectacled face rose and held out both hands to me and introduced himself as James Roose-Evans.

I discovered over lunch that he was the founder of the Hampstead Theatre the best and oldest Fringe theatre in London), the author of several books about the theatre and several TV documentaries for the BBC — and that he writes a popular series of children's books published by André Deutsch. (I labor mightily to bring forth a mouse of a book and I can't do anything else whatever.)

I sat next to Rosemary Leach, who was playing me in *84*, and across from David Swift, who was playing Frank Doel. Rosemary, a friendly outgoing soul who told me all about her actor husband and Mrs Brains, the family dog, is a big TV star in London.

'I've been acting in television for so long I can't believe I'm back in the theatre.'

We moved next door to the dining-room for lunch. If there were famous faces lunching there, I didn't recognize them. But there was a face at the center of one table that drew me like a magnet. It belonged to an elderly *grande dame* who was holding court at a table of younger admirers. Her beautiful white hair was framed by a black velvet hat — gently out of date and the only hat in the room — and in its discreet and expert make up her face looked serenely unlined. Her flowing print dress, like the hat, was deliberately out of fashion; it told you she preferred Yesterday. I've never seen anyone who had so perfected the art of combining old age and glamor.

Rosemary had never been in the Garrick Club before and we both wanted to look at those glass cases, so when lunch ended she asked James:

'Will it be all right if Helene and I stay and look at all the things out in the hall?'

— and James told us expansively to tour the building and stay as long as we liked. The others left and the two of us started slowly along the cases in the museum hall, examining every glamorous item.

There was a cast of Duse's hand, and a printed invitation to Bernhardt's funeral. There was a fan used on stage by Helena Modesta, Macready's stage garter worn in *Richard III*, a dog collar that had been worn by Edmund Kean's St Bernard, and Henry Irving's dog whistle. And Irving's powder box, 'Donated by Michael Redgrave.' And Charles Keane's shoe buckle and George Arliss's walking stick and Ivor Novello's cigarette case. And a walking stick thought to have belonged to David Garrick himself, 'Donated by Mr. Lunt, U.S.A.' Near the glass cases on a small stand was a bust of John Gielgud and on the wall above it a miniature portrait of Garrick 'made of the spun hair of Mr. and Mrs. Garrick.' And on a stand, a polished goblet that Garrick had had made for a fellow actor, from the wood of the mulberry tree in Shakespeare's garden.

We climbed another flight of stairs, the walls alongside lined with older paintings, and found on the top floor two dark, musty rooms, one full of faded portraits of long-forgotten stars, the other a library, its heavy brown shelves and tables piled high with three centuries of books on the theatre, in all sizes and shapes, some covered in faded silk, some in age-stained white vellum, some in thin leather so old and frail we were afraid to touch it.

As we left the club, Rosemary told me the cast was rehearsing all day every day and giving a preview performance every evening. Previews tell the director what scenes work and what ones don't, and he makes changes accordingly, but the changes can frazzle an actress.

'Before the preview Friday night, James told me the John Donne letter was being taken out,' Rosemary said. 'But when I got to rehearsal on Saturday morning, they'd changed their minds and the John Donne letter was back in. I don't know whether it'll be in or out tomorrow night.'

I told her I was avoiding the previews. I wanted to see the show fresh on Opening Night.

On Monday morning, the interviewing began to get out of hand. I was sitting down to my breakfast eggs when the phone rang and a man at the other end said:

'This is the *Sunday Express*. We'd like to interview you.'

'Fine,' I said, and was reaching for my date book when he began to interview me then and there while my eggs got cold. We hung up and I finished the eggs and was pouring my coffee when the phone rang again and a woman said:

'This is the *Express*. We'd like to interview you.'

'Somebody from the *Express* just did,' I said.

'That was the *Sunday Express*. This is the *Daily*,' she said – and interviewed me for fifteen minutes while my coffee got cold. I carried the coffee pot to the bedroom and was just pouring the coffee into the electric teakettle when the doorbell rang, announcing the first (scheduled) interviewer of the day.

On Tuesday, there was a company lunch at Futura, the paperback house. But Futura had been bought by Macdonald since my last lunch there, and when I walked into the office, all the '78 Upwardly Mobiles were gone, replaced by an entirely new set. The new ones were more relaxed and – sign of the times – there were young female faces sprinkled among the buttoned-down males.

What happened on Wednesday was so beyond imagining I have difficulty believing it even now. Ena came at noon to drive me to the remodelled building on Charing Cross Road that had once housed Marks & Co.'s bookshop. The small stone pillars that had flanked the shop's front door were still there, but they no longer bore the numbers 84. The old store had been split into two small stores. Both were new, unoccupied and unnumbered.

There was a small cluster of people gathered on the sidewalk. Abbe was there, and Leo Marks and Michael Redington, and André and half his staff, including Sheila Murphy, who informed me:

'We're the Rent-a-crowd.'

I was introduced to a bearded young man from the real estate firm that had remodelled the building, and he led me to the left-hand stone pillar. There was a small curtain on it with a drawstring. Two photographers were standing near it. One of them showed me where to stand and the other told me when to pull the drawstring. I pulled it and the curtain rolled aside, exposing a round brass plaque. On it, in neat block letters, was the inscription:

84
CHARING CROSS ROAD
THE BOOKSELLERS MARKS & CO.

WERE ON THIS SITE WHICH
BECAME WORLD RENOWNED
THROUGH THE BOOK BY
HELENE HANFF

Press agents and photographers were issuing instructions and in a fog, I moved where they told me to move and posed for pictures and didn't know I was posing with Leo, son-of-Marks-&-Co, with André, then with the bearded young man from the real estate office, until weeks later when the photos came in the mail.

I knew perfectly well that the plaque had been put up by the real estate firm as a sop to the neighborhood, which had fought a long, losing battle to save the old Charing Cross Road bookshops. Of course the realtors had had to get approval of the plaque from the London City Council, but I knew that real estate developers always had political connections. None of it mattered. Whatever the motives behind it, there was a plaque on a London wall with my name on it. Through more posed photographs I stared at the fact of it and couldn't make myself believe it.

The realtors had a lunch for us after the ceremony and as we walked toward the restaurant Michael told me:

'André will be sitting with you tomorrow night. You're in the second row.'

It horrified me.

'Oh, please don't trap me down front where Rosemary can't help seeing me!' I said. 'Can't I hang over the back rail, so I can flee to the lobby if I need to?'

'There is no back rail,' said Michael. 'The theatre has graduated tiers rising to the last row of the balcony. I'll put you in a box where there's an exit.'

It was five-thirty when I got back to the hotel on Thursday afternoon. The Opening Night curtain was to go up at seven and the theatre was only a few minutes' drive from the hotel. But knowing the perils of the telephone, I buzzed my friend the operator.

'Honey, do me a favor and don't put any calls through for the next hour,' I said. 'I have to bathe and dress and I want to take my time.'

'There's a call for you now,' she said. 'It's the last one I'll put through.'

It was Sheila calling.

'André will pick you up in a cab at six,' she said.

Six?

'Sheila,' I said. 'We could walk to the theatre in five minutes! Tell him six-thirty.'

'He doesn't want to be late,' said Sheila.

'Just tell him I can't be ready before six-thirty,' I said and hung up.

I got out my black velvet pantsuit and white blouse and then debated whether to wear the new shoes that hurt, or my old black velvet scuffs, as comfortable as old bedroom slippers and just as shabby. I decided to wear the new shoes and carry the scuffs in a Fortnum's shopping bag.

This weighty question settled, I ran a tub and had one foot in it when the phone rang. I went into the bedroom and picked it up.

'What happened?' I said to the operator.

'I'm sorry,' she said, her voice awed. 'It's Celeste Holm calling from Nottingham!'

Celeste was calling to wish me luck on the Opening.

At 6:15 the desk phoned to say Mr Deutsch was in the lobby. I made him wait five minutes and even so, we got to the theatre before 6:30. There was a crowd in the lobby and it seemed to me hundreds of people had turned and were staring fixedly at me. It made me nervous and I murmured to André:

'Why are they looking at me?'

'They recognize you,' he said. 'They've seen your picture in the newspapers all week and they've seen you on television. '

Not having seen the interviews, I hadn't realized Sue Hyman's press agency had made my face a household item.

We went upstairs to the bar – and all the way up, we were waylaid by theatregoers who thrust programmes at me to be signed. André brought me a martini but didn't let me finish it; he was convinced that if we didn't get to our seats fifteen minutes before the curtain it would rise without us. Till he led the way to it, it hadn't occurred to me that André felt obliged to sit with me in the upper box, where he couldn't see Rosemary's half of the stage at all. I've felt guilty about that ever since.

At a little after seven, the houselights dimmed and the curtain went up to reveal a split stage, with an old, shabby secondhand bookshop

on the right and an equally shabby bed-sitter on the left. And I heard
Rosemary's friendly voice read the date of the first letter:

'October 5, 1949.'

I'm not sure when it started, but the curtain hadn't been up very
long when I began to hear sniffles in the audience. It startled me.

There was nothing in the least sad taking place on stage. What was
going on a perfectly cheerful transatlantic conversation. It took me a
little time to realize that something profoundly different was going on,
in the minds of the people around me. They were caught up in a wave
of nostalgia. They were carried back to bombed-out postwar London,
to the grey years of food shortages when the arrival of a food parcel
from America was a red-letter event in their rationed lives. As the
evening wore on, everybody in the audience was reliving the sad
funeral of King George Vl and the high hopeful day of the young
Queen's coronation. Everybody, that is, but the lone American sitting
dry-eyed and restive in an upper box.

I was gratefully aware that Rosemary was reading my letters with
extraordinary warmth, wit and comprehension. But I'd read those
letters in Hugh Whitemore's TV script and heard them read over and
over every day for ten long days of rehearsal; I'd had to read them
again, in scripts submitted for my approval by amateur theatre groups
from Massachusetts to Hong Kong; I'd had to read James's script
before it opened in Salisbury and again after he'd made changes in it
for London. Now, at the Opening Night in London when I most
wanted to relive the correspondence for my own personal reasons, I
was finally sick to death of it.

After intermission Michael moved me to an empy seat in the upper
balcony.

'We want you to take a curtain call with the cast and it will be easier
to lead you down from here,' he said.

At the final curtain, the audience erupted in the kind of applause
you hear only at the opening of a hit. Michael came for me and led
me down the narrow balcony stairs to the mezzanine, on down to the
orchestra floor and then along the side aisle to the far end where a
door led around a corner to the backstage area. When we got there
the applause and the curtain calls were still going on.

Somebody took my arm and pointed to a door through which I
was to walk on to the stage. I didn't know, till I read it in one of the

reviews, that I was walking onstage through the door of my bookshop. Rosemary and David separated to make room for me between them and I stood blinking in the white glare of the footlights at the total blackness which was all I could see beyond. When the curtain finally came down to stay, the cast gave me a leather-bound copy of *84* with the complete cast list printed in it and their signatures alongside their names.

Gene Young and Little, Brown had presented me with a leather-bound copy of *Underfoot in Show Business* when it was reissued, and I never told her how it shocked me. I have my own standard of what books belong in fine leather covers and what ones don't. But the leather-bound *84* seemed to me then, and seems to me now, a fitting memorial to Marks & Co. and Frank Doel and all their vanished kind; and for their sakes I treasure it.

We assembled in the lobby – Leo and Ena, Michael and Ann Redington and James and I. (André had gone home; he was leaving early the next morning on a skiing vacation.) We were going to walk around the corner to the Opening Night party being held in the empty storefront at what had been 84, Charing Cross Road. But we were waylaid in the lobby by half the audience who knew one or another of us. The first familiar faces I saw belonged to Sheila and Mary Doel, accompanied by their husbands and the ghosts of their parents (Nora had died the year before). After that, it seemed to me every soul I'd ever met in London came up to congratulate me. Michael and James had far more friends to deal with, and it was an hour before we finally got out of the theatre.

We were only going around the corner, but the new shoes declined to walk that far. I stopped on the sidewalk, took them off, put on the scuffs, and gave the shoes to Leo to put in his overcoat pockets. I figured nobody at the party would be staring at my feet. As it turned out, nobody at that party could see anybody's feet.

The empy storefront was absolutely bare. There wasn't a table or a folding chair in it. The party had been in full swing for an hour and the room was wall-to-wall people. There must have been a bar at the other end because everybody had a glass in hand, but I never got far enough into the room to see the other end. Five feet inside the entrance I was stopped by a solid phalanx of tuxedos and evening gowns that somehow kept moving without going anywhere. People I knew and people I didn't know came up to congratulate me and somebody put a martini in my hand. In five minutes I'd lost sight of Ena and Leo, Ann and Michael and James. Ten more minutes and the sea of bodies had backed me into a corner between two walls.

It was after ten. I'd had nothing to eat since a hurried sandwich at noon, I was tired and hungry and I don't like big parties anyway.

'The hell with it,' I thought, and sat down on the bare floor and leaned back against the wall to finish my martini and think my thoughts. As I turned to put down my empty glass, I saw – lined up against the wall beside me in a neat row – four more martinis brought to me, I assume, by four separate well-wishers. I had doubts about the wisdom of another martini on my very empy stomach, but I picked up one of them – whereupon a passing male foot bumped into my hand, spilling half the martini on my right scuff. While I was mopping it up with tissue, a gentleman loomed above me, leaned down and said solicitously: 'Can I get you anything?'

'Yes,' I said. 'Leo Marks.'

The gentleman went off and a few minutes later, Leo appeared at the edge of the human sea and said:

'Yes, love?'

And I said simply:

'Get me out of here.'

And Leo, his baritone deepening at the crisis, said:

'Instantly, my darling!' and plunged back into the mob. Then miraculously Ena appeared at my elbow.

'Leo's gone for the car,' she said. We went to dinner and they drove me home, and by midnight I was crawling thankfully into bed.

Back in the days when New York, too, had eight daily newspapers, theatre people stayed up till four a.m. for the morning reviews and then went to bed and slept late.

They do it differently in London.

I woke the next morning at eight, to the prospect of a lovely, lazy morning with nothing to do but pack a suitcase before the arrival of the final interviewer at noon. I was having breakfast when Leo phoned to read me *The Times* review, which was wonderful. Then Ena got on the line and I asked her to come over and spend the morning with me and she said she was on her way.

A few minutes later, Abbe phoned.

'I thought I'd pick up the four morning papers and bring them to the hotel,' she said. And I said:

'Rush right over. Ena's coming and the coffee's hot.'

Ena and Abbe arrived together. We spread out the four reviews and read aloud to each other the small headlines proclaiming the show a hit. That was as far as we got when the desk phoned to say Mr and Mrs Redington were on the way up. Two minutes later, the desk rang again to say Mr and Mrs David Swift were on their way up. Then it was Mr Roose-Evans, then it was an executive from Futura and a wandering, unscheduled reporter, and after that I lost track.

I phoned Room Service and ordered coffee for ten, and a porter arrived with a banquet urn and ten cups and saucers. But so many people kept on coming that Ena and Abbe had to run back and forth from the living-room to the dressing-room sinks, to wash out cups for fresh arrivals at the reception nobody'd told me I was giving.

Some of the guests brought gifts – beautiful scarves that would go in the suitcase and beautiful books that wouldn't – and the Futura executive brought a gift I mean to take with me when I die, on the King Tut theory that you don't know what provisions will be available at the other end. It was a bottle of gin with the only genuine Private Label I ever saw. The printed label read:

GORDON'S
Special Dry
84, Charing Cross Road
London
GIN
Distilled by Futura Publications
for
Helene Hanff
to celebrate the opening of
'84, Charing Cross Road'
at the Ambassadors Theatre
26th November, 1981

The last of the guests departed only when and because the final interviewer arrived. He was still there when Sheila came with the car to take me to the airport.

It was December when I got home and through a hectic week of Christmas shopping the dream trip faded a little. Then one morning a thick envelope arrived in the mail from Sue Hyman, enclosing the afternoon reviews. One of them described my walk through the bookshop door to join the cast on stage and added:

'The audience rose to her.'

I hadn't seen that, in the blackness beyond the footlights.

I stared at the line till I couldn't see it for tears. Somehow, with that image, the dream week I'd lived through was suddenly, overwhelmingly real. The suite and the flowers and messages were real, the Opening Night was real, even the wildly improbable plaque on a London wall was real. Remembering the desolate evening when I'd learned of Frank Doel's death – when I'd been a failed writer with little to show for her past and no foreseeable future – I was in tears at how that life had been transformed in a single decade.

What fortune teller would ever have had the nerve to predict that the best years of my life would turn out to be my old age?

III 'It won't travel'

That winter and spring, everybody asked me whether the show was coming to Broadway. I answered by quoting a remark André once made, back in the early seventies when he first came to breakfast.

I'd just read Judith Viorst's *How to Be Hip over Thirty*. I was certain André would publish it if he read it, and when I set the breakfast table I put the book above his plate.

André arrived and stood in the kitchen doorway telling me an anecdote while I put the bacon and eggs on a platter. He was still telling the story as we moved toward the table. As we reached it he broke off in mid-sentence, pointed to the book, said: 'I read that, darling, it won't travel,' and went on with the story.

From where I'd sat in the Ambassadors Theatre, *84, Charing Cross Road* wouldn't travel. It was more than enough for me that the play was a hit in London. Thanks to James Roose-Evans I spent the winter and spring happily replacing my ragged drapes, my worn-out wall-to-wall carpet and a sofabed that was leaking powdered foam rubber. But late in the summer Alexander H. Cohen bought *84, Charing*

Cross Road for Broadway. He'd been a Broadway producer for forty years and I did not drop him a note telling him he was making a mistake.

In September, he phoned to tell me he'd signed Ellen Bursyn to play me and that the show was set to open on the first Tuesday in December. In October a mild interview epidemic began. In November Sheila and Mary Doel wrote to say they were coming to New York for the Opening (leaving their husbands behind as baby-sitters) and Alex Cohen with typical generosity offered to put them up at the Plaza for a week. My oldest friend, Maxine-the-actress, phoned from Hollywood to say she and her husband were coming in for the Opening, since she was a member of the cast of characters.

I went through those months feeling a slowly mounting excitement – and a peaceful sense of detachment. I knew that if a play of mine were about to open on Broadway, I'd be tense and hysterical by turns. But this was James's play. True, it was based on a book I'd written; but the verdict on the book was long in. Or, as I put it to myself placidly:

'It's James's rap.'

On the Friday evening before the Opening, I gave a supper party for Sheila and Mary Doel at which everybody (including the hostess) was riding the crest of pre-Opening excitement, heightened by the fact that we had all heard glowing reports from friends who had seen preview performances of *84* and had declared it was bound to be the hit of the season.

On Sunday afternoon, I went to a concert, a cocktail party and then on to dinner. I came home at ten P.M. to find the apartment filled with plants, flowers and telegrams which Dimitria, my excited neighbour across the hall, had taken in for me. The flower arrangement and plants were beautiful and they touched and gratified me, and in a one-room apartment there wasn't any place to put them. While I was distributing them around on tables and windowsills, with a few parked temporarily in the bathtub, the phone rang steadily. Out-of-town friends called to wish me luck; out-of-town fans called to say they were, or wished they were, here for the Opening.

On Monday, I was out for the evening and when I came home, there were more flowers and plants Dimitria had deposited on the sofa for lack of more suitable space. Since my sofa is also my bed, I was carrying two lovely flower arrangements to the kitchen when – at midnight – the phone rang. A couple from Chicago, ardent fans who had come in for the Opening, were at the other end.

'We know we didn't wake you,' the husband said. 'We've been trying you all evening.'

As I undressed I thought bleakly: 'I'll have to get an answering machine.' I hate answering machines, I love talking to fans when they call. But not if they were going to start calling at midnight.

On Tuesday evening, I walked to the theatre surrounded by family and closest friends. And the sight of my name on the Nederlander Theatre marquee brought a wave of memories of the noisy melodrama Maxine and I had lived through trying to crash the theatre.

I took my seat in a back row and as the houselights dimmed I reminded myself again complacently:

'It's James's rap.'

It was my rap.

I'd accepted congratulations for the words I'd written when they'd moved a London audience to tears: I had to accept responsibility for the same words when they fell with the dull thud of a flop in a Broadway theatre. My family and friends filled too many rows of seats that night. As the evening wore on, I began to feel acutely embarrassed at having lured them all there. I wanted to cut and run so I wouldn't have to face them afterward.

The final curtain fell to perfunctory applause and the briefest of curtain calls, and I bolted out to the lobby. But everyone who came to say hello to me there seemed in good spirits. So were all the friends who went to Sardi's with me afterward, for the usual party. The party went on till one A.M. – when somebody brought us the first edition of the *Times* with a devastating review of the play.

We picked up the other morning newspapers on the way home and reviews weren't much kinder. It was after two when I crawled into bed (having first had to dispose of a new batch of flowers and plants) and I was too tired to know what I felt.

But as I opened my eyes the next morning, a thought dropped gently into my mind:

'Thank God it flopped. I couldn't live like this.'

I sat bolt upright in shock.

'What kind of a thought was that!' I demanded aloud.

I got up and lit a cigarette and then sat on the edge of the bed and tried to make sense of myself. It wasn't hard to do.

Being a celebrity for a week in London had been the most fun I'd ever had in my life, and wonderful for the ego — but only because I'd known I was coming home at the end of it, home to the quiet, orderly, solitary, unglamorous life I was made for. To be forced to live a celebrity's life at home, even for a little while, had been a nightmarish possibility. It was gone in the morning, like any other nightmare.

'Peace,' I said to the understanding room. 'Peace.'

Q.E.D.

The Broadway production closed after three months, but James's play kept right on going. First there were summer theatre tours, here and in England. Then I began to get letters from actresses playing me in Bath and Edinburgh and Winnipeg – and phone calls from 'Helenes' in amateur productions of the play in New Jersey and Delaware and Oregon. Fans sent me programmes from productions in Houston, Ontario and Melbourne and a flock of far-off towns I'd never heard of. Not forgetting the American Beauty roses that arrived from the young players in a production at Sierra College in Rocklin, California, or the bowl of dried flowers airmailed to me by an actress named Liz Caiacob who was playing me in Perth, West Australia.

It was – and is – the best of both worlds: the peaceful life of a nobody, with enough fan mail, gifts and phone calls to assure me I'm really somebody. It ought to keep me in a permanent state of gratitude and contentment, and most of the time it does.

But there came an evening last winter when I was curled up in the armchair, too depressed to read. A new book I'd been working on for a year was getting worse instead of better. I wanted to abandon it, but the material in it was all I had to write about. I wondered, if I abandoned it, whether I'd ever write another book.

I thought of *84*, the miracle of my life I would never understand. I thought of *The Duchess*, the trips to London, the dazzling moments that had happened to me there. And like a resentful child when the party's over, I thought:

'What have you got to show for it all?'

I looked around the room. The Futura gin bottle (carefully preserved under a bell jar) stood on a breakfront shelf. The leatherbound *84* was up on a bookshelf. A framed photograph of the plaque hung on an alcove wall. In a long storage cabinet, installed under the bookshelves a few years ago, was a videotape of the TV show alongside a large manila envelope full of brochures from the literary tour and the lovely drawings Ena had made for me of Mama Deutsch's flat and Jane Austen's house. On the bottom shelf of the cabinet were the London reviews.

'Trinkets,' I thought sourly, 'and yellowing paper.'

Then I remembered the sign that had once hung outside Marks & Co.'s bookshop and now occupied the side alcove wall. That, at least, was real. I couldn't see it from where I sat, and I got up, flipped on the alcove light and stepped back a little into the living-room to get a good view of it. And then I stood still, rooted – and stared. Not at the sign. At the rows of books that stretched along the back alcove wall.

Except for the few the Queen's bookbinder had restored, they were shabby, faded and discoloured. Some had cracked spines, some had covers detached, eaten away by heat and dust. Almost all of them were in some way ravaged by years and use. Like their owner.

'You don't even read them anymore!' I protested silently. 'How many do you take down in a year? Five? Six?'

It didn't matter. I had so much of them inside my head they were part of me now. And I was shaken by what I suddenly knew: If I live to be very old, all my memories of the glory days will grow vague and confused, till I won't be certain any of it really happened. But the books will be there, on my shelves and in my head – the one enduring reality I can be certain of till the day I die.

Of all the gifts in Q's legacy, the first still mattered most and would matter longest. If it took me a lifetime to learn that, Q won't mind. He knows I was never a very bright pupil.

Warner now offers an exciting range of quality titles by both established and new authors. All of the books in this series are available from:
Little, Brown and Company (UK) Limited,
Cash Sales Department,
P.O. Box 11,
Falmouth,
Cornwall TR10 9EN.

Alternatively you may fax your order to the above address. Fax No. 0326 376423.

Payments can be made as follows: Cheque, postal order (payable to Little, Brown and Company) or by credit cards, Visa/Access. Do not send cash or currency. UK customers: and B.F.P.O.: please send a cheque or postal order (no currency) and allow £1.00 for postage and packing for the first book, plus 50p for the second book, plus 30p for each additional book up to a maximum charge of £3.00 (7 books plus).

Overseas customers including Ireland, please allow £2.00 for postage and packing for the first book, plus £1.00 for the second book, plus 50p for each additional book.

NAME (Block Letters) ....

ADDRESS...

....

☐ I enclose my remittance for _____

☐ I wish to pay by Access/Visa Card

Number ☐☐☐☐☐☐☐☐☐☐☐☐☐☐☐☐

Card Expiry Date ☐☐☐☐